Guide to Building Regulations 1985

For England and Wales   A. J. Elder RIBA   Series editors Vincent Powell-Smith and Peter Pitt

Butterworth Architecture

London   Boston   Singapore   Sydney   Toronto   Wellington

Butterworth Architecture
is an imprint of Butterworth Scientific

 PART OF REED INTERNATIONAL P.L.C.

First published, 1986 by the Architectural Press Ltd
Second edition 1989 published by Butterworth Architecture

© A. J. Elder 1989

British Library Cataloguing in Publications Data

Elder, A.J. (Albert Joseph), *1918–*
    Guide to the Building Regulations 1985 for
England and Wales.—2nd ed.—(Butterworth
Architecture library of building control),
    1. England. Buildings. Construction. Law:
Building regulations 1985 – Commentaries
    I. Title
    344.203′7869

ISBN 0-408-50013-1

Library of Congress Cataloging-in-Publication Data

Elder, Albert Joseph.
    Guide to the Building Regulations, 1985.

    Bibliography: p.
    Includes index.
    1. Building laws––Great Britain.   2. Standards,
Engineering––Great Britain.   I. Title.
KD1140.Z9E44   1988   343.42′07869   88-26196
ISBN 0-408-50013-1

Typeset by Mid-County Press, 2a Merivale Road, London
SW15 2NW
Printed and bound in Great Britain by
Anchor Press Ltd, Tiptree, Essex

Contents

The publishers announce with great regret that A. J. (Bert) Elder died in October 1988, not long after he had completed his work on the final proofs of this *Guide* (some account of his work appears on the back cover).

He was born in Hull in 1919, qualified in 1940 and practised in Teeside. Many architects and others have over the years had reason to be grateful for the down-to-earth, concise and reliable guidance he gave them through the pages of this book. As an author he was courteous, meticulous and hardworking. Readers of his novel *The Rubicon File* will able to infer something of the person, and the feelings about his profession, of a man who was himself deeply professional.

C.C.G. November 1988

Introduction

Some form of building control has been with us for a very long time. When man first started congregating in cities which grew up without any form of control other than that imposed by land ownership, the environment which developed must have been quite dreadful. In this country, the occurrence of events such as the Great Plague and the Great Fire of London led to efforts being made to prevent a recurrence, in other words to take positive steps to ensure the health and safety of the inhabitants. It is these two aspects which have dominated the provisions of building regulations ever since. More recently, the conservation of fuel and power and the prevention of waste or misuse of water have been added.

This history of modern building legislation goes back to 1845 when the first Public Health Act was passed. Housing was the primary concern and the defects to be cured were mainly damp, structural instability, poor sanitation, fire risk and lack of light and ventilation. In 1877, the first model by-laws were produced as a guide for local authorities, with whom lay the responsibility for setting and enforcing minimum standards. They applied only to 'new streets and buildings', but in 1936 new legislation was enacted covering all buildings and requiring all local authorities to make and enforce 'building by-laws'. At this time, although guidance from central government was given, local authorities still held direct responsibility for building standards and issued their own by-laws which, although generally similar, had individual differences which made it necessary for architects, designing buildings for the first time in a particular local authority area, to make sure of obtaining and studying a copy of the By-laws; undoubtedly a time-wasting routine! The breakthrough came with the issue of the 1952 Model By-laws, series IV (amended 1953), which saw two major advances. Firstly, perhaps as a result of the development of a whole range of new materials, a different technique of control was used whereby standards of performance were stated, and these formed the mandatory part of the by-laws. Descriptions of actual structural minima, which previously had been mandatory, were now contained in the so-called 'deemed to satisfy provisions', leaving the way open for other newer methods and materials to be used, providing their performance could be established. This system has, of course, been effectively used ever since, and has enabled increasing reference to be made to advisory publications such as British Standard Specifications and Codes of Practice. Secondly, although the enforcement of the model by-laws was still a matter for local authorities, they were universally adopted throughout England and Wales (except by the LCC), and hence building control legislation became standard. They also contained major new controls introducing, for the first time, the concept of structural fire resistance periods in relation to building type and size.

This legislation really did cause all building design offices to pause, think, and realise that, for the first time, they had a significant control system to satisfy, and one which was going to affect all fundamental design traditions. For example, prior to the 52 Model By-laws a decision as between structural steel or reinforced concrete for a frame would be made purely on such criteria as convenience, time for erection and cost. Subsequently the cost and time taken to fireproof the steel sections could, and often did, sway the decision in favour of rc. With hindsight it can be seen that this was really the first, and probably still the most important step from ad-hoc by-laws, (suitable only for use when buildings were a simple matter of bricks and mortar) towards a rationalised system under which the controls would gradually develop to embrace most parts of a building's skeleton, cladding and services.

In 1961, a new Public Health Act was introduced providing for the preparation of a national set of building regulations for England and Wales, but excluding Inner London which had a different system of administration from other local authorities, and was apparently able to persuade the Government that this system suited the special circumstances pertaining in a metropolitan area better than the proposed new standard regulations. After a lot of work by the Building Regulations Advisory Committee (BRAC), the Building Regulations 1965 were produced and came into operation on 1 February 1966. The inevitable drafting mistakes made and, apart from these, the usual processes of development and invention called for alterations and, in all, a total of seven amendments were issued, the first coinciding with the issue of the Building Regulations themselves, and the seventh and last coming into operation on 1 November 1971. Most of these were a miscellaneous collection of amendments affecting several parts of the Building Regulations, but one at least, the famous fifth amendment, concerned only part D – *Structural stability* – and contained entirely new supplementary rules for

1

controlling the design of buildings over five storeys to give protection against accidental loads, such as local explosions. It was issued as a direct result of the enquiry following the Ronan Point disaster.

2   The 1972 Regulations

The issue of successive amendments to the Building Regulations 1965 had made the keeping of an up-to-date complete copy virtually impractical, and a re-issue was overdue. Clearly, the question of metrication was affecting the date for complete revision. Finally, on 29 March 1972, the new metric Building Regulations were laid before Parliament and came into operation on 1 June 1972. These regulations incorporated all seven amendments to the 1965 issue and, some additional miscellaneous alterations which might have become an eighth amendment had the revised issue not been made. The suggested metric values previously published were, in general, used without further alteration. In most cases, these are rounded off to the nearest appropriate metric unit, whether it be metres, millimetres, watts and so on. The millimetre is generally the smallest size dimension used. Thus an imperial half inch might become 12mm or 13mm, but there are a number of instances where 12.5mm is used.

The issue of metric regulations does not give local authorities the right to demand drawings in metric but, to comply with the regulations, any imperial sizes or quantities used must be at least equal to the exact imperial equivalent of the metric standard specified. This is the reverse of the previous situation.

During the life of the 1972 Regulations three amendments were issued in 1973, 74 and 75 respectively. These all had considerable impact and were by no means concerned only with minor adjustments. Amongst the more major changes were a new part dealing with means of escape from fire and a completely revised part on the thermal insulation of dwellings including for the first time control on heat losses through windows as well as through solid construction.

3   The 1976 Regulations

These consolidated the three amendments mentioned above but also included a number of changes which had not been previously contained in an amendment. As a document it was a good deal larger than its predecessor (307 pages against 187). Since their issue there have been four amendments. The first of these extended the requirements for thermal insulation to embrace all buildings instead of only dwellings as before. The second included a completely revised Part F (Thermal insulation of dwellings) and introduced two new parts, Part Q (Heating controls) and Part R (Insulation of pipes etc.). The third amendment contained Part S which was concerned only with unvented hot water systems and the fourth Part T with access for disabled persons.

4   The 1985 Regulations

In the mid to late 70s a good deal of critical comment started to appear in the technical press concerning the current state of Building Regulations. They were accused of being unwieldy, inflexible, unduly restrictive and confusing (some went so far as to say that they were written deliberately to confuse). In particular, the language in which they were written (parliamentary prose) was severely belaboured. The RIBA took the matter up and in 1978 *The Architects' Journal* ran an energetic campaign under the title 'Revise the Regs' with a view to stirring things up. Because of a coincidental change in government it did.

An attempt had been made to interest Reg Freeson, the Secretary of State at the DoE under the last Labour government, in a complete revision of the Regulations and their enforcement system. He was not convinced. Following the Tory victory of 1979 a new Secretary of State in the shape of Michael Heseltine, seeking something to impress his personality on his newly acquired department, took on the job with considerable enthusiasm.

The AJ argument (supported by others) was concerned (*inter alia*) with the waste of time caused not only by the unwieldiness of the legislation itself, but also by Local Authorities having to deal with a multitude of small applications from unqualified persons. It proposed a separate simple set of Regulations for simple buildings and permission for architects to certify their own buildings as complying. It got neither.

What emerged instead was a single set of Regulations cut down to brief functional requirements, supported by a series of Approved Documents considerably larger than the old Regulations, but with the advantage of being written in normal English (or as near to normal as the Civil Service can achieve) and supported by diagrams.

On the procedural side, instead of the hoped-for self-certification there emerged a piece of political dogma in the shape of a system of private certification to operate in parallel with the Local Authority system and the immediate imposition of fees. The system specifically requires approved inspectors to have no direct interest in the work whatever, with the exception of certain minor works of a domestic nature. This was the only sop offered to the self-certification lobby, and then only if the architect has taken the time and trouble, and accepted the expense involved, in becoming an 'approved inspector' for the doubtful privilege of being able to certify a few of his own minor jobs.

The system has so far not got off the ground, having been prevented by the problem of indemnity insurance, which is an essential prerequisite to working as a private inspector. This is all part of the general problem of open-ended liability still under review. Neither the professional institutes, who would have to make the appointments, nor the insurance companies appear to have any answers, and the DoE appears to be ignoring the problem. The only exception is the NHBC who have been appointed as a corporate body able to employ salaried inspectors, thus affording an alternative service to their members. Whether this really represents the absolute independence required by clause 9 of the Approved Inspectors Regulations is arguable.

Apart from the certification question, the new Regulations introduce several changes from previous practice. The most important one is the 'building notice' procedure, whereby an applicant is no longer obliged to submit full plans, but may instead supply only a site plan and certain written details of the building. However, where means of escape regulations apply *and* the building is to be put to a designated use under the Fire Precautions Act 1971, full plans must be submitted. At the moment this means only shops and offices, but presumably more building types will fall within this category when means of escape regulations are extended, as is the intention.

Other changes are some extension of the list of exempted buildings, delegation of *all* powers of relaxation and dispensation to Local Authorities, and a more restricted definition of the meaning of 'building' and of 'material change of use'.

5 This Guide

This Guide has a long history. It started as the *AJ Metric Guide to the Building Regulations 1965* running as a series in *The Architects' Journal* as a stop-gap to help architects through the change to metric. It was published in book form in 1969 and was succeeded by the *Guide to the Buildings Regulations 1972*, followed by a series of revised editions as amendments to the Regulations were published. The last was the seventh edition, and was followed by a supplement on the second amendment to the 1976 Regulations.

The original function disappeared long ago but there were several other objectives which remained valid.

In particular it was designed as a working tool, a single volume which designers could use without the need of constant reference to other publications. To this end graphical or illustrated representations of the contents of tables in the schedules and summaries of the more important British Standards referred to in the Regulations were included. Today such references are far more numerous, so this aspect of the Guide has been much extended.

Some of the other objectives, such as the translation of parliamentary prose into plain English and the extensive use of diagrams, have been partially overtaken by the new system of Approved Documents, which purport to achieve the same purpose. However the language of the Approved Documents remains firmly Whitehallese and the diagrams frequently lack realism. One wonders whether they have been drawn by someone who has never designed a building in his life. In this Guide some of the diagrams have been reproduced unchanged, but in most cases they have been replaced by something which gives a more realistic interpretation, and in some cases avoids misinterpretation of the text. In addition a good deal more of the information is presented in diagrammatic form than in the Approved Documents.

As regards the text, this has been restructured to avoid so far as possible repetition and pedantry (and there is a good deal of both) without omitting any essential content. The author believes that this makes the material more easily digestible (less stodgy).

In addition an attempt has been made to reduce the need for cross reference within the Approved Documents themselves. Civil Service draughtsmen always seem to prefer to give a cross reference in preference to saying what is in it (even if quite brief). In this Guide therefore instead of for example 'see G2 3.14,' a summary of the contents of that clause is given unless it is too lengthy. This can be quite a time saver.

Finally this Guide must now be useful to those working in Inner London who are meeting the Building Regulations for the first time.

6   Abbreviations and symbols

The following abbreviations and symbols are used in this Guide. The list is not necessarily comprehensive.

ADs	Approved Documents
BRs	Building Regulations
BBA	British Board of Agrément
BSI	British Standards Institute
BS	British Standard
CP	Code of Practice
CS	Civil Service
DoE	Department of the Environment
DES	Department of Education and Science
LA	Local Authority
MOLC	Material of limited combustibility
SoS	Secretary of State
m, m^2, m^3	Metre, square metre, cubic metre
mm, mm^2	Millimetre, square millimetre
dB	Decibel
K	Kelvin ($=1°C$)
°C	Degree Celsius
N, kN	Newton, Kilonewton
W, kW	Watts, Kilowatts (also used for width)
L	Litre ($1000L = 1m^3$)
S	Second
$>$	more than	eg $a > b$ a to be *more* than b
$<$	less than	eg $a < b$ a to be *less* than b
$\not>$	not more than	eg $a \not> b$ a to be *not more* than b
$\not<$	not less than	eg $a \not< b$ a to be *not less* than b
$\geq$	equal to or more than	
$\leq$	equal to or less than	
$=$	equal	
⌁	heat transfer	
max	maximum	
min	minimum	
W or w	width	(note W also means Watt)
H or h	height	
L or l	length	
B or b	breadth	
℄	Centre line	

ACTS, PRINCIPAL REGULATIONS AND RELATED MATTERS

7   The enabling legislation

Whereas this was previously contained in a number of different Acts they are now all concentrated in the Building Act 1984. This is simply a consolidating measure and contains no new legislation. It contains items drawn from 46 other Acts or Instruments, but principally from the following:

The Public Health Acts 1936 and 1961
The Health and Safety at Work Act 1974
The Housing and Building Control Act 1984.

PART I of the Act contains the powers to make and enforce Building Regulations. Within these are the so-called 'linked powers' which are activated by an application for approval under the Building Regulations, referred to in the Act as 'the passing of plans'. Since, under the new Regulations plans no longer need to be deposited, in the majority of cases they are presumably now activated also by the giving of a building notice. The powers referred to are contained in Sections 18 to 29 of the Act. Certain of these have since been transferred to the Regulations themselves. They are:

Section 23 Provision of facilities for refuse
Section 26 Provision of closets
Section 27 Provision of bathrooms
Section 28 Provision of food storage
Section 29 Sites containing offensive material

If Section 18 (building over a sewer) or Section 24 (exits) are involved, information must be supplied with the building notice, as must information on the provision of drainage (Section 21). Section 24 is interesting since it contains powers for a Local Authority to require certain buildings to have sufficient means of ingress and egress as they shall (after consultation with the Fire Authority) decide. The buildings are:

O   Theatres and other halls used by the public.
O   Restaurants, shops, stores or warehouses to which the public are admitted and more than 20 people are employed.
O   Clubs registered under the licensing Act 1964.
O   Non exempted schools and
O   Churches, chapels or other places of worship.

This in effect extends the requirements for means of escape in B 1 of Schedule 1 to a range of other buildings, although no written guidance is given on what would be considered satisfactory. This is left for the Local Authority and the Fire Authority to decide.

Section 24 does not apply to buildings included in B 1, Means of Escape, but at the moment this only excludes shops (and restaurants, which are included in the definition of shops in the Regulations).

Of the other sections in Part I:

Section 1 contains the power to make Building Regulations for the reasons mentioned earlier and refers to Schedule 1 (see later).

Section 2 extends this to continuing requirements which may be designated in Regulations to prevent their initial purpose being frustrated by subsequent negligence or misuse. So far these powers have not been used (but Part III contains powers relating to existing buildings).

Sections 3, 4 and 5 relate to exemptions. These specifically exempt schools or other educational buildings controlled by the Education Act 1980, buildings of the UK Atomic Energy Authority, British Airports Authority or Civil Aviation Authority, except for a house or, in the case of the BAA, a hotel or a building used as offices or showrooms not being part of a railway station or, in the case of the BAA and CAA part of an aerodrome owned by the authority.

Public bodies may also be made exempt from the procedural requirements whilst being required to comply with the substantive requirements. Those bodies include Local Authorities, County Councils and any other bodies acting under an enactment for public purposes and not for profit (eg Health and Water authorities).

Sections 6 and 7 deal with the status of Approved Documents.

Sections 8, 9 and 10 deal with relaxations on application to the Secretary of State, and these powers may be (and have been) delegated to Local Authorities. Public Bodies have similar powers.

Section 11 deals with power for the SoS to direct that a particular type of building matter may be eligible for relaxation generally instead of only a specific case. Similarly Section 12 allows for a particular type of building matter to be approved as complying and this power may be delegated. Some Local Authorities are already combining to agree certain house types which are being erected in all their areas as suitable for this type of treatment.

Sections 14 and 15 require consultation with BRAC and with the Fire Authorities.

Section 16 requires Local Authorities to either pass plans or reject them if they are defective or show that the work would not comply, within 5 weeks (or two months if the applicant agrees). They may however pass them subject to modifications or further information being provided. It also provides for the acceptance of certificates, issued by approved persons, stating that a certain part of the work will comply with the regulations, subject to the existence of an approved scheme of insurance. Section 17 contains the powers for approving such persons. The parts of the regulations currently designated for this purpose are Schedule 1, Part A (structure) and L 2 and L 3 (resistance to the passage of heat).

Sections 18 to 29 concern certain substantive requirements described above.

Section 30 refers to determination by the SoS where there is a dispute between the Local Authority and an applicant as to the relevance of, or conformity with, Regulations.

Section 32 provides for the effect of the deposit of plans to lapse if work is not commenced within three years.

Section 33 deals with tests for conformity.

Section 35 deals with penalties for a breach.

Section 36 contains the power to require work to be pulled down or altered if it does not comply (the issue of a Section 36 notice). If the owner fails to do so the Local Authority may execute the work itself and recover the cost from the owner. These powers lapse 12 months after completion of the work and do not apply if the work conforms to plans which the Local Authority has passed or not rejected within the time limit.

Section 37 allows a person receiving such a notice to have an independent report made, and if as a result the Local Authority withdraws its notice it must recompense the owner for the costs incurred.

Sections 39 to 43 deal with appeals:

○ To the Secretary of State against the refusal of a Local Authority to grant a dispensation or relaxation

○ To a Magistrates' Court against a Section 36 notice

○ To a Crown Court if aggrieved by the decision of a Magistrates' Court

○ In certain circumstances eventually to the High Court

○ Or the Secretary of State may arrange for the appellant and the Local Authority to appear before a person appointed by him for the purpose.

Section 44 makes work on buildings for Crown Authorities subject to the substantive requirements, but not to the procedural regulations.

Section 45 deals with application to the UK Atomic Energy Authority.

Section 46 deals with the application of Part I to inner London by reference to Schedule 3.

PART II contains the new legislation to allow the supervision of building work by private certifiers.

8 Other provisions of the Building Act 1984

PART III contains a lot of legislation which parallels that in Part I but consists of general powers not directly related to Building Regulations. It gives Local Authorities wide-ranging powers to ensure that all buildings have suitable arrangements to maintain public health and safety. Thus if it appears for example, that a building has defective drainage or has inadequate closet accommodation, it must issue a notice to the owner to correct the defect or deficiency. In the event of the owner not complying, there is provision to allow the Local Authority to carry out the work and recover the costs (Section 99) and for appeal against the notice to a Magistrates' Court (Section 102). The substantive requirements are similar to those in Part I and concern (amongst other things) drainage, sanitary conveniences, entrances and exits, water supply, food storage, dangerous and dilapidated buildings or neglected sites.

Section 72 lays a duty on Local Authorities, after consultation with the Fire Authority in regard to certain buildings, to ensure that there are such means of escape from fire as they deem necessary, and if not to issue a notice requiring the necessary work to be done. The buildings to which this applies are over two storeys high with a floor more than 20 ft above ground and:

(a) Let as flats or tenements

(b) Used as an inn, hotel, boarding house, hospital, nursing home, boarding school, childrens home or similar institution.

(c) Used as a restaurant, shop, store or warehouse having an upper floor containing sleeping accommodation for employees.

This does not apply if Regulation B 1 does.

Section 74 requires the consent of the Local Authority to be obtained for the construction of a cellar below the normal ground water level for a house, shop, inn, hotel or office, but not if it forms part of a premises where a Justices' license has to be obtained.

PART IV contains the general sections on the forms of documents, powers of enforcement, appeals, compensation, prosecution etc, and interpretation.

Section 121 gives a very wide definition of 'building' which includes virtually every type of structure, including even a vehicle, vessel or aircraft if the circumstances suggest that it is being used in the manner of a building. In the Building Regulations however, a much more restricted definition is given, which has removed the necessity of providing the long list of exemptions included in the Second Amendment to the 1976 Regulations as a result of the bringing into force of Section 74(1) of the Health and Safety at Work Act 1974, which contained this all-embracing definition.

PART V contains the transitional provisions, amendments, repeals etc. The Act in general came into effect on 1 December 1984, but certain sections are held back to come into force when the SoS shall decide. Most of these appear to be connected with the time lapse before the coming into operation of the new regulations on 11 November 1985.

There are seven schedules.

Schedule 1 deals in detail with matters which may be the subject of Building Regulations and with the methods by which they may be prescribed (Section 1(3)). These are too well-established to require much comment here. They now include provisions for the acceptance of certificates of compliance, and also for the issue by Local Authorities of certificates that certain defined matters will comply with Building Regulations. Also included is the power to make prescribed persons responsible for performing the functions of Local Authorities (ie private certification).

Within the list of substantive requirements there are, in addition to those already included in Regulations, a number of items for which Regulations have never been made. These include telecommunications, lifts, escalators etc, standards of heating, artificial lighting, air-conditioning, electrical power outlets and means of access to and egress from buildings.

Building Regulations may also repeal or modify certain sections of the Act. These include the substantive requirements in both Parts I and III, and also most of Part IV. They may also repeal or modify any provisions of any Act passed before 20 September 1974 if it appears to the SoS to be inconsistent with the Regulations.

Schedule 2 deals with applications for relaxation made after the work has been carried out (Section 9(4)).

Schedule 3 deals with inner London (Sections 46, 88 and 91(2)). It has five parts which deal respectively with:

I   The application of Part I of the Act

II   The application of Part III of the Act

III   Building and drainage specific requirements which replace the normal regulations for the rest of England and Wales

IV   By-laws relating mainly to the demolition of buildings. Who will make these in the absence of the GLC is not specified

V   Enforcement: this may be exercised by Local Authorities or District Surveyors (under the new arrangements there will be 14 of these).

Schedule 4 deals with the provisions which apply when a Public Bodies Notice is issued (Section 54). These are parallel to those which apply when a private certifier is engaged.

Schedules 5, 6 and 7 deal with transitional provisions, consequential amendments and repeals.

9   Other legislation

The Building Regulations form only one part (although a very important one) of a miscellaneous and widely disseminated mass of legislation affecting buildings. The following is a list of other legislation affecting building, not necessarily comprehensive:

Factories Act 1961.

Offices, Shops and Railways Premises Act 1963.

Clean Air Act 1956.

Highways Act 1980.

Town and Country Planning Acts 1962 and 1971.

Housing Act 1961.

Cinematograph Acts 1909 and 1952.

Fire Precautions Act 1971.

Water Acts 1945, 1973, 1981 and 1983.

Control of Pollution Act 1974.

Education Act 1980.

Local Government, Planning and Land Act 1980.

Various local acts (see note below)

Some Local Authorities, mainly County Councils with large urban populations, have considered the provisions of the various Acts to be inadequate to meet their requirements. To remedy this they have obtained parliamentary consent to the making of local Acts. These remain in force. There are 25 such Acts and they are each concerned with one or more of the following:

List of requirements of particular relevance, which appear in the Local Acts

(*a*)   Requirements as to safety requirements for parking places.

(*b*)   Access for the fire brigade.

(*c*)   Fire precautions in certain large buildings.

(*d*)   Fire and safety precautions in public and other buildings.

(*e*)   Further precautions against fire in high buildings.

(*f*)   Provision of means of escape from fire in certain buildings.

(*g*)   Separate drainage systems.

(*h*)   Retaining walls.

(*i*)   Requirements as to paving of yards and passages (extended to other buildings than houses).

10   The 1985 Documents

In order to deal with an application under the Building Regulations a considerable quantity of paper is now essential (also available on microfiche). The relevant documents are:

The Building Regulations 1985 (SI 1985 No 1065) known as the principal regulations.

The Building (Approved Inspectors etc) Regulations 1985 (SI 1985 No. 1066)

The Manual to the Building Regulations 1985

Mandatory rules for means of escape in case of fire		(E)
Approved document to support Regulation 7 (Materials and workmanship)		(B)
Approved Document A	Structure	(D)
Approved Document B	Fire spread	(E)
Approved Document C	Site preparation and resistance to moisture	(C)
Approved Document D	Toxic substances	(new)
Approved Document E	Resistance to sound passage	(G)
Approved Document F	Ventilation	(K, P)
Approved Document G	Hygiene	(new and P)
Approved Document H	Drainage and waste disposal	(N)
Approved Document J	Heat producing appliances	(L, M)
Approved Document K	Stairways, ramps and guarding	(H)
Approved Document L	Conservation of fuel and power	(F, FF)
Approved Document M	Access for disabled people	(T)

(Letters in brackets indicate the parts of the 1976 Regulations which dealt with the same or similar requirements)

The Building (Prescribed Fees) Regulations 1985

NOTE   The introduction of the Building Notice procedure and private certification (with reserve powers for the Local Authorities to take over should the certifier withdraw) have considerably complicated the fee structure. However the fee payable for a Building Notice application is still the same as if full plans were submitted.

11   The Manual

This is an excellent document. It contains what has never previously been available, a complete guide to the procedures required to obtain approval under the Building Regulations.

There are three sections dealing with the following:

Section 1   The application of the Regulations.

Section 2   The procedures to be followed.

Section 3   The regulations and supporting documents.

These are followed by a reprint of the Regulations themselves with explanatory notes on the facing pages.

The three sections cover the ground so well that there seems to be no need to go through them in detail. However a few introductory comments might be appropriate.

However, certain provisions of the London Building Acts (e.g. means of storage) continue to apply in Inner London.

Application

The Regulations apply throughout England and Wales and since 1 July 1987 to inner London also*. They apply to building work in general, controlled services and fittings and to material change of use. There are some exemptions (see Schedule 3).

Repair work is not controlled, but if this involves a major reconstruction it may be.

Two systems of control

An applicant now has two options. He can apply to the Local Authority or alternatively appoint an approved private inspector. The procedures for both are set out in detail.

In practice the second alternative does not exist at the moment, since private inspectors must be covered by an approved scheme of insurance (approved by the SoS) and to date none exist (except for special arrangements made by the NHBC)

As regards the Local Authority system there are now also two options.

Full plans

The first is to deposit 'full plans'. This means plans sufficient to show that the work complies with the Regulations, with the exception of L 4 and L 5 which relate to heating systems. This is the same as the previous system and in practice is not always easy to achieve. Local Authorities building control departments vary in the amount of information they wish to see on drawings. However certificates of compliance are now permitted by Section 16(a) of the Act to be given by approved persons. The parts currently designated for this purpose are Part A (structure) and L 2/3 (energy conservation).

When full plans are submitted the Local Authority is obliged to either pass or reject them. If they pass them they are no longer able to require work to be pulled down or altered (the Section 36 procedure) if it is built in accordance with the plans.

Plans may be passed subject to specified modifications or subject to the submission of further plans. The latter allows plans to be dealt with in stages, which may be convenient both for the applicant and the Local Authority.

Building Notice

The second option is to submit only a 'Building Notice' together with a site plan and certain specific information. The developer is then not protected as described in the paragraph above. If the building is one to which B 1 (means of escape) applies and is also designated under the Fire Precautions Act 1971, full plans must be submitted. This presently applies only to offices and shops.

If the building is one of the other designated classes, ie factories, railway premises, hotels and boarding houses, consultation with the Fire Authority is essential to avoid subsequent alteration becoming necessary as a condition of issuing a fire certificate. It is in fact always advisable in all but the simplest of buildings.

Contraventions

These are dealt with under Sections 35 (fines) and 36 (removal or alteration of work) of the Act, both of which may be used in any particular case.

Other procedures

The Manual explains the procedures to be followed when seeking a dispensation or relaxation. These powers are now all delegated to Local Authorities with a right of appeal to the SoS if refused.

The situation is somewhat changed from previous procedures, because earlier Regulations were in many cases specific, and therefore needed to be relaxed or dispensed with in situations where they could be said to be unreasonably restrictive. This now only applies in the case of B 1 (mandatory means of escape rules) and L 2/3 (resistance to the passage of heat). The other requirements of Schedule 1 are 'functional', frequently simply requiring that matters be 'adequate' or 'reasonable'. Guidance on this is given in the Approved Documents and any dispute is now likely to turn on the interpretation of these in relation to the actual work, or on the 'adequate' nature of alternative methods if the Approved Document is not being followed. There is no advice as to how such disputes are to be resolved, but if the Local Authority could not be persuaded it would presumably reject the plans (where these had been deposited) under Section 16, which carries a right of appeal to the SoS.

Alternatively, if the Building Notice procedure were being used, the Local Authority would have to use a Section 36 notice and the developer would have a right of appeal to a Magistrates' Court (under Section 40). However the SoS may also be asked to determine the issue of whether the plans conform to the Regulations or the work has been executed in accordance with the plans, and it is now possible for a developer to apply for such a ruling without having the agreement of the Local Authority, as was previously the case. Presumably such a determination could deal with the question of whether plans which did not follow the recommendations of an Approved Document would meet the requirements. There appears to be no such facility where only a Building Notice has been given; perhaps another good reason for depositing plans.

12 The principal Regulations

The Manual reproduces these with explanatory notes which are useful. However, where appropriate the contents of these have been included in the notes on the Approved Documents which follow.

The notes which follow here are the author's interpretation and comments, which are intended to be complementary to, and may bring out a few points not mentioned in, the Manual.

The new document is quite short, containing only 20 Regulations and 4 Schedules.

PART I General Title, commencement and application

1   This is simply the citation and a note that they do not apply to Inner London, which has since been changed. They came into force on 11 November 1985.

Interpretation

2   This is a list of definitions. Some of these are self-evident or are described elsewhere in the Regulations. Such cases are not included here.

(1) 'Area' means the area of the finished internal surface. However, more detailed rules are given in Part B 2/3/4.

'Basement' see sketch below.

'Building' means any permanent or temporary building, but not any other kind of structure or erection. *The term includes a part of a building.*

This is a much narrower definition than the one in Section 121 of the Building Act 1984 (see item 8 above).

'Dwelling' includes a house and a flat.

'Dwelling house' does not include a flat or flat block.

'Flat' means a self-contained dwelling, divided horizontally from other parts of the building. It includes a maisonette (although in the Approved Document to Part B of Schedule 1 care is taken to always state 'flat or maisonette' as though the terms are not synonymous).

'Floor area': see diagram below.

'Height' see diagram below.

'Institution' a hospital, home, school or the like, used as living accommodation for, or treatment, care or maintenance of, persons with disabilities due to illness, old age or other disability, or under five years old, where such persons sleep on the premises.

'Office' premises used for administration, clerical work of all types including drawing and editorial work, handling money, telegraph or telephone operating.

'Shop' means premises used for retail trade (including the sale of food and drink for immediate consumption, auction sales, book lending for profit and hairdressing) and

Height

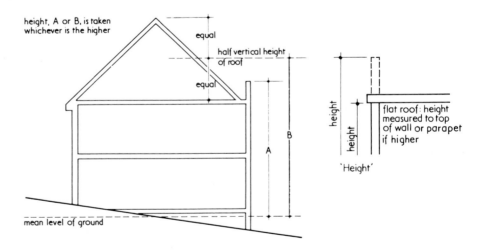

"Basement"

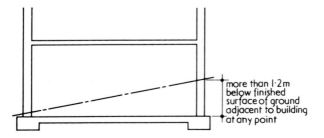

Floor area of storey of building or compartment

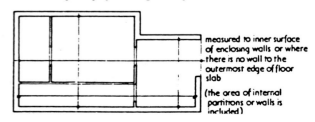

premises which the public enter to deliver items for repair or other treatment, or where they themselves carry out those processes.

These are some other definitions which are also given in paragraph L 1 of Schedule 1 and so not repeated here (see the Approved Document to Part L).

(2)   'Public building' a building containing:

(*a*)   A theatre, hall or other place to which the public are admitted, or

(*b*)   A school or other educational establishment not exempted by Section 4(1)(c) of the Act (these are schools etc controlled by the DES), or

(*c*)   A place of public worship;

but not a building containing a shop, store or warehouse or a private house to which members of the public are occasionally admitted.

(3)   A basement is not counted as a storey except in relation to A 3 of Schedule 1 (this deals with disproportionate collapse in buildings of five or more storeys including any basement levels). See also Part M.

(4)   This deals with the meaning of the words 'adversely affecting' in relation to works of alteration or extension of buildings (see Regulations 3(2) and 4(2)). It is deviously expressed, but means in effect that when a building is altered or extended the new work itself must comply with all relevant requirements and also must not cause the existing building:

(*a*)   Not to comply with any requirement with which it previously complied.

(*b*)   Not to comply with any requirement which did not previously apply to it.

(*c*)   To comply with any requirement to a lesser degree than it did.

This means that it will not generally be necessary to bring the existing part of the building up to full Regulation standard, but in certain cases it would be: e.g. the addition of a storey to a four-storey building would bring the whole building within the ambit of A 3 of Schedule 1 (disproportionate collapse). This however would not affect the application of others parts of Schedule 1 to the building.

(5)   This is even more obscure and the Manual has nothing to say on the subject. One feels that perhaps even the authors of that were baffled. What it seems to say, after omitting the fine print, is that when deciding whether the existing building will be 'adversely affected' it must be assumed:

(*a*)   That the altered or extended building is being erected in its proposed form.

(*b*)   That the existing building is being newly erected in its existing form.

What this seems to add up to is that the existing building has to be treated as being subject to the latest Regulations (not those that applied when it was built) when assessing the effect of an extension or alteration for the purpose of deciding whether they have an adverse effect.

(6)   When deciding whether any requirement of Schedule 1 or 2 applies and if so would be made less satisfactory, regard must be had to the intended use of the building after completion (some requirements of Schedule 1 apply only to specific types of building, e.g. B 1 applies to dwelling houses, some flats, shops and offices, Part E (resistance to sound) applies only to dwellings). In (4) to (6) above any reference to a building being erected includes also any provision of controlled services or fittings (controlled by the Regulations).

PART II Control of building work
Meaning of building work

3(1)   'Building work' means:

(*a*)   The erection or extension of a building.

(*b*)   The material alteration of a building.

(*c*)   The provision, extension or material alteration of a controlled service or fitting.

(*d*)   Work required by regulation 6 (material change of use)

(2)   'Material alteration' means:

(*a*)   Any work which by itself (i.e. unless other work is done), at any stage, would adversely affect the existing building in relation to Part A (structure) B 1 (means of escape) B 3 (internal fire spread structure) B 4 (external fire spread) M (access for disabled people). NOTE   This does not include, perhaps surprisingly, B 2 (fire spread, internal surfaces). Some examples of such alterations are given in the Manual as:

Removing part of a loadbearing wall, necessitating a beam.

Altering a three-storey house, requiring additional work to maintain the means of escape from the third storey.

Removing part of a non-load-bearing wall which is, however, required for fire resistance.

Removing a sanitary convenience suitable for disabled people if requirement M 3 is thereby no longer met.

(*b*)   The insertion of insulating material into a cavity.

(c)   Underpinning.

(3)   'Controlled service or fitting' means those to which G 2/3/4, H, J, and L 4/5 of Schedule 1 apply (bathrooms, unvented hot water systems, sanitary appliances, drainage and waste disposal, heat producing appliances, boiler controls and insulation of pipework etc).

Notes

○   An alteration to a service or fitting would be unlikely to affect any of the requirements mentioned in (2) above except possibly B 3, if a service penetrates separating structure. Structural alterations are a different matter.

○   'Erection' is not defined in the regulations but Section 123 of the Act states that any reference to 'construction' or 'erection' includes the carrying out of such operations (whether for the reconstruction of a building, the roofing over of an open space between walls or otherwise) as may be designated in building regulations as operations to be treated as the construction or erection of a building for regulation purposes.

○   The insertion of insulating material into a cavity must comply with C 4 (resistance to moisture) as well as with D 1 (toxic substances).

Requirements relating to building work

4(1)   Building work must be carried out so that:

(a)   It complies with the relevant requirements of Schedule 1 and

(b)   The method of complying with a requirement does not result in the failure of part of the work to comply with another.

NOTE   As mentioned above some requirements only apply to certain types of building, or are limited in other ways (see Schedule 1).

(2)   The work must be carried out so that no existing building (including any controlled service or fitting) which is extended or materially altered [see 3(2)] is adversely affected as regards compliance with the relevant requirements.

Meaning of material change of use

5   This is now more restricted than it was, as in the 1976 Regulations all types of buildings were covered, but to a varying degree. Now only the following circumstances constitute a material change of use – that the building:

(a)   Becomes a dwelling when previously it was not.

(b)   Contains a flat when previously it did not.

(c)   Is used as a hotel or institution when previously it was not.

(d)   Is a public building when previously it was not.

(e)   Was an exempted building (in classes I to VI of Schedule 3) and no longer is.

The Local Authority must always be informed of a change of use even if no work will be required. A change which does not concern the Regulations may still involve the Fire Authority (e.g. from domestic to office use).

Requirements relating to material change of use

6(1)   Where the change concerns a whole building the completed building must comply with the following parts of Schedule 1:

(a)   In all cases,

B 1   (means of escape).

B 2   (internal fire spread, surfaces).

B 3   (internal fire spread, structure).

B 4(2)   (external fire spread – roofs).

F 1 and F 2 (ventilation).

G 1   (food storage).

G 2   (bathrooms).

G 4   (sanitary conveniences).

H 4   (solid waste storage).

J 1 to J 3   (heat producing appliances).

(b)   In cases described in 5(e) A 1 to A 3 (structure) and

(c)   If the building exceeds 15 m in height B 4(1) (external fire spread – walls).

(2)   If the change applies only to part of a building, that part only need comply with the requirements in (1)(a) and (b) above. However if (1)(c) above applies (over 15 m high) then the whole building must comply with B 4(1).

NOTE   Although the whole building, after the change of use, need only comply with the above requirements, any new work that is done in the process is 'building work' (see 3(1)(d)) and hence must comply with all relevant requirements.

| **Materials and workmanship** | **7** Building work must be carried out with proper materials and in a workmanlike manner. This is a masterpiece of brevity and it is necessary to refer to the Approved Documents (see later) to decide what it means. |

| **Limitation on requirements** | **8** To comply with the requirements of 7 above and Schedule 1, nothing more need be done than is necessary to ensure the health and safety of persons in or about the building or others who may be affected by a failure to comply.
NOTE   This is something over which there has previously been much heart-searching, as it was felt that Regulations in the past were tending to become a standard of good practice, going beyond the terms of the enabling powers which refer specifically to ensuring health and safety. Just where the line may be drawn in specific circumstances may be difficult to determine. However the notes preceeding the Approved Documents do say that the acceptable levels of performance given in some of these should not be seen as the minimum standard, and that there may be cases where something less will meet the requirements. This seems something of a paradox, since something less than an acceptable level would logically be an unacceptable level, but apparently not so. In any case the so called acceptable levels of performance given in Approved Document are generally in no way specific. |

| **Exempt buildings and work** | **9** Schedule 3 contains details of six classes of buildings which are exempt, both as to their erection, and also as to any work later carried out which does not result in them becoming non-exempt. There is also a Class VII, covering such minor extensions as a carport, conservatory, greenhouse, porch, covered yard or way. |

| **PART III   Relaxation of requirements**
Powers to dispense with or relax requirements | **10**(1)   This Regulation delegates to the Local Authorities powers of the SoS under Section 8(1) of the Act to relax or dispense with any of the requirements.
(2)   If the Local Authority refuses an application it must inform the applicant of the contents of Section 39(1) and (3) of the Act (appeals against refusals etc). If the Local Authority does not notify the applicant of its decision within two months, a refusal is assumed and an appeal can be made. Under the Act an appeal must be lodged within one month of the date of the notification of refusal. The notice of appeal must set out the grounds on which it is based. It is submitted to the SoS via the Local Authority. |

| **PART IV   Notices and plans**
Giving of a building notice or deposit of plans | **11**(1)   A person intending to carry out building work or make a material change of use may either:
(*a*)   Give a Building Notice (see Regulation 12), or
(*b*)   Deposit full plans (see Regulation 13).
(2)   If the building is one to which B 1 applies and is also designated under Section 1 of the Fire Precautions Act 1971 full plans must be deposited.
In practice this means shops and offices only at the moment, although any extension of B 1 to other building types or additions to the designations under the Fire Precautions Act could change this.
A glance at the two lists below will make this clear |

Included in B 1	*Designated under the Fire Act*
Dwelling houses of 3 or more storeys*	Factories
Flats, buildings of 3 or more storeys	Offices
Offices	Shops
Shops	Railway premises
	Hotels
	Boarding houses

* Including extensions and material changes of use.

Thus if, for example, hotels or factories became subject to the means of escape requirements of B 1 it would become necessary to deposit full plans for them also.
In any case any one using the Building Notice procedure in connection with a designated

building not covered by (2) above should consult with the Fire Authority, as they will in due course require a fire certificate. In cases which are covered by (2) above the Fire Authority cannot normally ask for structural alterations as a condition of issuing a certificate.

(3)   If the work consists only of the installation of a gas heating appliance by or under the supervision of the Gas Corporation it is not subject to the Regulations.

(4)   If Regulation 18 of the Building (Approved Inspectors) Regulations 1985 applies, it supplants this Regulation.

This is where work is being supervised by an approved inspector who withdraws before it is complete. The Local Authority can then require plans of the work to enable them to take over the inspector's duties.

(5)   For the purposes of Sections 219 to 225 of the Highways Act 1980(c) which refer to advanced payments, the giving of a Building Notice is treated as the deposit and passing plans (this rule was inserted by Regulation 19(1) of the 1985 Fees Regulations (SI 1985 No 1576).

Particulars and plans where a building notice is given

12   This is a long Regulation which lists the information which must be supplied with a Building Notice.

(1)   The notice must state the name and address of the applicant, be signed by him or his agent and be accompanied by:

(*a*)   A statement that it is given in accordance with regulation 11(1)(a).

(*b*)   A description of the work or material change of use, and

(*c*)   Details of location and intended use.

(2)   In the case of the erection or extension of a building:

(*a*)   A plan to a scale of not less than 1/1250 showing:

     (i)   Its size and position in relation to adjoining boundaries.

     (ii)   The boundaries of the curtilage and the size, position and use of every other building or proposed building within that curtilage.

     (iii)   The width and position of any street on or within the said boundaries.

(*b*)   A statement of the number of storeys.

(*c*)   Particulars of:

     (i)   The provision for drainage

     (ii)   If Section 24 of the Act applies, exits etc in certain public buildings (see list of these under item 7 of these notes, p. 5), details of these.

     (iii)   If Section 18 applies (building over a sewer etc) the precautions to be taken.

     (iv)   Steps to comply with any local Act.

The item (*c*) above concerns the linked powers in the Building Act which have not been transferred to the regulations. For some reason Section 25 (water supply) is omitted. Where Section 18 is involved the Local Authority may require the owner to enter into an agreement (regarding future access).

(3)   Where the work involves the insertion of insulation into cavity walls details must be provided of:

(*a*)   The name and type of material.

(*b*)   Whether or not it is approved by the British Board of Agrément or conforms to a British Standard.

(*c*)   Whether or not the installer has a BSI certificate of registration or is approved by the BBA (see the Approved Document to C 4).

(4)   Where the work involves a hot water storage system to which G 3 relates (unvented hot water systems) the following details must be supplied:

(*a*)   The name and type of the system.

(*b*)   Whether approved by the BBA.

(*c*)   Whether the installer has been approved by the BBA (see Approved Document to G 3).

(5)   When the building notice procedure is being used, the applicant must nevertheless give to the Local Authority such plans as are necessary for the discharge of their functions as specified by them in writing. Plans in this context include drawings, specifications and any other information concerning the building (e.g. structural calculations).

NOTE   This power might be used in widely differing degrees by various Local Authorities and in some circumstances could result in the Local Authority requiring almost as much information as if full plans were being deposited. As an example Local Authorities are required to enforce the rules on means of escape in B 1 and so far as shops and offices are concerned they will have full plans to enable them to check these (regulation 11(2)). However B 1 also covers certain houses and flats which are not designated under the Fire

Precautions Act, and they might well consider that it would be inadvisable to leave the checking of means of escape in, say, large blocks of flats until they are built.

(6)   Neither a Building Notice, nor any plans given under (5) above are treated as 'deposited' (but subject to Regulation 11(5): see above).

This is to say that the Local Authority has no duty to pass or reject them and they do not confer on the applicant the protection afforded by Section 36(5) of the Act, i.e. that the Local Authority may not issue a Section 36 Notice (to pull work down) if the work is built in accordance with plans that they have passed.

Full plans

13(1)   These must be accompanied by a statement that they are deposited in accordance with Regulation 11(1)(b).

(2)   They must be in duplicate and the Local Authority may keep one copy

NOTE   Local Authorities have often in the past required more than two copies (e.g. one for the Fire Authority), but it appears that they can only request this.

(3)   Full plans shall consist of:

(*a*)   A description of the building work or change of use and all the particulars required under 12(1) to (4) above.

(*b*)   Such other plans as are necessary to show compliance with the regulations except for L 4 and 5 of Schedule 1 (heating controls and insulation of heating pipework etc).

Local Authorities can reject plans on the grounds of incomplete information, and frequently do. Under Section 16 of the Act a notice of rejection must specify the defects, or the grounds on which they have been rejected. A notice that the plans have been passed may make this subject to one or more conditions.

Notice of commencement and completion of certain stages

14(1)   The Local Authority must be notified of the following in writing, or by other means if they agree:

48 hours beforehand.

(*a*)   commencement of work

(*b*)   the covering up of:

○   Excavation for foundations.

○   The foundations themselves.

○   A damp proof course.

24 hours beforehand

○   Any concrete or other material laid over site

(*c*)   haunching or covering up of a drain or private sewer

no more than 7 days after completion

(*d*)   work involved in laying, haunching or surrounding a drain with concrete or other material and backfilling trenches

(2)   In calculating the time in hours for the above the usual weekends public holidays or any special days are not counted.

(3)   If the above notices are not given the Local Authority may, by notice, require the person carrying out the work to 'cut into, lay open or pull down' as much of the work as is necessary to check compliance with the Regulations.

(4)   where the Local Authority has issued a notice specifying the manner in which work contravenes the Regulations, and the person carrying out the work has carried out further work to correct this, he must inform the Local Authority in writing of the completion of this work 'within resonable time'.

(5)   Notice in writing, or by other means if agreed, must be given of:

(*a*)   the erection of a buildng not more than seven days after completion and (if any part is occupied before completion) not less than seven days before occupation.

(*b*)   any other work not more than seven days after completion.

PART V   Miscellaneous Testing of drains and private sewers

15   This gives Local Authorities powers to test drains for compliance with Part H.

Sampling of material

16   This gives them power to take samples for testing as necessary to check compliance with any part of the Regulations.

Supervision of building work other than by LAs	**17**(1) This disapplies Regulations 11, 14, 15 and 16 when an initial notice has been given under Section 47 of the Act, or a Public Bodies Notice under Section 54. (2) Regulations 15 and 16 do not apply to any work for which a final certificate has been given under Section 51 of the Act or paragraph 3 of Schedule 4 of the Act (in the case of public bodies) and accepted by the Local Authority. This means that the private or self certification procedure has been adopted and the Local Authority has no further duties other than checking certificates issued by the private certifier or public body. After completion the Local Authority's powers to test drains and take samples remain disapplied.
Repeals	**18** Sections 23(1) and (2) and 26 to 29 of the Act are repealed. These are the 'linked powers' concerning refuse, closets, bathrooms, food storage and sites containing offensive material which have now been included in the Regulations themselves (see C 2, G 1, G 2, G 4 and H 4 of Schedule 1).
Revocations	**19** These are specified in Schedule 4 and comprise the Building Regulations 1976 and subsequent four Amendments.
Transitional provisions	**20**(1) This is the usual arrangement to cover cases in the pipeline. Thus the new regulations do not apply to: (*a*) Plans deposited before 11 November 1985 or (*b*) Work carried out in accordance with such plans, whether or not any departure or deviation is made and in such cases the regulations and enactments specified in 18 and 19 above continue to apply.
Schedule 1 Requirements	This contains the substantive requirements and has 12 parts which broadly correspond to the parts of the 1976 Regulations (see item 10 of these notes, p 8). They are set out in the form of functional requirements and the terms 'sufficient', 'adequate' and 'reasonable' are used throughout as the means of specifying the standards required (except in B 1 and Part L where specific performance standards are set). These may clearly be subject to widely differing interpretations and hence it is necessary to refer to the Approved Documents, one or more of which are provided for use with each part (see later). The actual requirement of each part of Schedule 1 is restated at the beginning of each Approved Document.
Schedule 2 Facilities for disabled people	The original Schedule 2 contained the requirements for access for disabled people. It has now been revoked and replaced by Part M of Schedule 1 and the accompanying Approved Document. This is similar to Schedule 2 but extends the term 'relevant premises' to include the principal entrance storey of all factories, schools and public buildings which were previously restricted to single storey buildings of these types (see AD M). This limitation to certain types of building is due to lack of authoritative published material and it is expected to include further categories as more becomes available.
Schedule 3 Exempt buildings and work	Because of the more limited definition of 'building' in Regulation 2 it is no longer necessary to include the previous long list of exemptions. The revised A 5 and Schedule 2 in the second amendment to the 1976 Regulations had two parts relating to wholly and partially exempted buildings. Most of those in Part I have now been eliminated by the change mentioned above. Part II had nine classes of building, each of which was subject to several specified Regulations which varied according to the type of building. These included in each case B 1 (materials) plus two or more of the following C (site and water resistance) D (structure) E (fire) L, M (heating appliances etc) N (drains) P (sanitary conveniences). Schedule 3 has seven sections which include types of buildings very similar to those in Part II of the old Schedule 2 mentioned above. They are however now wholly exempt. A brief summary follows; for more detail refer to Schedule 3 itself.

Class I   Buildings controlled under other legislation
1   The Explosives Acts 1875 and 1923.
2   The Nuclear Installations Act 1965 (except if used as a dwelling office or canteen).
3   The Ancient Monuments Act 1979.

Class II   Buildings not frequented by people
Detached buildings not normally used by people, or visited only for the inspection of plant or machinery.

Class III   Greenhouses and agricultural buildings
1   A greenhouse unless mainly used for packing, retailing or exhibiting.
2 (1)   A building used for agriculture sited not less than 1½ times its height from any building containing sleeping accommodation, and with a fire exit not more than 30 m from any point within the building, unless the main purpose is retailing, packing or exhibiting.
2 (2)   A wide definition of agriculture is given which includes not only growing things, but also dairy or fish farming and the keeping of livestock.

Class IV   Temporary buildings
1   A building intended to remain for less than 28 days.
2   A mobile home (see the Mobile Homes Act 1983).

Class V   Ancillary buildings
1   An estate office.
2   Builders' site huts.
3   An office or showroom to a mine or quarry and not containing a dwelling.

Class VI   Small detached buildings
1   Not exceeding 30m² floor area, contains no sleeping accommodation and either:
(*a*)   More than 1m from a boundary, or
(*d*)   Single storey and of wholly non-combustible material.
2   A detached shelter against any form of attack if:
(*a*)   The floor area does not exceed 30m², and
(*b*)   The excavation is sited at a distance at least equal to its depth plus 1m from any other building.

Class VII   Extensions
The addition at ground level of:
(*a*)   A greenhouse, conservatory, porch, covered yard or way or
(*b*)   A carport open on at least two sides
in each case having a floor area not exceedng 30m².
NOTES
○   Previously only porches of 2m² or less were exempt.
○   The 30m² area limit would just allow for a carport for 2 cars,
○   Conservatory means one with a transparent or translucent roof.

Schedule   See Regulation 19.
4   Revocations

---

13   The Approved Documents

These have a somewhat curious status. They are issued by the SoS under the powers in Section 6 of the Act. Under this section they may also be issued by a body designated for that purpose by the SoS, such designation to be in the form of a Statutory Instrument, but this power has not been exercised to date. No doubt one such body could be the BSI.

They give guidance on ways of meeting the requirements and they bear a marked similarity to the old 'deemed to satisfy' regulations, but they are not now part of the law and do not need parliamentary approval for their issue or amendment. Hence they no longer need to be couched in the language of parliament or the law and can contain diagrams.

They are not mandatory and a designer can choose to use other solutions, providing these meet the requirements. Since these are based on matters being 'adequate' or 'reasonable' it may well be difficult to decide when another solution does satisfy the requirements (see item 11 under 'other procedures' p 9).

The same problem existed previously in respect of the 'deemed to satisfy' Regulations, but since there was no Building Notice procedure, the problem was not quite the same and could always be dealt with at the plans stage. It would seem that a designer would be well advised to deposit full plans if he is not using an Approved Document as the basis for any part of this design.

Although they are not the law it is stated that following the guidance in the Approved Documents will, in the event of any dispute, tend to show compliance with the Regulations. If the guidance is not followed it may be necessary to demonstrate this by other means, bearing in mind that it is only necessary to secure reasonable standards of health and safety. However, not following the guidance may be used as evidence tending to show non-compliance with the Regulations.

Approved Documents basically give three kinds of guidance:

1   Acceptable levels of performance
These amplify the requirements themselves and are sometimes helpful, but sometimes only say the same thing as the requirement in different words. Not all Approved Documents have them.

2   Technical solutions
These give detailed guidance on widely used construction methods and details. In general they contain the same material as the earlier definitive or 'deemed to satisfy' Regulations.

3   Alternative approaches
These are virtually all based on British Standards. In any case much of the material in the technical solutions has clearly been drawn from BSS, so that the alternative is not all that different. However BSS do generally give a lot more guidance which may often be helpful to a designer, regardless of Regulations.

In drawing up the Approved Documents the opportunity has, in many cases, been taken to update and expand upon the earlier Regulations. Just one example of this is Part H (drainage and waste disposal) which goes well beyond the range of the old Part N and takes in quite a lot of the latest BS on which it is based. This kind of approach seems to go against the original Heseltine approach which seemed to favour cutting down Regulations to the minimum basic requirements and leaving the rest to designers. It seems that this approach has been found impractical, probably because it would leave Local Authorities with too little guidance as to acceptable standards. It is of course true that the principal Regulations have been cut to a fraction of their former size, but the accompanying documents increase the whole thing to well beyond the size of the 1976 Regulations.

In this Guide comments are included on changes from the earlier Regulations where these appear significant.

14   Approved Inspectors

As stated earlier, the powers necessary to establish the proposed system of private certification are contained in Part II of the Act (Sections 47 to 58). In addition to private certification it also provides for self certification by specified public bodies. These are the big national corporations which are run on a profit-making basis (or theoretically should be) such as for example British Gas, British Rail, National Coal Board etc. There are about 20 of them.

The system is controlled by the Building (Approved Inspectors etc) Regulations 1985, but apart from public bodies, and a corporate scheme set up by the NHBC, is so far not operational. This is because a basic and clearly essential component is the existence of a scheme of liability insurance required in each case to protect the employer of the approved inspector against damages arising from inadequate inspection. Unlike Local Authorities, Approved Inspectors are not permanent continuing establishments. They will in due course pass on, and even whilst still here are unlikely to have the sort of resources needed to meet a hefty claim for damages. The insurance industry is known to be sceptical about the number of unknown factors and lack of experience in dealing with liability of this type and the current state of the Law Reform Committee's recommendations does not help.

It is not therefore proposed to go into any detail in this Guide, but very briefly the system is put into operation by the issue of an 'initial notice' by the Approved Inspector. This may be accompanied by, or followed by, a plans certifcate which is not essential, but if issued provides similar protection to the deposit of full plans in accordance with the principal regulations. Thereafter the Approved Inspector is responsible for supervising the work as regards the Building Regulations, provision of drainage and Section 24 of the Building Act (ingress and exits).

On completion, a final certificate that the work has been carried out in accordance with the regulations is issued. Should circumstances prevent the issue of a final certificate the LA has powers to take over.

There are provisions for the designation of bodies to approve inspectors and such approvals may specify a limitation on the extent of their field of operation (there may be more than one class of inspector).

Adequate insurance and total independence of inspectors are essential parts of the system.

15   Inner London

The Building (Application to Inner London) Regulations 1985 are now in force. They apply to the Inner London Boroughs, the Temples and the City and bring into action not only the Building Regulations 1985, but also the Building (Approved Inspectors) Regulations 1985 and the Building (Prescribed Fees) Regulations 1985 in these districts. There are the usual transitional arrangements for plans or work in the pipeline.

In the past control has been exercised by means of the London Building Acts and byelaws made under them administered by the GLC and District Surveyors. However matters concerning sanitary conveniences, drainage and waste disposal were administered by the inner London Boroughs under local byelaws.

With the abolition of the GLC, the whole of the national Regulations will be administered by the boroughs. However some parts of the London Building Acts will remain in force in modified form, and these will still be enforced by a reduced body of District Surveyors (14 instead of the previous 28).

There are three schedules:

Schedule 1 contains amendments to the three sets of Building Regulations (principal, approved inspectors and fees) consequential upon their application to inner London.

Schedule 2 contains modifications to various sections of the London Building Acts (Amendment) 1939 and the LCC (General Powers) Act 1955.

In particular, Section 20, which concerns special precautions against fire in large buildings, is modified. The section now applies only in special circumstances where precautions are needed beyond those imposed by building regulations. It applies to buildings over 28m high and buildings of the warehouse class, or used for trade or manufacture, exceeding 7100m^3 unless sub-divided in the manner required to form a 'separate part' in the Regulations. It allows for the provision of fire alarms, extinguishers, smoke control and access for the fire brigade. Special provisions may also be required when mechanical plant is installed or inflammable substances are stored.

For these buildings the builder will still have to supply full details of the scheme as at present, and the Council may impose conditions.

Similar powers have been taken by Councils in large conurbations by means of local Acts. In the future these powers may be transferred to the regulations as a functional requirement supported by an Approved Document.

Powers are also retained in respect of special and temporary structures and rights of adjoining owners (Sections 29 and 46).

Section 34 is retained to control means of escape from fire in buildings not covered by Part B 1 of the Regulations.

Part VII (dangerous and neglected structures) is also retained.

Schedule 3 repeals various parts of the London Building Acts, LCC and GLC general powers legislation and the whole of the Thermal Insulation (Industrial Buildings) Act. The latter is no longer required since all buildings are now covered by Part L of the Regulations, including those in London.

The repeals include *all* of the provisions of the London Constructional Byelaws and District Surveyors' fees byelaws and all references to byelaws in the London Building Acts have been repealed.

This is an amending measure, and as such it cannot be used without reference to a great many other documents, which will make life very difficult for those operating in Inner London. It is to be hoped that in future a consolidating measure will be produced, say in the shape of a special set of regulations for London which will include those parts of the London

Building Acts which remain in force, or at least a document containing only those parts to be used alongside the national Regulations.

However since virtually all the requirements of the Building Regulations now apply, this Guide should be equally useful in Inner London.

16   Fees

Because of the other changes the fees Regulations have had to be changed. It seems a pity that a matter of legal administration for the public good should have to be subject to fees at all, but the first act of the 1979 Tory government in changing the regulation system was to rule that it should be 'totally self-financing'.

Logically one could have said the same thing about the police, fire brigade or health service. Nevertheless the first change made was the imposition of fees for Building Regulations procedures, followed in short order by a similar system for planning applications. What springs to mind when looking at the latest revision, viz the Building (Prescribed Fees) Regulations 1985 is part of the old saw 'Oh what a tangled web we weave'. The institution of the Building Notice procedure and the private certification system has necessitated the introduction of new scales. In practice these are not too complicated as the fees for a Building Notice application are the same as those where full plans are submitted (one does not get any reduction because plans no longer have to be passed or rejected). As regards private certification, a fee known as a reversion fee becomes payable if the Local Authority has to take over due to the cancellation of an 'initial notice' (i.e. because the private certifier is for some reason unable to continue his supervision). In this case the fees chargeable by the Local Authority are the same as if a new application had been made.

No fees are payable where the work is solely for the benefit of disabled people.

There are four schedules giving the fee scales:

Schedule 1
(a)   For single small domestic buildings where the fee is £65 for each dwelling in the building, plus an extra for dwellings over 64m^2.
(b)   In a multiple scheme, which might comprise single dwellings or a group of buildings containing several dwellings, there is a formula which is an extrapolation of (a) above.

Schedule 2
This deals with small garages and carports and small domestic extensions or alterations for which fixed fees are set beteen £32 and £64 inclusive. The size limit here is 40m^2 but note that carports upto 30m^2 are now exempt under Schedule 3 of the principal regulations.

Schedule 3
This deals with all other cases where the fee is based on 70 per cent of 'a reasonable written estimate' of the cost of the building, which has to be supplied with the deposited plans or Building Notice. As before, there are two scales, a plans fee and an inspection fee which is 3 times the plans fee. A Building Notice fee is equal to the total of both.

The same anomaly as before persists; namely that at the lower end of the scale the total fee amounts to 1.2 per cent of the cost (at £1,000) reducing as one might expect to 0.42 per cent at £1,000,000. Thereafter however it increases to 0.79 per cent on each successive million.

Schedule 4
This deals with fees for the determination of questions by the SoS.

The most recent amendment is the Building (Amendment of prescribed fees) Regulations 1988 (SI 1988 No 871) which merely raises fees for small domestic buildings in line with inflation.

17   References and sources

The publications listed here are all published by HMSO (unless otherwise stated).

Acts of Parliament
The Fire Precautions Act 1971.
The Health and Safety at Work Act 1974.
The Building Act 1984.

Ministry of Public Building and Works
The Building Regulations 1965 Technical Memoranda Fire-Stairs-Space.

Ministry of Housing and Local Government/Welsh Office
The Building Regulations 1965 Town Centres and Shopping Precincts (MHLG 19/69 WO 22/69).
Circular 17/68 and 11/68 The Building Regulations 1965 Multi-storey car parks.

Department of the Environment/Welsh Office
The Building Regulations 1976 (SI 1976 No 1676).
The Building (First Amendment) Regulations 1978 (SI1978 No 723).
The Building (Second Amendment) Regulations 1981 (SI 1981 No 1338).
The Building (Third Amendment) Regulations 1983 (SI 1983 No 195).
The Building (Fourth Amendment) Regulations 1985.
The Future of Building Control in England and Wales (Command Paper 8179 of February 1981).
The Building Regulations 1985 (SI 1985 No 1065).
Manual to the Building Regulations 1985.
Mandatory rules for means of escape in case of fire 1985.
Approved Documents to Regulation 7 and Parts A to M of Schedule 1.
The Building (Approved Inspectors) Regulations 1985 (SI 1985 No 1066).
The Building (Prescribed Fees) Regulations 1985.
The Building (Disabled People) Regulations 1987 (SI 1987 No 1445)

Department of Education and Science
Design Note 18 (1984) Access for disabled people to educational buildings.

British Standards Institution
Specifications and Codes of Practice as listed at the end of each set of notes on the Approved Documents.

Addresses of organisations whose publications are referred to in the Approved Documents:
Association of Structural Fire Protection Contractors and Manufacturers, 45 Sheen Lane, London, SW14 8AB (01-876 4415).
British Standards Institution, Sales Office, Linford Wood, Milton Keynes, MK14 6LE (0908 320066).
BSI Certification and Assessment Service (Kitemarks), PO Box 375, Milton Keynes, MK14 6CO (0908 315555).
Building Research Establishment (BRE), Garston, Watford, WD2 7JR (09273 674040).
Chartered Institution of Building Services Engineers, Delta House, 222 Balham High Road, London, SW12 9BS (01-675 5211).
Constrado, NCA Tower, Addiscombe Road, Croydon, CR9 3JH (01-688 2688).
Fire Offices' Committee, (now part of the Association of British Insurers), Aldermary House, 10 Queen Street, London, EC4N 1TT (01-248 4477).
Fire Protection Association, 140 Aldersgate Street, London, EC1A 4HX (01-606 3757).
Fire Research Station, Melrose Avenue, Borehamwood, Herts, WD6 2BL (01-953 6177).
HMSO, PO Box 276, London, SW8 5DT.
Institution of Electrical Engineers, Savoy Place, London, WC2R 0BL (01-240 1871).
NATLAS Accreditation Scheme for Testing Laboratories, National Physical Laboratory, Teddington, Middx.

APPROVED DOCUMENT TO SUPPORT REGULATION 7
Materials and workmanship

Unlike the other ADs all of which relate to one of the 11 parts of Schedule 1, this relates directly to one of the principal Regulations. It is a masterpiece of brevity, as follows:

Materials and workmanship

   7 Any building work shall be carried out with proper materials and in a workmanlike manner.

As the Manual points out, it supplements Schedule 1, all parts of which are subject to its requirements.

It replaces Part B of the 1976 Regulations and also A16 (short-lived and unsuitable materials), but contains more points of reference than Part B, which referred only to British Standards. The authors have clearly been faced with the problem that afflicts all specifiers; how to define an acceptable standard without asking for perfection.

There is a list of acceptable levels of performance which expand on the regulation itself as follows:

0.1   Materials should be:

(*a*)   Of a suitable nature and quality in relation to the purposes and conditions of their use, and

(*b*)   Adequately mixed or prepared, and

(*c*)   Applied, used or fixed so as to perform adequately the functions for which they are intended.

Materials include products, components, fittings, items of equipment and backfilling for excavations in connection with building work.

0.2   For Parts A to K of Schedule 1 the standards of material and workmanship need to be no more than necessary to ensure the health and safety of persons in or about the building.

NOTE   It would seem that herein lies the safeguard against the possibility of too high a standard being demanded by the controlling authority.

0.3   For Part L they need to be no more than needed to restrict calculated heat losses to the levels set out in the Schedule.

0.4   For schedule 2 they need be no more than necessary to serve their purpose (this hardly needs saying!).

0.5   The Regulations contain no provisions for continuing control over the use of materials following completion of the building.

NOTE   The inclusion or otherwise of continuing control has been raised in the past, but not adopted. However Section 76 of the Building Act 1984 does give Local Authorities power to take remedial action where they consider that premises are in a 'defective state' (prejudicial to health), or require the owner to do so.

The Approved Document is divided into two sections, Materials (1) and Workmanship (2). Part B concerned itself with materials only.

A number of aids to establishing the fitness of both are described. These are not mandatory (see 1.1 below) but it remains to be seen how Local Authorities will react to the emphasis now being placed on reference to increasingly numerous standard-setting bodies. Is it going to become necessary to back up applications by references to compliance with BSI or other standards for virtually every item in the building? Even today drawings submitted for approval are usually peppered with notes reading 'Type No. 000 to BS 0000: 1985' and the like, although the designer (and possibly the Building Control Officer) may well have little knowledge of the contents of that particular British Standard. Sticking the reference on the drawing covers them both. It is already clear that the new Regulations herald the advancement of a period (already well started) of living with an increasingly complex set of technical standards, the understanding of which requires a breadth of technical knowledge way beyond the average designer or specifier. Even to track down the relevant parts of a BS may be a time-consuming operation, and it is one of the objectives of this Guide to make life a bit easier by summarising the most essential parts of British Standards or other references.

Section 1   Materials

1.1   The Approved Documents contain references to materials and products likely to be suitable by reference to BSS or Agrément Certificates which cover them. Such references are not exclusive and other materials may be suitable in particular circumstances.

Ways of establishing fitness
1.2   The following aids may be useful:

BS 000

[**10**] *BSI Kitemark*

(*a*)   *Past experience* The material may be considered suitable because it has behaved satisfactorily in a building in use.

(*b*)   *Agrément Certificates* The material and the conditions of use are in accordance with the certificate.

(*c*)   *British Standards* The material and conditions of use conform to an appropriate British Standard.

(*d*)   *Independent certification schemes* The only one referred to is the BS Kitemark scheme (see illustration [10])

If so marked the material can be taken to conform to the relevant BS, but unmarked materials may still conform.

(*e*)   *Quality schemes* The material is covered by a scheme complying with BS 5750 *Quality Systems*. The BSI operate a number of schemes of 'Registration of Firms of Assessed Capability' relating to specific groups of products or processes (e.g. cavity foam filling) which may or may not also be covered by a BS.

(*f*)   *Tests and calculations* It can be shown by test or calculation that the material can perform adequately. The NATLAS accreditation scheme for testing laboratories is one way of ensuring that the tests are conducted to recognised standards.

(*g*)   *Sampling* Local Authorities have power to take such samples as they deem necessary to establish compliance with Schedule 1 (Regulation 16).

Short-lived materials
This is a rather sloppy section which gives very little guidance on which materials might be considered unsuitable and much will now depend on the judgement or prejudices of the individual building control official.

It replaces A16 of the 1976 Regulations. This drew its authority from Section 53 of the Public Health Act 1936 which allowed Local Authorities to reject plans showing the use of materials, specified in Building Regulations, which in the absence of special care were liable to rapid deterioration, or to impose a time limit on the building or conditions as to its use. This is now replaced by Section 19 of the Building Act 1984 (Section 20, which is similar but covers a wider field may replace Section 19 by order of the Secretary of State). A.16 defined such materials by reference to Schedule 5 which contained two tables listing materials for the weather resisting parts of walls and roofs and in addition any material, flexible or rigid, which formed the skin of an air supported structure.

This was surely preferable to the new Regulations which are not specific and the Approved Document which is not much more so.

The following is a summary:

1.3   Some materials in the absence of special care may be unsuitable because of their rapid deterioration in relation to the life of the building. It is not possible to lay down specific criteria in relation to the Regulations (although the old Regulations did). Often the choice is influenced by economic factors which are not proper considerations as matters affecting health and safety.

1.4   Short-lived materials which are readily accessible for maintenance or replacement may be acceptable if the consequences of failure are not likely to have a serious effect on health or safety.

1.5   Such materials, if not readily accessible and where failure is likely to have a serious effect on health or safety are unlikely to be suitable. However if failure is likely to have only a minor effect on health or safety the use of the materials may be admissible.

The last item seems to be a built in source of controversy.

Resistance to moisture etc.
Here we are on firmer ground.

1.6   Any material which may be adversely affected by condensation, ground moisture, rain or snow will meet the requirements if:

(*a*)   The construction will resist the passage of moisture to the material, or

(*b*)   The material is treated or protected from moisture

1.7   Any material in contact with the ground should be able to resist attacks by deleterious substances in the subsoil such as sulphates (see Approved Document C1/2/3 Section 2).

High alumina cement (HAC)

1.8   Any material containing high alumina cement should only be used as a heat-resisting material and never in structural work or foundations.

House longhorn beetle

1.9   In the areas specified softwood used for roof construction, or within the roof space (including ceiling joists), should be treated with a suitable preservative to prevent infestation by the house longhorn beetle (*Hylotrupes bajulus L.*)

The earlier B 4 was more detailed and gave two specific treatments, plus a reference to BS 4072: 1974.

Geographical area

The District of Bracknell

The Borough of Elmbridge

The Borough of Guildford (other than the area of the former borough of Guildford)

The District of Hart (other than the area of the former urban district of Fleet)

The District of Runnymede

The Borough of Spelthorne

The Borough of Surrey Heath

In the Borough of Rushmore, the area of the former district of Farnborough

The District of Waverley (other than the parishes of Godalming and Haslemere)

In the Royal Borough of Windsor and Maidenhead, the parishes of Old Windsor, Sunningdale and Sunninghill

The Borough of Woking

Section 2   Workmanship

This is really just a repeat of 1.2 above.

2.1   The following aids may be useful in establishing the adequacy of workmanship:

(*a*)   *Past experience* A method of workmanship may be shown to be adequate because of its performance in use.

(*b*)   *Agrément certificates* The method specified and the conditions of use are in accordance with the terms of the certificate.

(*c*)   *British Standards* The method is covered by an appropriate British Standard.

(*b*)   Quality assurance schemes The method is covered by a scheme which complies with BS 5750 *Quality systems*, such as a scheme of registration of firms of assessed capability. These schemes may relate to products which are also covered by a BS.

(*e*)   *Tests* Regulation 15 enables Local Authorities to make tests for compliance with Part H of Schedule 1 for:

(i)   Sanitary pipework and drainage.

(ii)   Cesspools, septic and settlement tanks.

(iii)   Rainwater drainage.

Guidance on testing is contained in Approved Documents H 1 and H 3.

Approved Document A: Structure

Part A contains three requirements. There are two Approved Documents – the first and largest covers requirements A1/2 – *Loading and ground movement*, the second, A 3, deals with *Disproportionate collapse*. The first covers the same ground as the old D 3 – *Foundations* and D 8 – *Structure above foundations*, with their attached 'deemed-to-satisfy' clauses. The second is equivalent of D 17 – *Further requirements for the structure of certain buildings*, designed to prevent undue damage arising from accidental causes and introduced in 1970 following the Ronan Point collapse.

A 1/2   LOADING AND GROUND MOVEMENT

The new regulations read as follows:

	Requirement	Limits on application
	Loading	
Structure	A 1. – (1) The building shall be so constructed that the combined dead, imposed and wind loads are sustained and transmitted to the ground—	
	(a) safely, and	
	(b) without causing such deflection or deformation of any part of the building, or such movement of the ground, as will impair the stability of any part of another building.	
	(2) In assessing whether a building complies with sub-paragraph (1) regard shall be had to the imposed and wind loads to which it is likely to be subjected in the ordinary course of its use for the purpose for which it is intended.	
	Ground movement	
Structure	A 2. The building shall be so constructed that movements of the subsoil caused by swelling, shrinkage or freezing will not impair the stability of any part of the building.	

General

The first thing to note is that there is an essential difference from D 3 and D 8 which referred to loads being transmitted in such a way as not to 'impair the stability or cause damage to' the building. This is no longer required provided the loads are transmitted 'safely' and do not impair the stability of *another* building. This is following through the principle that building regulations should be concerned only with matters of 'health and safety'. The cost and inconvenience of repairing damage is for someone else to worry about.

There are two sections each covering A 1 and A 2 jointly. Section 1, which contains five parts is concerned only with 'certain structural elements of houses and other small buildings', a very limited field. It may seem *prima facie* a little odd therefore that it occupies some 48 out of the total 54 pages in the document. However, on reflection, it may be observed that this class of building forms a very large part of the output of the building industry. Furthermore, it is far from being simply a set of statutory requirements, but is in fact a valuable guide for designers, who in this case do not need to be highly specialised structural engineers. Where else would we have obtained our wall thicknesses and timber sizes in the past without schedules 6 and 7 and their predecessors? For the purist this, no doubt, is stepping outside the true field of the regulations, but it has the advantage of satisfying both designers' requirements and the law at the same time. Its removal would provoke a storm of protest. Section 2 covers the remainder of the field and is simply a list of references to British Standards covering the various structural forms, with one or two specific directions as to their use.

Introduction to the provisions

This outlines the general philosophy regarding structural safety.

0.1   The safety of the structure depends on the successful combination of design and construction, particularly:

(*a*)   Loading, where dead and imposed loads should be in accordance with BS 6399: Part 1 and wind loads in accordance with CP 3: Chapter V: Part 2.

(*b*)   Properties of materials.

(*c*)   Design analysis.

(*d*)   Details of construction.

(*e*)   Safety factors.

(*f*)   Workmanship.

0.2   Defines three approaches to meeting the requirements by using:

(*a*)   Section 1 Relevant to small buildings of traditional masonry construction. Part B (timber elements) and C (walls) are the important parts, and strangely there is a difference in the types of buildings to which each refers – single family houses for Part B and residential buildings, annexes and small buildings for Part C (see later for fuller description).

(*b*)   Section 2 Relevant to all building types. Where the building codes are not precise regard is to be had to 0.1.

(*c*)   Other approaches. If these are used, regard to be had to 0.1. Numerical values of safety factors, explicit or implicit, in equations or design values to be derived from the aspects of design and construction given in 0.1 *as a whole*. Any change in one aspect may affect safety. Loads used are to allow for possible dynamic, concentrated and peak effects.

Section 1

Sizes for certain structural elements for houses and other small buildings

1.1   The section is arranged in five parts:

A   Basic requirements for stability.

B   Sizes of timber members in single family houses not over three storeys high.

C   Masonry walls in certain residential buildings not over three storeys and small single-storey buildings and annexes.

D   Masonry chimneys.

E   Strip foundations of plain concrete.

Comment

Why there is a difference in the designations of the building types to which B and C apply is not (and never has been) clear.

1.2   Parts B to E may be used independently of each other.

Definitions

The following are given (wording summarised):

Buttressing wall designed to afford lateral support to a wall at right angles, extending from base to top.

Compartment wall: constructed to meet requirements of Regulation B 3(2).

Dead load: due to weight of all walls, permanent partitions, floors, roofs, finishes, services and all permanent construction.

Imposed load assumed to be produced by occupancy or use including movable partitions, distributed, concentrated, impact, inertia and snow loads but excluding wind loads.

Pier: a thickened section at intervals along a wall.

Separating wall: common to adjoining buildings to satisfy Regulation B 3(2).

Spacing: least distance between centres of adjacent timber members of the same type (see diagram [1.3])

Span: distance between centre of bearings, except in Part B where spans for timber members are clear spans between faces of supports (see diagram [1.4]).

Supported wall: one to which lateral support is given by buttressing walls, piers or chimneys in conjunction with floors and roofs.

Wind load: due to effect of wind pressure or suction.

PART A   Basic Requirements for Stability

A 1   This part is to be used in conjunction with parts B and C.

A 2   Trussed rafter roofs to be braced as recommended in BS 5268: Part 3: 1985. Traditionally framed roofs without sufficient built in stability (e.g. hips, rigid sarking, etc) should also be braced in a similar way.

A 3   If the roof is braced as above, adequately anchored to the structure below and walls designed as in part C, no special provisions should be needed against wind loads.

Part B   Sizes of certain timber floor, ceiling and roof members in single family houses

B 1/2   The part applies only to single family houses not exceeding 3 storeys and is to be used with Part A.

B 3   The following assumptions are made:

(*a*)   Dead and imposed loads will not exceed the values given in the tables. (NOTE The imposed loads are the same as those given in BS 6399: Part 1 – see Section 2)

(*b*)   Species and grades of timber to be used are stated in table **B 1**. There is a more comprehensive table in BS 5268: Part 2: 1984.

(*c*)   Floor boarding is to comply with BS 1297: 1970(1980).

B 4   Strength classes, species, grades etc. are as defined in BS 5268: Part 2: 1984.

B 5   Sectional dimensions are basic sawn sizes as given in BS 4471: Part 1: 1987 and the tables cannot be used if these have been reduced by planing etc. North American sizes (indicated by an asterisk) are surfaced sizes. NOTE These seem only to occur in the 38 mm width. Sometimes this timber may be resawn to BS 4471 requirements.

B 6   Notches and holes – see diagram [**1.5**].

B 7   Bearing areas and workmanship are to comply with BS 5268: Part 2.

Spans and spacing

B 8   In tables B 3 to 28 all spans, except floorboards, are clear spans between faces and spacings are between centres, see diagrams [**1.3–1.4**].

Tables [**1.1**] *Flat roofs: includes all pitches up to 10°.*

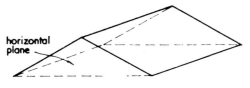

Tables [**1.2**] *Measurements per m² are to be in horizontal plane.*

[**1.1–5**] *Illustration of terms and rules for timber construction.*

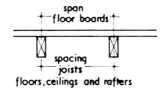

floors, ceilings and rafters

[**1.3**] *Span: floorboards.*

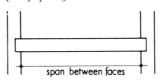

B 8 [**1.3**] *Span: joists*

Table B 1
For convenience this is included below.

Table to **B 1** **Common species/grade combinations,** which satisfy the requirements for the strength classes to which Tables B 2 to B 28 relate[1]

| Species | Origin | Grading rules[2] | Grades to satisfy strength class | |
			SC3	SC4
Redwood	imported	BS 4978	GS, M50	SS, M75†
Whitewood	imported	BS 4978	GS, M50	SS, M75†
Douglas Fir-Larch	Canada	BS 4978	GS	SS
	Canada	joist and plank	No. 1, No. 2	select
		structural light framing	No. 1, No. 2	select
Hem-Fir	Canada	BS 4978	GS, M50	SS, M75
		joist and plank	No. 1, No. 2	select
		structural light framing	No. 1, No. 2	select
Spruce-Pine-Fir	Canada	BS 4978	GS, M50	SS, M75
		joist and plank	No. 1, No. 2	select
		structural light framing	No. 1, No. 2	select
Western Whitewoods	USA	BS 4978	SS	
		joist and plank	select	
		structural light framing	select	
Southern Pine	USA	BS 4978	GS	SS
		joist and plank	No. 1, No. 2, No. 3	select
		structural light framing	No. 1, No. 2, No. 3	select
		light framing	Construction*	
		stud	Stud*	
Douglas Fir	UK	BS 4978	M50, SS	M75
Scots Pine	UK	BS 4978	GS, M50	SS, M75†
European Spruce	UK	BS 4978	M75	
Sitka Spruce	UK	BS 4978	M75	

Notes

[1] The common species/grade combinations given in this Table are for particular use with the other Tables in this Part and for the cross section sizes given in those Tables.
Definitive and more comprehensive tables for assigning species/grade combinations to strength classes are given in BS 5268: Part 2: 1984.

[2] The grading rules for American and Canadian Lumber are those approved by the American Lumber Standards Board of Review and the Canadian Lumber Standards Accreditation Board respectively (see BS 5268: Part 2 1984)

* Only 38 mm × 89 mm cross section.

† These species/grade combinations given under SC4 may qualify for SC5 but have been listed here for use with the table.

AUTHOR'S NOTE Although the machine grades MGS and MSS are not mentioned in the table, BS 5268 includes them as being equal to GS and SS respectively.

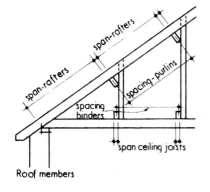

B 8 [**1.4**] *Span: roof members.*

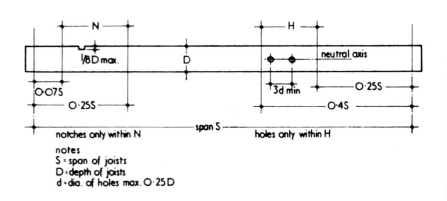

notes
S = span of joists
D = depth of joists
d = dia. of holes max. 0·25 D

B 6 [**1.5**] *Notches and holes.*

Notes on British Standards	Generally the recommendations given in Approved Documents (previously in deemed-to-satisfy Regulations), such as the foregoing, are drawn from British Standards (BSS). In addition the reader is often referred to the standards themselves, which usually provide a great deal more useful information, although it may take some time and trouble to track down. To assist the reader, in accordance with the general policy of this Guide, a brief description of those used in this Part is given below.
BS 1297: 1970	This gives rules regarding the timber quality, defects and manufacture of floorboards.
BS 4471: Part 1: 1978	This defines the rules as to sizing. Generally softwood for carcassing is sawn and any further treatment, planing, machining etc involves reduction of sizes by allowances which are specified. This means they are not acceptable as full sized structural sections. Some Canadian timber is however supplied surfaced (known as CLS) and is marked in the tables.
BS 4978: 1973	This deals with 'timber grades for structural use', previously contained in CP 112: 1971 (now superseded). Originally it specified four grades, GS and SS, (visually graded), MGS and MSS (machine graded). These were applied to the tables of sizes in schedule 6, the SS and MSS grades being rated higher than the other two. The BS had been much amended (the last in 84) firstly to bring back the grades M70 and M75 from CP 112, which are also machine graded, and more recently to introduce reference to strength classes as defined in BS 5268: Part 2: 1984. It does not define the stresses appropriate to these grades, this being done in BS 5268.
BS 5268: Part 2: 1984	This replaces CP 112: Part 2: 1971. It introduces the concept of 'strength classes' of which two (SC 3 and SC 4) are used in the tables to Part B. It includes more comprehensive tables for assigning species and grades to strength classes than are given in Table B 1 above. The grades are those defined in BS 4978 and also those set by the Canadian and USA Lumber Standards Boards. In addition to allocating grades to strength classes, the BS also gives comprehensive tables showing the actual stresses (shear, bending, compression etc) which can be taken by the various species/grade combinations. In assigning these to strength classes account cannot be taken of compression stresses at bearing, which must be individually calculated. The BS also requires lateral stiffening of one or both flanges, or between, as the depth to width ratio increases. This is not required in the tables although it is common practice to use strutting between floor joists. It is also interesting to note that part B defines spans as clear spans whereas the BS gives them as between centres of bearings. The BS assumes that its contents will be used by qualified designers, e.g. civil or structural engineers. There is a comprehensive section on workmanship including moisture content, machining, joints, storage, assembly, inspection and maintenance.
BS 5268: Part 3: 1985	This is mentioned in part A. It replaces CP 112: Part 3 for trussed rafter construction. This includes recommendations for bracing which may also be applied to other roofs (see A 2). It also deals with potential condensation problems requiring ventilation.

Table B 2
This is the key to the 26 tables which give sizes for all the normal timber members used in this type of building (B 3 to B 28). They have always been one of the most useful (as opposed to restricting) parts of the regulations. They are not included in BS 5268 which merely gives the necessary data for designing them, and they represent a considerable body of work.
For quick reference table B 2 is summarised below

Members	Table numbers
Floor joists	3 and 4
Ceiling joists	5 and 7
Binders for ceiling joints	6 and 8
Common rafters	9, 11, 13, 15, 17, 19
Purlins supporting rafters	10, 12, 14, 16, 18, 20
Roof joists	21, 22, 23, 24
Purlins for sheeted roofs	25, 26, 27, 28

All categories include two separate strength classes, SC 3 and SC 4. The figures for rafter roofs include 3 different slopes and those for sheeted roofs 2 different slopes. Figures for flat roofs include for those with maintenance access only and with normal access. The strength classes are as determined in Table B 1. Each table has a diagram illustrating the meaning of the terms span and spacing in relation to the members involved. These are shown in the general illustration following B 8.

Notes to tables
Each table has a note to the effect that the dead load is the load supported by the member excluding its selfweight and a note concerning the superimposed loads allowed. These are taken from BS 6399: Part 1: 1984. (see Section 2).

Comparison with Schedule 6
The tables are generally very similar to (but not the same as) those in the 1976 Regulations Schedule 6. The differences are:
(1)   There are two more tables resulting from splitting the last category, purlins for sheeted or decked roofs, into two sections, those from 10° to 30° and 30° to 35° pitch. The more restrictive are those over 30°, but only by about 2 per cent which hardly seems worth the trouble. Schedule 6 did not specify any maximum slope for this type of roof.
(2)   Spans are given as clear spans whereas in Schedule 6 they were between centres of bearings. In effect, assuming a normal effective bearing of 75 mm at each end, this means that the spans as listed in the new tables would be 75 mm shorter. A general check through shows them to be shorter, but not to that extent, which suggest that improved accuracy in grading technique etc has allowed slightly higher stresses to be used.
(3)   The loadings now used are those given in BS 6399, basically 1.5 kN/m² for floors and 0.75 kN/m² for roofs, whereas schedule 6 used the slightly reduced figures allowed for this type of building, viz. 1.44 and 0.72 respectively, in the regulations. This hardly worth while deviation from the BS was a leftover from Imperial standards which now seems to have been abandoned. This change would also suggest a reduction in the allowable spans which has not in fact happened.
(4)   Some additional sizes have been included, both imported and UK, so the tables are now longer.
(5)   The 44 mm width has been dropped in favour of 47 mm. The reason for this is unclear since 44 mm was the half way mark between the sizes on either side.

Floorboards
These are to be tongued and grooved and at least 16 mm for joists up to 450 mm centres, 19 mm over 450 and up to 600 mm centres. Where spans of continuous members (e.g. rafters, purlins) are unequal the larger span is to be used (which hardly needed saying).

Comment
(1)   As stated earlier the span figures in the tables are generally slightly more generous than those in Schedule 6, although this is partly concealed by the use of clear span, instead of centre to centre figures. It is also interesting to note that although rafter spans increase as the roof pitch rises, due to the decrease in the imposed load, the spans of the purlins supporting them actually decrease. This may have to do with the effect on the moment of resistance of the purlin being set at right angles to the roof (instead of vertically), but this did not show up in Schedule 6.
(2)   Spans are given to two places of decimals (i.e. metres and centimetres). Care is needed when adding small dimensions given in mm not to misplace the decimal point.
Readers are referred to Tables B 3 to B 28 for the selection of timber sizes (but see below).

Tables B 3 to B 28	The tables each present a formidable block of dimensions which are anything but easy for quick reference. Furthermore, they give no visual impression of the relationship between the four variables of size, span, load and spacing. The graphs which follow do however give an immediate picture of these relationships, and they should be useful for making a rapid assessment of the alternative possibilities available in any particular element of structure.

In the interests of clarity not all of the tabulated figures are charted. For example, the joist tables give sizes for dead load values of under 0.25 kN/m², 0.25 to 0.5 kN/m² and 0.5 to 1.25 kN/m², and for spacings of 400mm, 450mm, and 600mm centres. The graphs show directly only the 0.25 to 0.5 kN and 0.5 to 1.25 kN/m² figures and the 400mm and 600mm figures, but it is a simple matter visually to interpolate between the appropriate graph lines whenever an intermediate value is desired. Even the tables do not cover all possibilities, and spacing of joists frequently has to be something in between the figures given. The figure of 0.25 to 0.5 kN/m² has been chosen as the lower of the two dead load figures in preference to under 0.25 kN/m² as the lower figure would be unlikely to occur often in practice. Similar principles have been adopted in other tables where different dead load brackets are used: i.e. in each case one load classification is left out and the other two brackets only are shown. The tables also show a 47mm timber width which has been omitted, as have the three Northern American sizes which are intermediate between some of the 25mm depth increases. Here again, using the graphs it is easy to interpolate for any intermediate size.

Table B 3: floor joists.
Joist sizes to take an imposed load of 1.5 kN/m² plus a dead load of not more than 0.5 kN/m² or 1.25 kN/m² for spacing of joists as shown. Strength class SC3.

Joists at 400mm centres shown as continuous line.
Joists at 600mm centres shown as broken line.

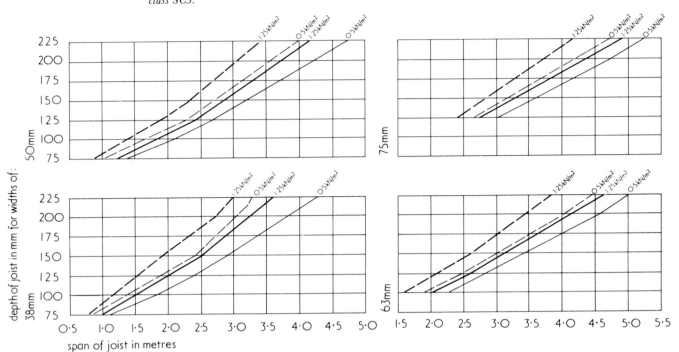

Table B 4: floor joists.
Joist sizes to take an imposed load of 1.5 kN/m² plus a dead load of not more than 0.5 kN/m² or 1.25 kN/m² for spacing of joists as shown. Strength class SC4.

Joists at 400mm centres shown as continuous line.
Joists at 600mm centres shown as broken line.

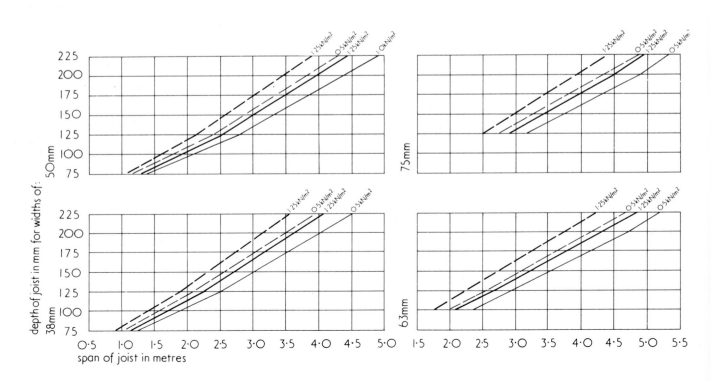

Table B 5: ceiling joists.
Joist sizes to take an imposed load of 0.25 kN/m² plus
a concentrated load of 0.9 kN acting together and a
dead load of not more than 0.25 kN/m² or 0.5 kN/m²
for spacing of joists as shown. Strength class SC3.
Joists at 400mm centres shown as continuous line.
Joists at 600mm centres shown as broken line.
NOTE   On these graphs the 600mm spacing with a
0.25 kN/m² dead load follow the same line as the
400mm spacing with 0.50 kN/m² dead load.

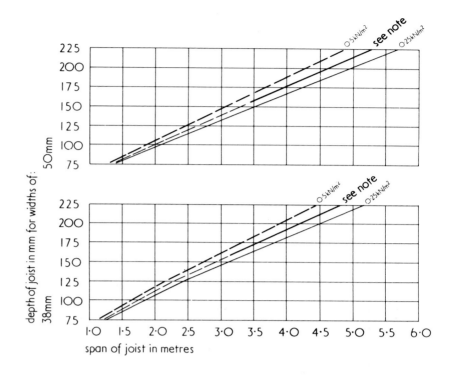

Table B 6: beams or binders supporting ceiling joists
(Table B 5).
Sizes of beams to support joists in Table B5 where the
dead load supported by the joists is not more than
0.25 kN/m² or 0.5 kN/m² for different spacing of
beams as indicated. Strength class SC3.

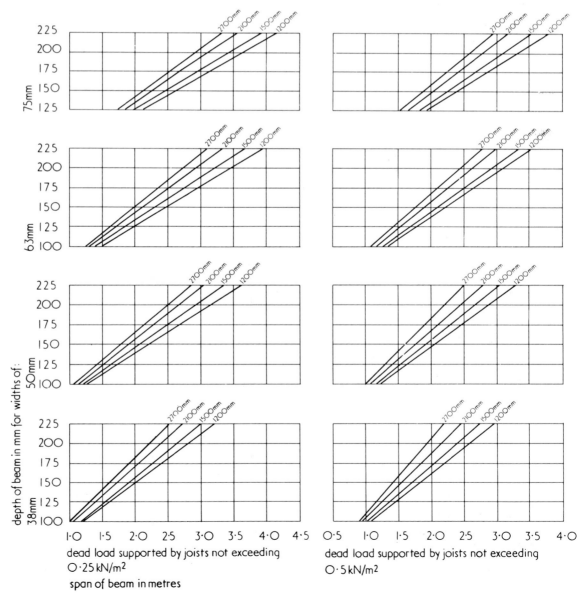

dead load supported by joists not exceeding
O·25 kN/m²

span of beam in metres

dead load supported by joists not exceeding
O·5 kN/m²

Table B 7: ceiling joists.
Joist sizes to take an imposed load of 0.25 kN/m² plus
a concentrated load of 0.9 kN acting together and a
dead load of not more than 0.25 kN/m² or 0.5 kN/m²
for spacing of joists as shown. Strength class SC4.
Joists at 400mm centres shown as continuous line.
Joists at 600mm centres shown as broken line.
NOTE   On these graphs the 600mm spacing with a
0.25 kN/m² dead load follow the same line as the
400mm spacing with 0.50 kN/m² dead load.

Table B 8: beams or binders supporting ceiling joists
(Table B 7).
Sizes of beams to support joists in Table B 7 where
the dead load supported by the joists is not more than
0.25 kN/m² or 0.5 kN/m² for different spacing of
beams as indicated. Strength class SC4.

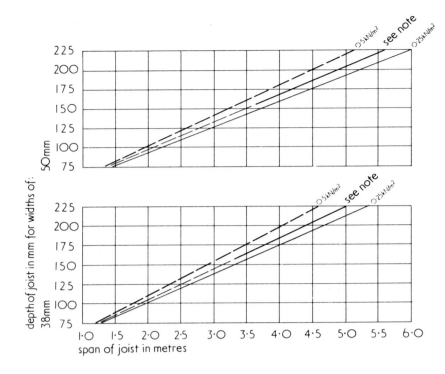

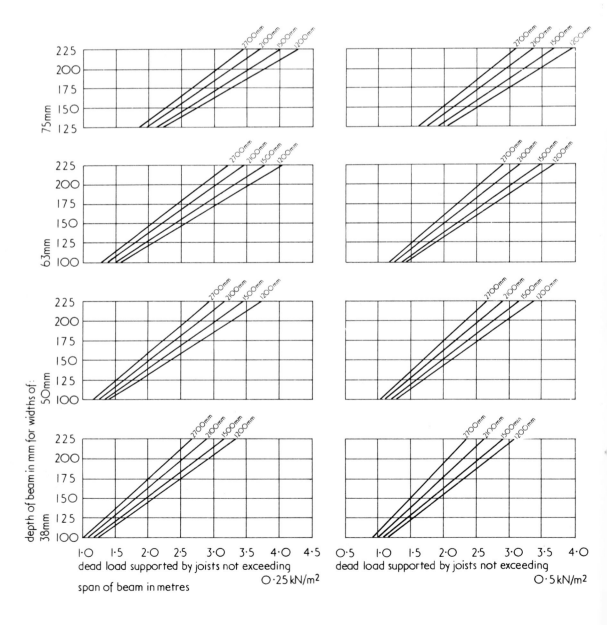

Tables B 9, 13 and 17: common or jack rafters.
Sizes of common rafters for roofs of pitch indicated
when dead load carried by the rafters is not more than
0.5 kN/m² or 1.0 kN/m² for spacing of rafters as
shown. Imposed load up to 30° pitch 0.75 kN/m² or a
concentrated load of 0.9 kN, over 30° pitch

0.75 kN/m², reduced by 50 N/m² for every 3° above
30° pitch. Strength class SC3.
Rafters at 400mm centres shown as continuous line.
Rafters at 600mm centres shown as broken line.
When spans are unequal use the longer span.

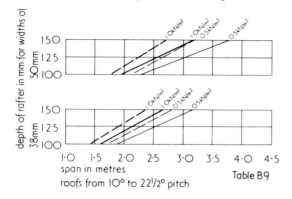

Table B 9
roofs from 10° to 22½° pitch

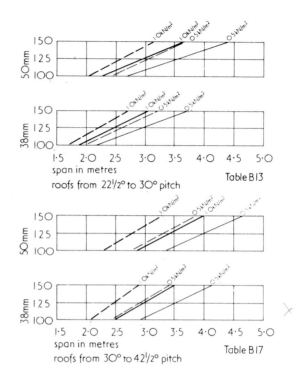

Table B 13
roofs from 22½° to 30° pitch

Table B 17
roofs from 30° to 42½° pitch

Table B 10: purlins supporting rafters to which Table
B 9 refers.
Sizes of purlins in roofs from 10° to 22½° pitch for
various spans when the dead load supported by the

rafters is not more 0.5 kN/m² or 1.0 kN/m² and the
purlins are spaced at the indicated distances. For other
spacings interpolate as appropriate. For imposed loads
see table for rafters. Strength class SC3.

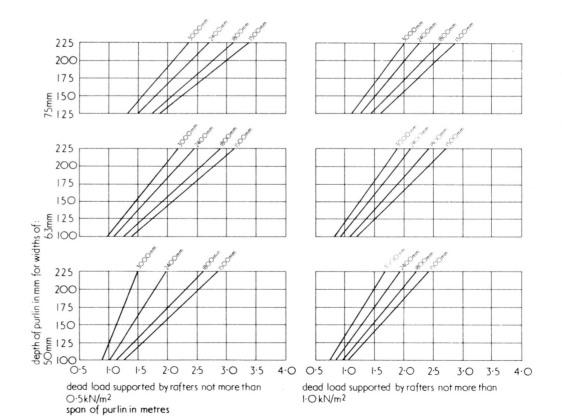

dead load supported by rafters not more than
0.5 kN/m²
span of purlin in metres

dead load supported by rafters not more than
1.0 kN/m²

Table B 14: purlins supporting rafters to which Table B 13 refers.
Sizes of purlins in roofs from 22½° to 30° pitch for various spans when the dead load supported by the rafters is not more 0.5 kN/m² or 1.0 kN/m² and the purlins are spaced at the indicated distances. For other spacings interpolate as appropriate. For imposed loads see table for rafters. Strength class SC3.

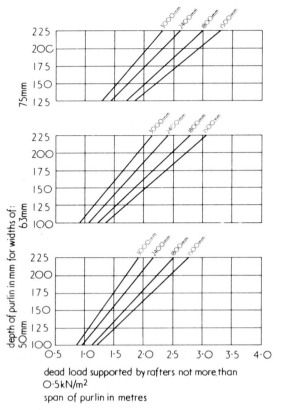

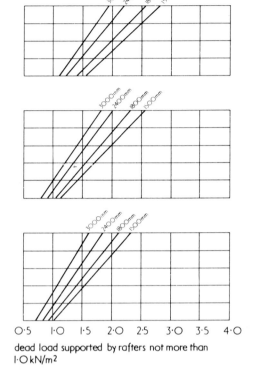

dead load supported by rafters not more than O·5kN/m²
span of purlin in metres

dead load supported by rafters not more than I·O kN/m²

Table B 18: purlins supporting rafters to which Table B 17 refers.
Sizes of purlins in roofs from 30° to 42½° pitch for various spans when the dead load supported by the rafters is not more 0.5 kN/m² or 1.0 kN/m² and the purlins are spaced at the indicated distances. For other spacings interpolate as appropriate. For imposed loads see table for rafters. Strength class SC3.

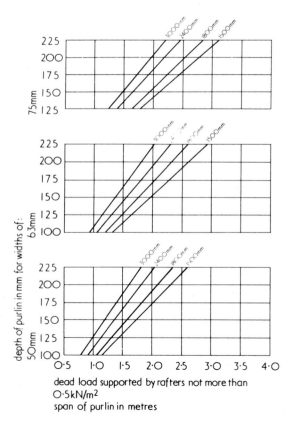

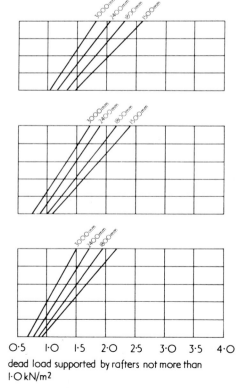

dead load supported by rafters not more than O·5kN/m²
span of purlin in metres

dead load supported by rafters not more than I·O kN/m²

Tables B 11, 15 and 19: common or jack rafters.
Sizes of common rafters for roofs of pitch indicated
when dead load carried by the rafters is not more than
0.5 kN/m² or 1.0 kN/m² for spacing of rafters as
shown. Imposed load up to 30° pitch 0.75 kN/m² or a
concentrated load of 0.9 kN, over 30° pitch

0.75 kN/m², reduced by 50 N/m² for every 3° above
30° pitch. Strength class SC4.
Rafters at 400mm centres shown as continuous line.
Rafters at 600mm centres shown as broken line.
When spans are unequal use the longer span.

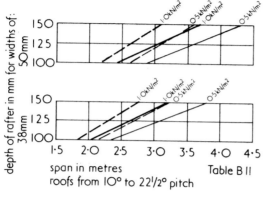

roofs from 10° to 22½° pitch
Table B 11

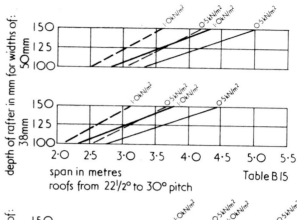

roofs from 22½° to 30° pitch
Table B 15

Table B 12: purlins supporting rafters to which Table
B 11 refers.
Sizes of purlins in roofs from 10° to 22½° pitch for
various spans when the dead load supported by the
rafters is not more 0.5 kN/m² or 1.0 kN/m² and the
purlins are spaced at the indicated distances. For other
spacings interpolate as appropriate. For imposed loads
see table for rafters. Strength class SC4.

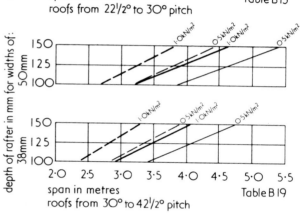

roofs from 30° to 42½° pitch
Table B 19

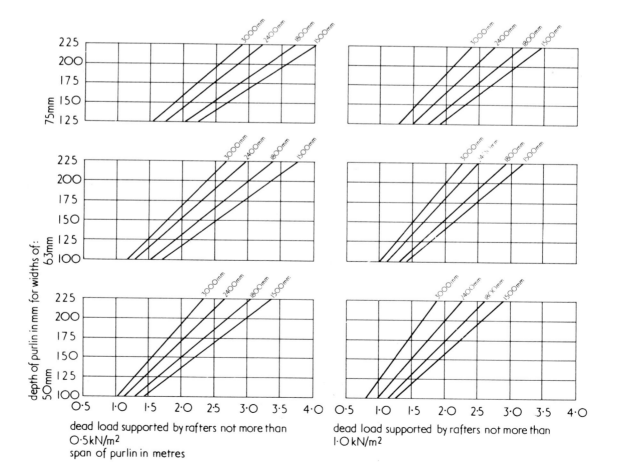

dead load supported by rafters not more than
0·5kN/m²
span of purlin in metres

dead load supported by rafters not more than
1·0kN/m²

Table B 16: purlins supporting rafters to which Table B 15 refers.
Sizes of purlins in roofs from 22½° to 30° pitch for various spans when the dead load supported by the *rafters is not more 0.5 kN/m² or 1.0 kN/m² and the purlins are spaced at the indicated distances. For other spacings interpolate as appropriate. For imposed loads see table for rafters. Strength class SC4.*

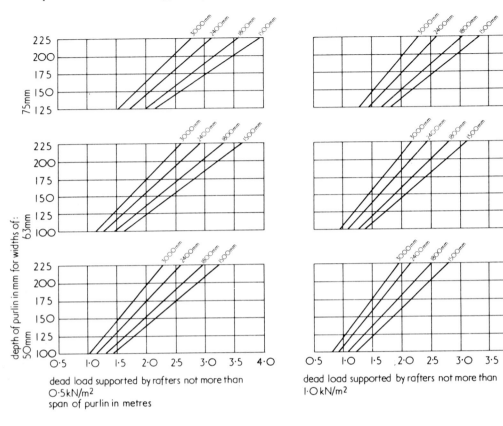

dead load supported by rafters not more than
0·5kN/m²
span of purlin in metres

dead load supported by rafters not more than
1·0 kN/m²

Table B 20: purlins supporting rafters to which Table B 19 refers.
Sizes of purlins in roofs from 30° to 42½° pitch for various spans when the dead load supported by the *rafters is not more 0.5 kN/m² or 1.0 kN/m² and the purlins are spaced at the indicated distances. For other spacings interpolate as appropriate. For imposed loads see table for rafters. Strength class SC4.*

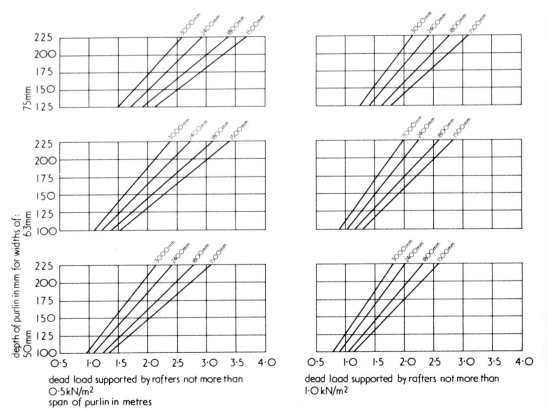

dead load supported by rafters not more than
0·5kN/m²
span of purlin in metres

dead load supported by rafters not more than
1·0 kN/m²

Table B 21: joists for flat roofs with access only for
maintenance or repair.
Joist sizes to take an imposed load of 0.75 kN/m² or a
concentrated load of 0.9 kN plus a dead load of not
more than 0.5 kN/m² or 1.00 kN/m² for spacing of
joists as shown. Strength class SC3.
Joists at 400mm centres shown as continuous line.
Joists at 600mm centres shown as broken line.

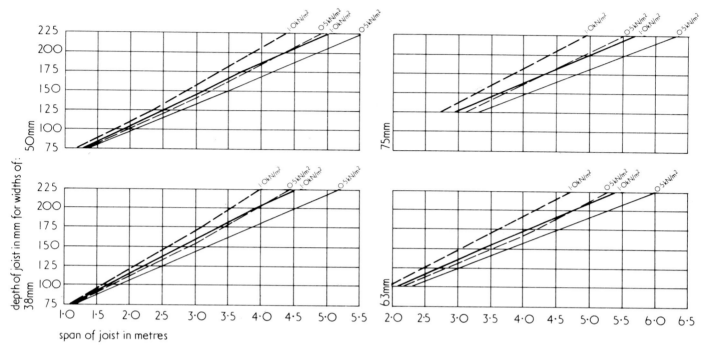

Table B 22: joists for flat roofs with access only for
maintenance or repair.
Joist sizes to take an imposed load of 0.75 kN/m² or a
concentrated load of 0.9 kN plus a dead load of not
more than 0.5 kN/m² or 1.00 kN/m² for spacing of
joists as shown. Strength class SC4.
Joists at 400mm centres shown as continuous line.
Joists at 600mm centres shown as broken line.

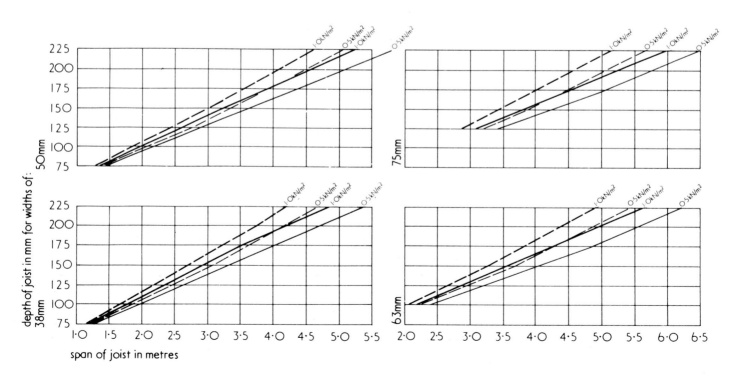

Table B 23: joists for flat roofs with general access.
Joist sizes to take an imposed load of 1.5 kN/m² plus
a dead load of not more than 0.5 kN/m² or
1.00 kN/m² for spacing of joists as shown. Strength
class SC3.
Joists at 400mm centres shown as continuous line.
Joists at 600mm centres shown as broken line.

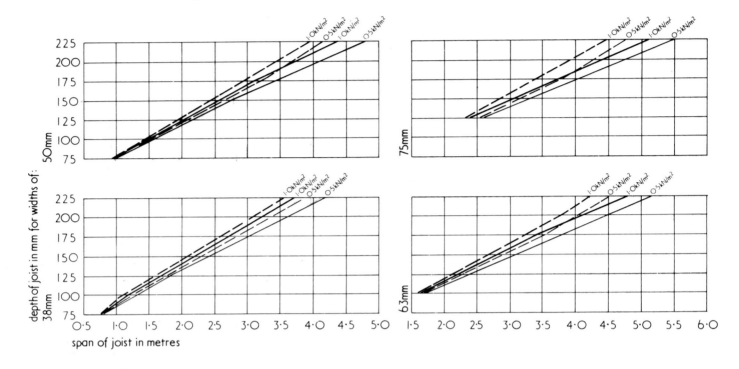

Table B 24: joists for flat roofs with general access.
Joist sizes to take an imposed load of 1.5 kN/m² plus
a dead load of not more than 0.5 kN/m² or
1.00 kN/m² for spacing of joists as shown. Strength
class SC4.
Joists at 400mm centres shown as continuous line.
Joists at 600mm centres shown as broken line.

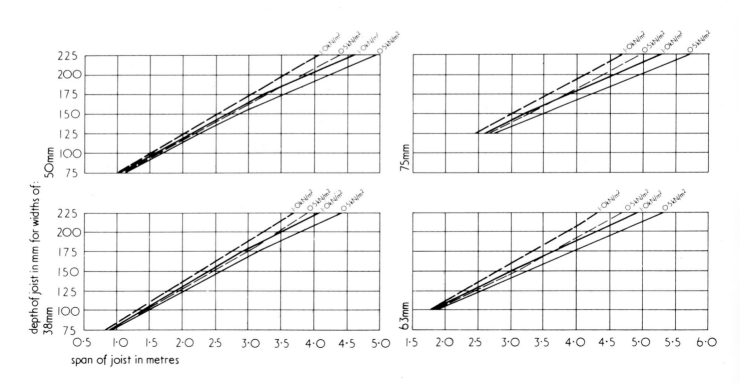

Tables B 25 and B 27: purlins supporting sheeting or decking to pitched roofs.
Sizes of purlins when the dead weight of the sheeting is not more than 0.25 kN/m², 0.5 kN/m² or 0.75 kN/m² as indicated and the purlins are spaced at the indicated distances apart (centre to centre) with maximum imposed load of 0.75 kN/m² (0.70 kN/m² for roofs over 30° pitch). For other spacings interpolate as appropriate. Strength class SC3.
Roofs from 10° to 30° pitch shown as continuous line.
Roofs from 30° to 35° pitch shown as broken line.

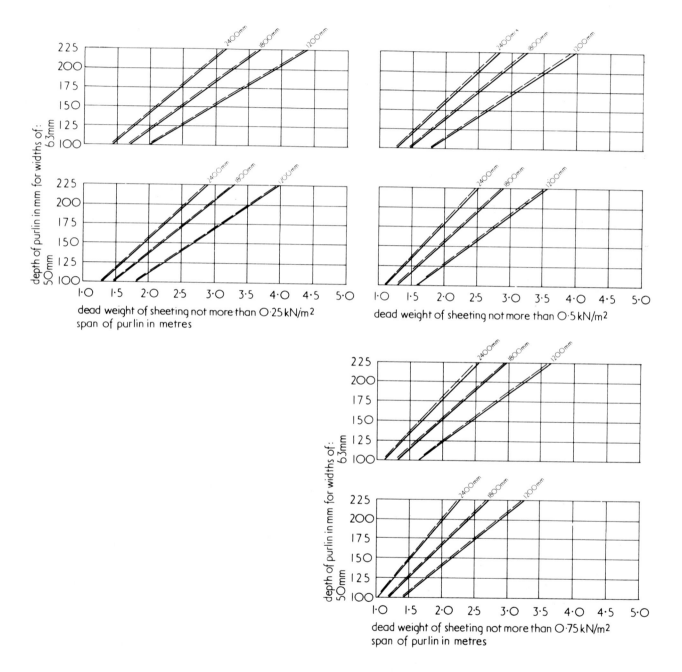

Tables B 26 and B 28: purlins supporting sheeting or decking to pitched roofs.
Sizes of purlins when the dead weight of the sheeting is not more than 0.25 kN/m² , 0.5 kN/m² or 0.75 kN/m² as indicated and the purlins are spaced at the indicated distances apart (centre to centre) with maximum imposed load of 0.75 kN/m² (0.70 kN/m² for roofs over 30° pitch). For other spacings interpolate as appropriate. Strength class SC4.
Roofs from 10° to 30° pitch shown as continuous line.
Roofs from 30° to 35° pitch shown as broken line.

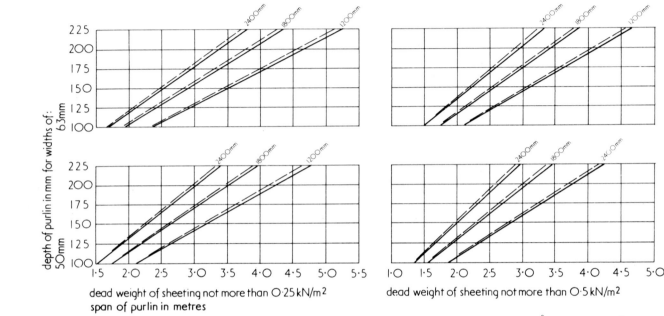

dead weight of sheeting not more than 0·25 kN/m²
span of purlin in metres

dead weight of sheeting not more than 0·5 kN/m²

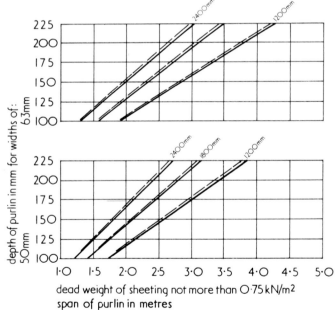

dead weight of sheeting not more than 0·75 kN/m²
span of purlin in metres

PART C   Thickness of walls in certain small buildings

C 1   The part applies to:

(*a*)   Residential buildings up to three storeys

(*b*)   Small single-storey non-residential buildings

(*c*)   Small annexes to residential buildings (including garages and outbuildings).

C 2   Only the following wall types are considered:

1   External walls

2   Internal loadbearing walls

3   Compartment and separating walls

Item (3) does not apply to categories (*b*) and (*c*) above.

C 3   (*a*) Part A is to be used with this part.

(*b*)   If the wall thickness is to be determined by using C 4 to C 13 'all appropriate design considerations given in this part must be satisfied' This is to say that these cannot be used separately in conjunction with other data drawn from elsewhere.

(*c*)   Walls are to comply with the relevant parts of BS 5628: Part 3 except as regards the conditions in C 14 to C 40. These are those relating to limiting dimensions, materials, supporting structure etc, which differ from similar recommendations in BS 5628. The essential difference is that the BS gives general recommendations to be used in conjunction with structural calculations, whereas this document supplies a convenient set of rules of thumb which can only be used within the strictly limited conditions set by C 1 and C 2 above. Here again we have an example of the Regulations providing a useful design tool.

(*d*)   To allow of the use of such simplified rules the worst combination of circumstances has to be used. Some minor departures on the basis of experience or judgement, in respect of a particular aspect of a wall, may be permissible, especially if supported by calculation.

(*e*)   The guidance given in this part is based on the use of three compressive strengths (see C 22) for masonry units. Advice on the use of other design strengths is given in BS 5628.

Arrangement

In addition to the general clauses above, the Part is divided into the following main sections:

Thickness of walls C 4 to C 13.

Conditions relating to the building C 14 to C 17.

Conditions relating to the wall C 18 to C 38.

External walls of small single storey buildings and annexes C 39/40.

Thickness of walls

Wall thicknesses

C 4   May be as specified in C 6 to C 13 providing the conditions in the remaining paragraphs C 14 to 40 are met. This is laid out in a much lengthier and quite unnecessary way in diagram C 1, which is therefore not reproduced.

Bay windows

C 5   The rules do not apply to wall sections, including gables, forming parts of bay window structures above ground floor sill level.

Thickness

C 6   For solid walls in coursed brickwork or blockwork the minima are illustrated in diagram [1.6].

key to min thickness

‖ 190 mm   also no wall to be less than 1/6 th storey height

▌ 290 mm

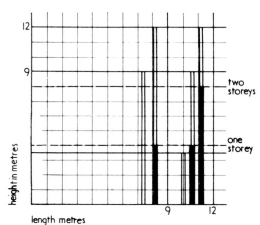

C 6 [**1.6**] *Thickness of external compartment and separating walls.*

Solid walls of uncoursed stone, flints etc

C 7   These including those formed of 'clunches of bricks or other burnt or vitrified material' should be at least 1.33 times the thickness specified in C 6.

Cavity walls

C 8   For cavity external compartment or separating walls the rules illustrated in diagram [1.7] apply.

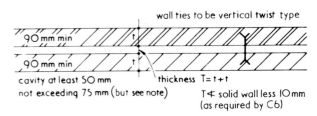

C 8 [**1.7**] *Cavity walls.*
Note that if vertical twist type ties are used at 750 mm horizontal spacing, the cavity may be up to 100 mm. Also if courses do not permit spacing may be varied if the number of ties per unit area is maintained.

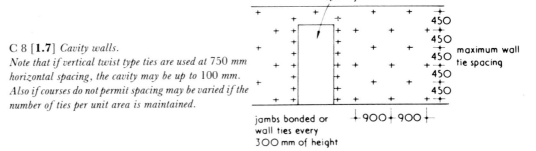

Walls providing vertical support to other walls

C 9   These must never be less in thickness than the supported wall.

Internal loadbearing walls of bricks or blocks

C 10   These (excluding compartment or separating walls) should have a minimum thickness of half the thickness specified in C 6 less 5 mm, but with a minimum of 140 mm for walls on the lower floor of a 3 storey building which carry a load from both upper floors.

Parapet walls

C 11   The minimum thickness is to be as shown in diagram [1.8].

C 11 [**1.8**] *Parapet walls: thickness.*

C 11   *Parapet walls – thickness*

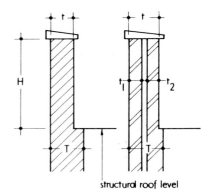

Max. Height. H.	Minimum thickness	
	Solid t.	Cavity $t_1 + t_2$
600	150	200
760	190	–
860	215	250

Also t ⊉ T.

structural roof level

NOTE   There is a change here: previously in Schedule 7 rule 15 a thickness not less than ¼ height, with no maximum height was specified.

Single leaves of certain external walls

C 12   This says that 'the single leaves of external walls of small non-residential buildings, and of annexes, need only be 90 mm thick, notwithstanding paras C 39 and 40'. It has to be assumed that the buildings referred to are those described later under that heading in C 14, which defines certain limiting sizes. C 39 and 40 also deal with the same type of building and make rules regarding the provision of buttressing walls and piers. This rule seems to be suggesting that these provisions are not needed, in which case why are they there? Rule 14 of

Schedule 7 specified the same maximum sizes as are now given in C 14 and included the rules regarding piers etc. now set out in C 39/40. The only possible interpretation is that the rules are really unchanged but are now confusingly spread out amongst 3 separate items each of which has to be inter-related. In other words such walls may be only 90 mm thick in buildings described in C 14(b) and (c) if limited or supported as described in C 39/40.

Modular bricks and blocks

C 13   Where modular units derived from BS 6750: 1986 are used prescribed wall thicknesses may be reduced by an amount not exceeding the deviation from work size allowed by a BS for units of the same material. It may be noted that the reduction of 10 mm in minimum thicknesses from round figures (300 to 290, 200 to 190 etc) made some time ago assisted in the use of modular systems.

Conditions relating to the building

Size

C 14   Limitation on the height and proportions of buildings are shown in diagram [1.9].

C 14 [**1.9**] *Limits on size and proportion of buildings.*

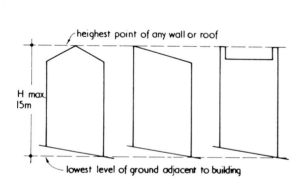

(a) *Residential buildings.*

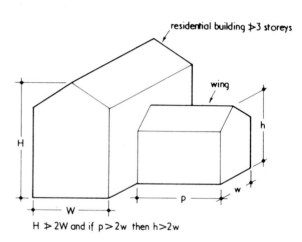

$H \not> 2W$ and if $p > 2w$ then $h > 2w$

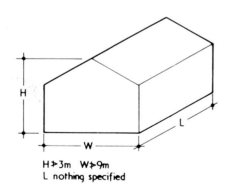

$H \not> 3m$ $W \not> 9m$
L nothing specified

(b) *Small single storey non residential buildings.*

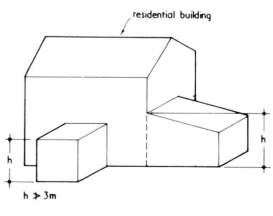

$h \not> 3m$

(c) *Annexes*

Note on item (b) If this is meant to be an interpretation of Rule 14 of Schedule 7 it is in error because that rule in relation to small single-storey buildings refers to the maximum height of the *walls* (not the building) and according to the general rules this should be measured to half way up the gable, not to the ridge.

C 15 [**1.10**] *Sizes of subdivisions.*

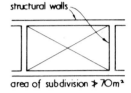

any structural wall

area of subdivision ≯ 30m²

structural walls

area of subdivision ≯ 70m²

Maximum floor areas

C 15   These are limited as shown in diagram [1.10].

Imposed loads

C 16   These must not exceed the following:

	Distributed		Concentrated
Floors above ground storey	2.0 kN/m²	or	1.8 kN
Roofs	0.75 kN/m²	or	0.9 kN
Ceilings	0.25 kN/m²	plus	0.9 kN
	or	0.75 kN/m²	

Design wind speed (V_s)

C 17   This must not exceed 44 m/sec. V_s is the result of multiplying the basic wind speed (taken from the map in CP3: Chap V: part 2: 1972) by 3 factors thus:

$$V_s = V \times S_1 \times S_2 \times S_3 \text{ where:}$$

S_1 is the topography factor and is nearly always taken as 1.0

S_2 covers a number of circumstances (ground roughness, building size etc). A class B size building is to be assumed, which in effect means allowing for a 5 second gust duration. Allowance must also be made for locations near the edge of a cliff or escarpment.

S_3 the probability factor is to be taken as not less than 1.0. In practice, apart from assessing loads during construction, it never is, nor is it often taken as more than 1.0. For more detail on CP 3: Chap V: Part 2 see Section 2.

NOTE   A 3 states that provided the specified structural recommendations are met, no special provision should be needed for wind loads.

Conditions relating to the wall

Dimensions and measurement

C 18/19   The Part does not deal with walls longer or higher than 12 m. Lengths are measured centre to centre of supports (buttressing walls etc). Heights are measured as shown in diagram [1.11].

C 19 [**1.11**] *Wall and storey heights*

Key

(a) Measuring storey heights

A   *is the ground storey height if the ground floor is suspended timber floor or a structurally separate ground floor slab*

A₁   *is the ground storey height if the ground floor is a suspended concrete floor bearing on the external wall*

B   *is the intermediate storey height*

B₁   *is the top storey height for walls which do not include a gable*

C   *is the top storey height where lateral support is given to the gable at both ceiling level and along the roof slope*

D   *is the top storey height for walls which include a gable where lateral support is given to the gable only along the roof slope*

(b) Measuring wall heights

H₁   *is the height of a wall that does not include a gable*

H₂   *is the height of a compartment or separating wall which includes a gable*

H₃   *is the height for a wall (except a compartment or separating wall) which includes a gable if the parapet height is more than 1.2 m add the height to H_1*

NOTE   In C 11 parapet walls are limited to 860 mm high.

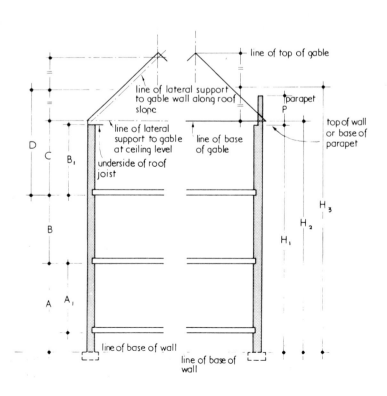

Wall ties

C 20   These are to comply with BS 1243: 1978 (or other not less suitable). In severe exposure conditions austenitic stainless steel or non-ferrous ties are to be used. Refer to BS 5628: Part 3 for definition of 'severe exposure'. (BS 5628 gives a table and graph of exposure categories using a 'local spell index' which is based on meterological data to show the maximum quantity of wind driven rain falling on vertical surfaces during the worst likely spell of bad weather).

Brick and block construction

C 21   Walls are to be properly bonded and solidly put together in mortar using:
(a)   Clay bricks or blocks to BS 3921: 1974 or BS 6649: 1985 or
(b)   Calcium silicate bricks to BS 187: 1978 or BS 6649: 1985 or
(c)   Concrete bricks or blocks to BS 6073: Part 1: 1981 or
(d)   Square dressed natural stone to relevant parts of BS 5390.

Compressive strength of bricks and blocks

C 22   The requirements vary according to the location within the building. The strengths, when tested in accordance with the appropriate BS, to be at least those in diagram [1.12].

C 22 [**1.12**] *Compressive strength of bricks and blocks.*

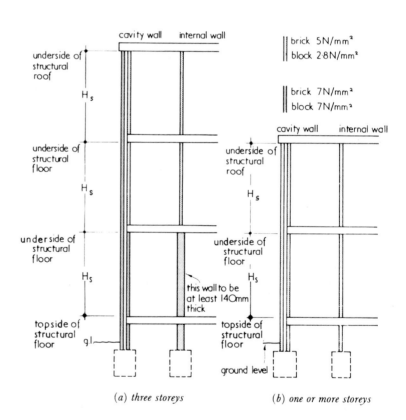

NOTES
1   *If H_s is not greater than 2.7 m, the compressive strength of bricks or blocks should be used in walls as indicated by the key.*
2   *If H_s is greater than 2.7 m, bricks or blocks with a compressive strength of at least 7 N/sq mm should be used.*
3   *If the external wall is solid construction, the bricks or blocks should have a compressive strength of at least that shown for the internal leaf of a cavity wall in the same position.*

(a) *three storeys*   (b) *one or more storeys*

Mortar

C 23   Mortar should be:
(a)   To the proportions given in BS 5628: Part 1: 1978 designation (iii) or 1:1:6 cement/lime/fine aggregate by volume dry, or
(b)   Of equivalent or, if appropriate, greater strength which is compatible with the masonry units and situation.

Comment

The rules regarding measurement, materials and strengths are generally unchanged, but with the usual tendency to quote BS references, rather than rely on accepted trade descriptions (e.g. bricks and blocks, previously described as 'composed of burnt clay, siliceous sand and lime, crushed siliceous rocks and lime and concrete'). Rule 9 of Schedule 7 also stated that blocks could be hollow if the volume of solid material was at least 50 per cent.

Maximum spans of floors

C 24   These are not to exceed 6 m measured centre to centre of bearings (not clear span as used in Part B). The sketch illustrating this in the Approved Document is reproduced here as [1.13].

C 24 [**1.13**] *Span of floors.*

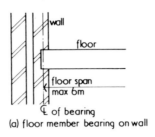
(a) floor member bearing on wall

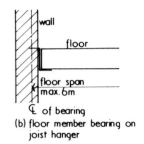
(b) floor member bearing on joist hanger

NOTE   It is usual for joists built in to bear on the full thickness of the inner leaf and for joist hangers illustrated in BS 5628: Part 1: 1978 as suitable for forming floor to wall connections to do the same, being also bent over to provide some effectiveness in tension.

Other loading conditions

C 25   Vertical loading on walls should be distributed. This can be assumed for concrete floor slabs, precast or in-situ and timber floors complying with Part B. For lintels over 1200 mm span, 150 mm bearing is required, if less 100 mm.

The combined dead and imposed loads at the base of the wall must not exceed 70 kN/m run. Walls must not be subject to any lateral loads, other than from wind or a limited difference in levels of ground or fill at each side: see diagram [1.14].

C 25 [**1.14**] *Loading conditions.*

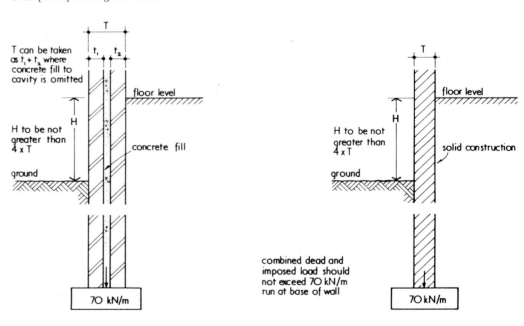

Buttressing walls, piers and chimneys

C 26/27/28   The length of a wall, which is limited to 12 m, is measured from centre to centre of end and intermediate supports, which can take the form of buttressing walls, piers or chimneys. These must be provided at each end whatever the length (but see C 39 for exception) and in all cases the supports must extend from the base to the full height of the supported wall. Diagrams [1.15, 1.16] show the criteria for the design of these supports.

C 27 [**1.15**] *Buttressing walls, openings.*

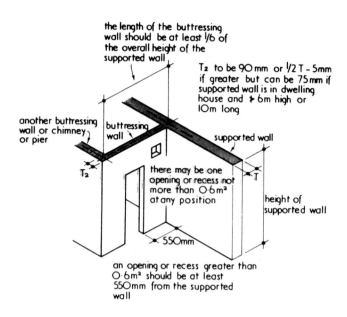

NOTES

1   The buttressing wall should be bonded or securely tied to the supported wall and at the other end to a buttressing wall, pier or chimney.

2   Openings or recesses in the buttressing wall should be as shown – the position and shape of the openings should not impair the lateral support given by the buttressing wall.

3   Buttressing walls may themselves be supported walls.

4   Refer to diagram [1.11] for the rules for measuring the height of the supported wall.

C 28 [**1.16**] *Buttressing piers and chimneys.*

The plan area of solid material in a chimney should be at least equal to that required for a pier.

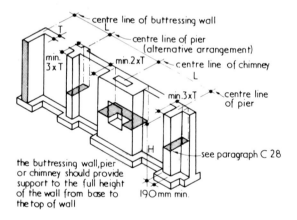

Comment

These are just a repeat of the same rules in Schedule 7 and do clarify what was a confusing bit of CS jargon. However the diagram to C 27, which is modified to include items of text but basically unchanged from the original, is ambiguous about the height of the support. C 19 gives the definition of 'height' and C 26 requires the support to extend 'from the base to the full height of the supported wall', which can mean from foundation level up through 3 storeys, and the one-sixth length of the buttressing wall is related to this total height.

The diagram to C 28 shows a depth requirement of only 2 × T for a chimney (including the wall) against 3 × T for a pier. It is questionable whether this is a true interpretation of Schedule 7 Rule 4(5), but more importantly whether it makes sense structurally.

Openings and recesses

C 29/30   The general rule is that the number, size and position of these must not impair the stability of a wall, or the lateral support afforded by a buttressing wall: rules about the latter are in C 27. Construction above openings must be adequately supported. Specific criteria are given in diagram [1.17] (NOTE No distinction is made between openings and recesses whatever the depth).

C 30 [**1.17**] *Dimensional criteria for openings and recesses.*

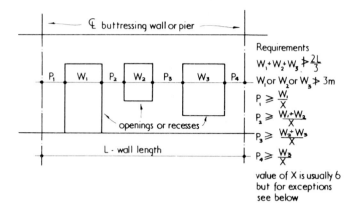

Value of X where less than 6

Nature of roof span	Wall or inner leaf min. thickness	Span of floor into wall – max.			
		Timber		Concrete	
		4.5 m	6.0 m	4.5 m	6.0 m
Timber into wall	100 mm	6	5	4	3
max 9 m	90 mm	4	4	3	3

NOTES

1   *Where roof span is parallel to wall X = 6 except if a concrete floor over 4.5 m spans into wall, when it is 5.*

2   *When floor spans are parallel to wall value of X is always 6.*

3   *If compressive strength of bricks or blocks is at least 7 N/mm² value of X is always 6.*

Comment

There has been a technical change here, as previously the divisor 6 (see diagram) was universal, regardless of circumstances. Obviously some further research has taken place.

Chases

C 31   The number and position of chases must not be such as to impair stability particularly where hollow blocks are used.

There are limitations as to the depth of vertical and horizontal chases, shown in diagram [1.18]. It is interesting to note that the limitation for horizontal chases if applied to the walls of domestic buildings with 75 mm inner leaf means that such chases are restricted to only 12.5 mm in depth. Clearly, this rule could easily be broken on most domestic work.

C 31 [**1.18**] *Chases:*

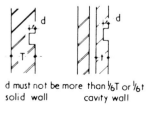

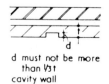

d must not be more than ⅙T or ⅙t
solid wall   cavity wall

d must not be more than ⅓t
cavity wall

d must not be more than ⅓T
solid wall

(a) horizontal

(b) vertical

Overhangs

C 32   The amount of any projection must not impair the stability of the wall. This is not very helpful, but there is more guidance in BS 5628: Part 3.

Lateral support by roofs and floors (C 33–37)

C 33/34   Walls must extend the full height of each storey and have lateral supports to restrict movement at right angles, as shown in the diagram [1.19].

C 33/34 [**1.19**] *Floor lateral support and roof lateral support. Connections (C) must be adequate to transmit lateral forces (see C 36, 37).*

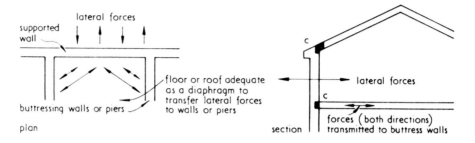

C 35   The requirements apply to external, compartment or separating walls at every junction with every floor or roof (but not applicable in the case of floors only if the wall is less than 3 m long) also to internal loadbearing walls at the top of each storey.
NOTE   This rule appears more onerous for internal load-bearing walls below 3 m in length than for external, separating or compartment walls. This is presumably because such walls may be thinner (see C 10).

C 36   Generally walls should be strapped to all floors above ground level (NOTE   It is not clear whether this includes a suspended ground floor, but since the height of a ground storey is taken from foundation level, one presumes not: Schedule 7 was even less explicit on this point), using galvanised mild steel straps 30 × 5 mm cross section. No minimum length is specified either here or later (or in BS 5628 for that matter). In a considerable number of cases they are not essential. These are illustrated in diagram [1.20].

C 36 [**1.20**] *Situations where strapping to floors is not required.*

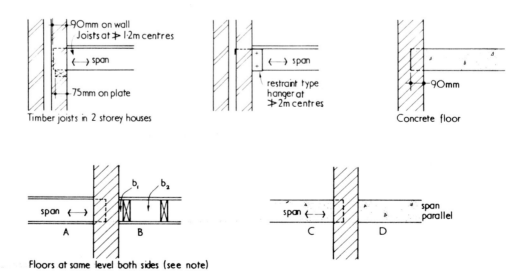

NOTE
Where floors abut on both sides contact must be continuous (eg concrete) or at not more than 2 m intervals. This suggests that in Type B blocking would

be needed at b_1 and probably also at b_2 but no advice is given. Floors at each side to be about the same level and where contact is intermittent the points of contact should be in line (or almost so).

Where strapping is required the arrangement should be as indicated in the next diagram [1.21].

C 36 [**1.21**] *Strapping.*

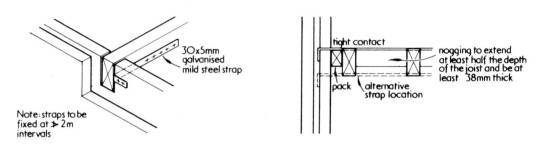

C 37   Walls should be strapped to roofs at gables of end or separating walls as indicated in diagram [1.22 (*a*) and (*b*)] which are lateral connections. C 37 also requires vertical strapping at eaves level, except where the construction is as shown in (*c*). This in fact will probably cover the majority of cases.

C 37 [**1.22**] *Wall to roof connections.*

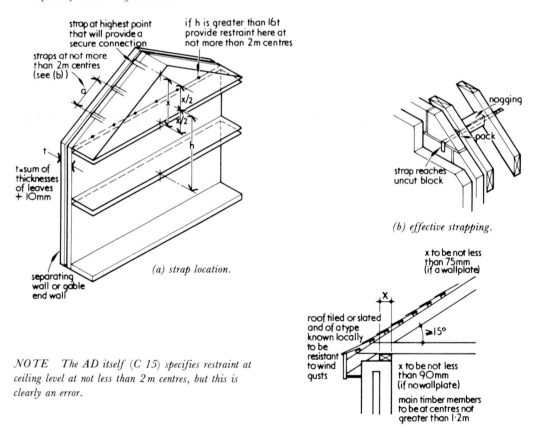

(*a*) strap location.

(*b*) effective strapping.

(*c*) where vertical strapping need not be provided.

NOTE   The AD itself (C 15) specifies restraint at ceiling level at not less than 2 m centres, but this is clearly an error.

Comment

The object of strapping in the context of this Part is to ensure interaction between wall and floor or roof in order to provide lateral bracing to the wall. Vertical strapping usually has a different function in preventing roofs from being lifted by wind suction when their self-weight is insufficient, such straps being usually taken down to a joint 5 or 6 courses down the wall. This would not necessarily contribute anything to the lateral stiffness of the wall. However BS 5628: Part 3 does show a vertical strap detail for a flat joisted roof using a twisted strap to connect joist to wall. Schedule 7 made no mention of vertical strapping, but was generally less than specific.

Interruption of lateral support

C 38   An opening for a stairway or the like is permitted adjacent to a supported wall under the circumstances illustrated in diagram [1.23].

C 38 [**1.23**] *Interruption of lateral support.*

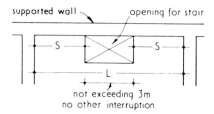

NOTE
Where anchors are not used the conditions along the supported length (S) must be as normal. Where anchors are used the spacing of anchors along the lengths (S) must be reduced so as to result in the same number as would have been used if full length (L) had been available.

Small single story non-residential buildings

C 39/40   These are the buildings illustrated in C 14 (*b*) and (*c*). They may have single-leaf external walls of bricks or blocks if not subjected to any load apart from the roof and wind loads. They are limited to 2.5 m in height and width unless bonded to piers or buttressing walls as in diagram [1.24] (see also C 12).

C 39/40 [**1.24**] *Buttressing to single leaf walls.*

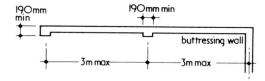

Note the minimum thickness of 90 mm required by Rule 14 of Schedule 7 is now included in C 12.

Part D   Chimney stacks

Application. This is not specifically restricted in the same way as Parts B and C, but 0.2(a) at the beginning of the document states that Section 1 'is relevant to small buildings of traditional masonry construction', which presumably in the case of Parts D and E includes buildings of any purpose group. (The same rules in the 1976 regulations were not restricted in application).

Where these are not adequately supported by ties or otherwise securely restrained the dimensions are limited as shown in diagram [1.25].

*Part D [***1.25***] Chimney stacks.*

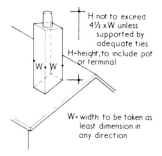

Part E   Strip foundations of plain concrete

Application. See Part D.

This is a straightforward repeat of Regulation D 7 and specifies widths and depths of simple strip foundations in relation to loading and type of ground, under the following conditions:

The ground

E 1   (*a*) There must be no made ground or wide variation of subsoil type in the loaded area.
(*b*)   no weaker type of soil below the foundation subsoil at a depth which could impair stability.

The foundation design

E 2   (*a*) They are to be centrally placed below walls

(*b*)   The concrete is to be of cement to BS 12: 1978, fine and coarse aggregate to BS 882: 1983 and either:

At least 50 kg cement: 0.1m³ fine aggregate: 0.2m³ coarse aggregate or

Grade C15P to BS 5328: 1981 or

Grade 15 to CP 110: 1972 (to be succeeded by BS 8110)

(*c*)   Minimum thickness 150 mm or more as illustrated

(*d*)   Stepped foundations must overlap as illustrated

(*e*)   Foundations to piers chimneys etc to project the same distance as for the wall (see diagram [1.26]).

E 2 [**1.26**] *Foundation design.*

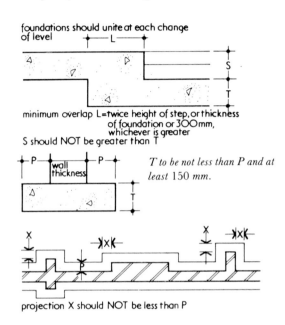

foundations should unite at each change of level

minimum overlap L=twice height of step, or thickness of foundation or 300 mm, whichever is greater

S should NOT be greater than T

T to be not less than P and at least 150 mm.

projection X should NOT be less than P

NOTE   Diagram E 1 of the Approved Document suggests that if footings are provided the width of the foundations should be increased by the extent of their projection on each side. This was not the case in Schedule 7, nor is there any structural logic in it, so it must be presumed to be an error. The intention is surely that the projection P can be measured from the outer edge of the footings, but not that it should affect the foundation width.

Widths

E 3   Subject to E 1 and E 2 the recommended widths in the table may be used. The table has been converted into illustrations [1.27] which show the effect of the rules on width and depth for walls of four thicknesses. Since various masonry units may be used, these have been chosen to represent walls built up of 100 mm wide units with 10 mm joints or 50 mm cavities.

E 2 [**1.27**] *Foundation dimensions for different*
loadings and subsoils.

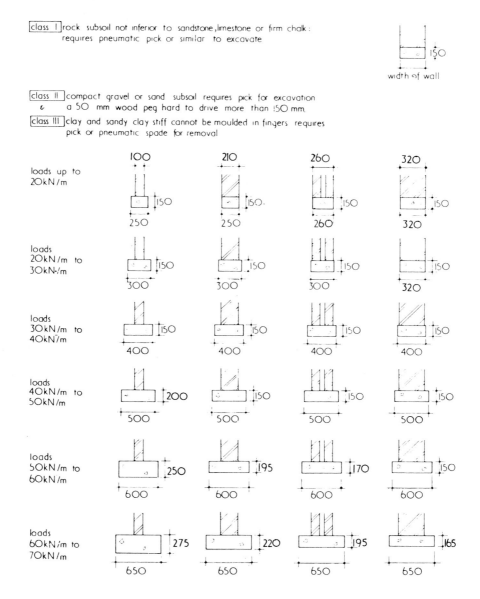

class I rock subsoil not inferior to sandstone, limestone or firm chalk : requires pneumatic pick or similar to excavate

class II compact gravel or sand subsoil requires pick for excavation & a 50 mm wood peg hard to drive more than 150 mm.

class III clay and sandy clay stiff cannot be moulded in fingers requires pick or pneumatic spade for removal

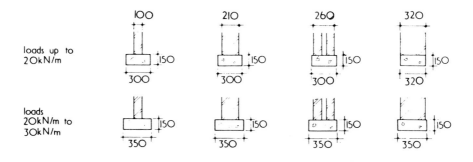

class IV clay or sandy clay, firm : can be moulded by substantial pressure with fingers. can be excavated with graft or spade

[**1.27**] E 2 *(continued)*

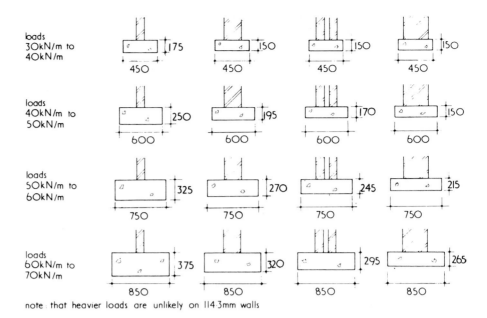

loads
30kN/m to
40kN/m

loads
40kN/m to
50kN/m

loads
50kN/m to
60kN/m

loads
60kN/m to
70kN/m

note: that heavier loads are unlikely on 114·3mm walls

class V : sand, silty sand, clayey sand, (loose)
can be excavated with spade, 50mm square wood peg can easily be driven in

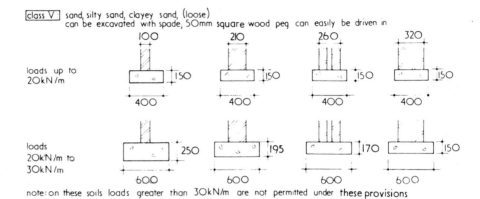

loads up to
20kN/m

loads
20kN/m to
30kN/m

note: on these soils loads greater than 30kN/m are not permitted under these provisions

class VI   silt, clay, sandy clay, silty clay (soft)
fairly easily moulded in fingers and readily excavated

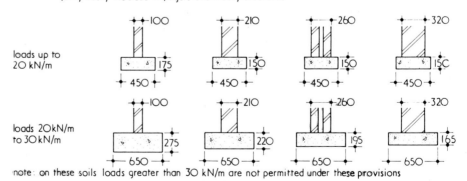

loads up to
20 kN/m

loads 20kN/m
to 30kN/m

note: on these soils loads greater than 30 kN/m are not permitted under these provisions

E 2 [**1.27**] *Foundation dimensions for different*
loadings and subsoils (concluded)

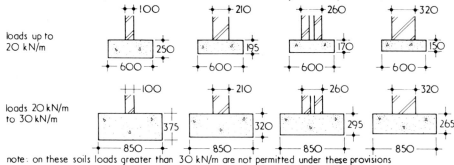

class VII   silt, clay, sandy clay, silty clay (very soft)
        natural sample in winter conditions exudes between fingers when squeezed in fist

note: on these soils loads greater than 30 kN/m are not permitted under these provisions

Comment

As Parts D and E form part of Section 1, they must be presumed to be relevant only to the classes of buildings described at the beginning (see 0.2). In the 1976 Regulations (and previously) however, these requirements were not specifically restricted to these classes (small residential up to 3 storeys etc).

This is another of those parts which is as much a handy design tool as a regulation.

Note on BS 5628 – CP for structural use of masonry

There are 3 parts of which only Parts 1 and 3 are referred to.

Part 1: 1978 Unreinforced masonry

This replaces CP 111: 1970 which is to be withdrawn in April 1987. Both may be used at the moment, but not together. It makes use of the 'limit state' philosophy of design (see Section 2), employing partial safety factors and contains guidance on resistance to lateral loading, as well as the limitation of the effects of accidental damage.

It covers the design of unreinforced masonry of bricks, blocks, square dressed natural stone and random rubble.

It assumes that the design will be entrusted to 'chartered structural or civil engineers, or other appropriately qualified persons'.

The contents include sections on:

Materials, components and workmanship.

Design objectives and general recommendations, which deals with stability, loads, partial safety factors and strengths of masonry in compression, shear and flexure.

Detailed design, including slenderness ratios, eccentricity, vertical loads, shear stresses, bearing and lateral loads and accidental damage.

There is a useful appendix on floor connections using metal anchors and joist hangers.

Part 3: 1985 Materials and components, design and workmanship

This covers a different field from Part 1, being concerned primarily with the effectiveness of masonry walls in relation to weather penetration, durability, fire resistance, insulation of heat and sound, as well as structural soundness.

It contains a wealth of useful information, well illustrated where appropriate on the detailing of masonry construction, as well as sections on materials and workmanship on site. Thermal and moisture movement are also well covered and although structural design is left largely for Part 1, there are some useful guidelines which can be applied to small structures without requiring specialist knowledge. It replaces CP 121: Part 1: 1973 which is withdrawn.

Section 2 | All building types, Codes and Standards

The design and construction of a structure should bein accordance with the relevant recommendations of the following Codes of Practice and British Standards.

Where alternative codes and standards have been listed, the whole of the design for the same material should normally be based on one of the codes only.

Loading

BS 6399: Part 1: 1984 Code of Practice for dead and imposed loads and CP3: ChV, Part 2 for wind loads

Where certain factors result in snow depths which are not uniform, guidance to be sought from BRE Digest 290. (NOTE   BS 6399 supersedes CP 3: Ch V, Part 1 as used in the 1976 Regulations).

CP 3: Ch V: Part 2: 1972 for wind loads and in no case shall the factor S_3 be taken as less than 1.0 (which is normal).

Exceptionally if actual loads are known to be greater than those given in BS 6399: Part 1 the actual load is to be used.

As these are important criteria, applicable to all types of building and forms of construction, a fairly comprehensive summary of their requirements follows:

The new BS replaces CP 3: Ch V: Part 1. It is very similar, the principal revisions being new and more extensive load tables and the inclusion of rules for vehicle barriers in car parks.

The BS defines its scope as covering:

1   New buildings and structures.

2   Alterations and additions to existing buildngs and structures.

3   Material change of use of an existing structure, but NOT maintenance or replacement of parts not accompanied by a change of use.

Nor does it cover:

(*a*)   Loads on bridges (see other Codes: eg BS 5400).

(*b*)   Wind loads.

(*c*)   Internal pressure loads (eg bunkers, silos, tanks).

(*d*)   Machinery vibration (except some gantry cranes, see later).

(*e*)   Loads due to lifts (see BS 2655).

(*f*) (*g*)   Incidental construction loads or test loads.

(*h*)   Accidental loads.

Clause 3   Dead loads

Partitions

For fixed partitions allow actual weight. Movable partitions are now considered as imposed loads.

Tanks, receptacles, etc.

The weight of tanks or other receptacles are considered as dead loads and account must be taken of both full and empty conditions in assessing their effect.

Clause 4   Imposed floor loads

The loads appropriate to different uses (table 1 of the previous code) are now split into 8 tables, 5 to 12, covering all normal types of building including a vehicle occupancy (table 12). At first sight this looks like a reversion to the original 8 classes in the 1952 code, but the grouping is different. The tables give a distributed load in kN/m^2 and a maximum concentrated load for each case. The latter are to be considered as acting where they would produce the maximum stress or maximum deflection, whichever is the limiting factor. They are assumed to be acting on a point (whereas previously a square of 300 mm side was specified) for bending and shear, but for local effects (punching/crushing) to act over the actual area of application [1.28].

[**1.28**] *Basis for assessing loads. Use distributed or concentrated load – whichever produces greater stress. Do NOT use both together.*

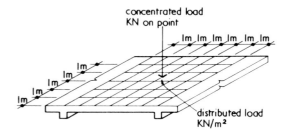

The tables are too extensive to reproduce here. Loads vary from a minimum of 1.5 kN/m² in dwellings to 20 kN/m² in foundries. For storage applications a figure per metre of available height is given.

The general recommendations do not apply to atypical usages such as mechanical stacking, plant etc.

For movable partitions the allowance per m² is not less than ⅓ the weight per metre run of partition with a minimum of 1 kN/m².

The distributed loads apply to both slabs and beams. Where no concentrated loads are given, the distributed load is considered an adequate basis for design. Sometimes only concentrated loads are given (e.g. catwalks – 1 kN at 1 m centres.)

Stairways and landings

The basis of the design is the horizontal area of the stair (L × B). This is not stated in the CP but may be inferred from the general rules applying to the tables [1.29].

Loadings vary according to occupancy and are given in the Tables.

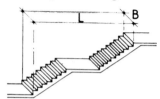
[**1.29**] *Loadings on stairways and landings.*

Ceilings

For members supporting ceilings, access hatches etc, (excluding glazing).

(*a*)   Without access: nil.

(*b*)   With access: 0.25 kN/m² distributed.
                                  0.9 kN concentrated.

Clause 5 Reduction of imposed loads

When an area of slab (L × B) is supported by one single span of beam and exceeds 40m² reductions in the imposed load for the beam can be made as follows:

exceeding 40 m²	5 per cent
exceeding 80 m²	10 per cent
exceeding 120 m²	15 per cent
exceeding 160 m²	20 per cent
exceeding 200 m²	25 per cent

These are not applicable to roofs. Reductions for intermediate areas may be taken by linear interpolation, diagrams [**1.30, 1.31**].

[**1.30, 1.31**] *Permissible reduction of imposed loads on beams and vertical supports.*

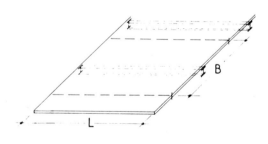

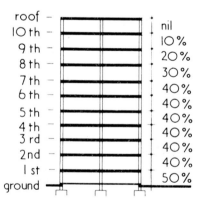

Exceptions

Except as stated below, the reductions shown above can be made in the total calculated imposed load on columns according to the number of floors supported by them.

1   In warehouse and garage buildings the full load on each floor must be assumed.

2   Where floors are designed for 5 kN/m² or more the total load calculated in this way must not be less than an average of 5 kN/m² over the whole area of the building.

3   No reduction shall be made in respect of some areas of office floors (heavy file storage and so on) or buildings used for storage purposes generally.

NOTE: In arriving at column loadings either type of reduction may be used if applicable but both types may *not* be used together on the same member. No reduction shall be made in respect of any fixed plant, machinery or equipment the actual weight of which is specifically allowed for. For purposes of reductions in the total imposed load, roofs may be regarded as floors.

Clause 6 Imposed loads on roofs

The rules are described in the following diagrams. The imposed loads stated include an allowance for snow loads, but not for wind loads which must be added where applicable. The rules for flat roofs include all roofs up to 10° pitch. The rules, illustrated by diagrams, are as follows:

The effective area of the roof is to be calculated on the horizontal plane [1.32].

How the loads are to be applied. [1.33]

Loads on roofs with access *only* for maintenance and repair – any building type [1.34].

Flat roofs – with or without access – any building type [**1.35**].

Curved roofs [1.36].

All roof coverings (except glazing) [1.37].

[**1.32**] *Calculation of roof area.*

[**1.33**] *Application of loads.*

[**1.34**] *Roofs with access only for repairs. Distributed loads.*

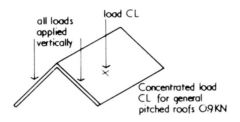

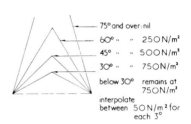

[**1.35**] *Flat roofs with and without access other than only for repair or maintenance.*

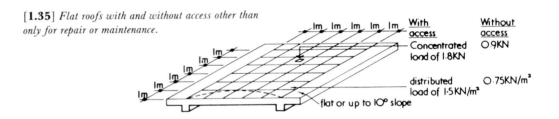

[**1.36**] *Curved roofs.*

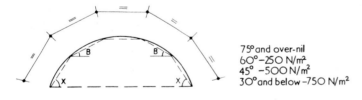

[**1.37**] *All roof coverings (except glazing).*

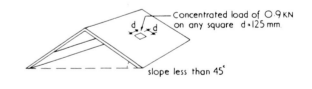

Clause 7 Crane gantry girders

The BS does give guidance on allowances to be made in the support system of gantry cranes to cover 'forces set up by vibration, shock from slipping of slings, kinetic action of acceleration and retardation and impact of wheel loads', diagram [1.38].

BS 6399: Part 1 Clause 7 [**1.38**] *Gantry cranes.*

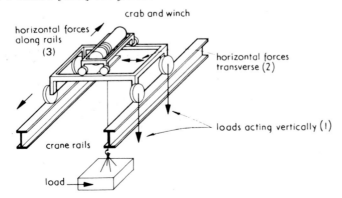

Loads (1) Max static wheel loads increased by 25 per cent for electric crane, 10 per cent for hand crane.

Loads (2) Horizontal force taken as 10 per cent of combined weight of crab and load for electric crane, 5 per cent for hand crane.

Loads (3) Force along rails taken as 5 per cent of static wheel loads whether electric or hand operated.

Forces (2) or (3), but not both, are to be taken as acting simultaneously with force (1). These rules apply only to simple single gantry cranes. Heavy, high speed or multiple cranes are to be treated as a special problem.

Clause 8 Dynamic loading (excluding wind)	The values in the tables allow for small dynamic effects, such as those due to normal movement of people, furniture etc, but not for machinery, fork lift trucks etc, or dynamic loads due to crowds. In such cases, the magnitude of the load effect depends on the response of the structural system, and can be much higher than the normal static load effect. Special design consideration is needed.

Clause 9 Parapets and balustrades	Table 4, which gives appropriate figures, has been expanded to include several new categories. The loads are expressed as acting horizontally 1.1 m above datum (finished level of platform or pitch of stairs) [1.39].

*Clause 9 [**1.39**] Parapets and balustrades.*

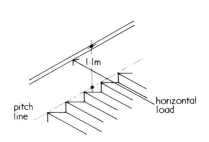
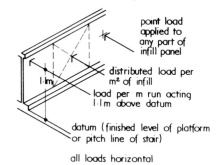

In addition to a horizontal UDL per m run (as previously) two other figures are given – a UDL per m² applied to the infill and a point load applied to any part of the infill (see also Approved Document for K 2/3).

Clause 10 Vehicle barriers for car parks	This is a new section. It gives a formula for general use, based on vehicle weights etc, and a figure of 150 kN/ for each 1½ m run for car parks housing cars and light vans up to 2500 kg gross mass. The force is considered as acting horizontally at 375 mm above floor level in this case. For barriers to access ramps the conditions are different, as illustrated in [1.40].

*Clause 10 [**1.40**] Vehicle barriers for car parks (cars and light vans up to 2500 kg gross mass).*

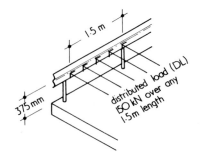
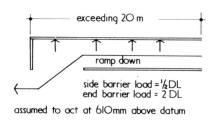

CP 3: chapter V; part 2: 1972. Code of practice for wind loads	Although the general policy throughout this guide is to make the necessity for reference back to the Regulations or other publications as infrequent as possible, CP 3: chapter V: part 2: 1972, is rather a special case. In the first place it is due for revision. Secondly, much of the basic design criteria is presented in the form of tables which cannot really be simplified or presented in any better way. This section is, therefore, presented as a general explanation of the principles involved and a description of the method of calculation to be used, with diagrams where appropriate. The reader is, however, referred to the tables in the CP itself when making an assessment of wind forces in a specific case.

The effect of wind	When wind blows against the face of a building it is slowed down, resulting in a build up of pressure against that face. At the same time it is deflected and accelerated around the sides

and over the roof with a consequent reduction of pressure (ie suction) on those surfaces. A large eddy also forms behind the building, resulting in a negative pressure or suction to the rear wall. The greater the speed at any particular point the greater will be the resulting suction, diagram [1.41].

[**1.41**] *Wind effects.*

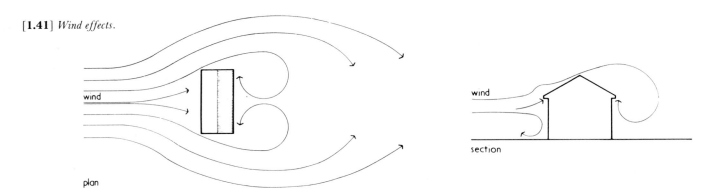

plan

section

Restricted gaps between or through buildings (eg an open ground storey) can cause higher than normal wind speeds due to the differential pressures on opposite sides of the gap, which in turn results in higher than normal suctions on surfaces facing towards the gap.

The suction on a roof, particularly a low pitched roof, is frequently the most severe load experienced on any part of the building and may often considerably exceed the dead weight of the structure, requiring firm fixings to prevent it being lifted. Suction or negative pressure will occur even on the windward slope of roofs up to 30° pitch but roofs of 35° pitch and over usually develop a positive pressure on the windward side. Even then, however, there is a zone near to the ridge where suction occurs and roof coverings may be dislodged. Lee slopes always experience suction. When the wind blows parallel to the ridge, all roofs – regardless of pitch – experience suction, particularly next to the windward gable.

Wind tunnel experiments have shown that external pressures due to the wind vary over the whole surface of the building according to the velocity and direction and the shape and size of the building. These pressures can be shown by means of a contour diagram. Such diagrams would have to be drawn for various wind directions and, since every part of the building has to be designed to resist the forces created by wind from any direction, it is more convenient for practical purposes to make adequate allowances for the increased local pressures which occur at corners and the intersections of surfaces, diagram [1.42].

The diagram shows the location of high local pressures. The variation in pressure is expressed for convenience in terms of a co-efficient by which the normal dynamic pressure of the wind is multiplied. This can vary between a positive factor of +0.7 in the centre of the windward side and a negative factor of −2.0 near to the windward edges of roofs. Upward positive pressure is generated below the overhangs of roofs and balconies on the windward side. This must be taken into account when assessing the total uplift on a roof, and the intensity is to be taken as the same as that on the adjoining wall surface.

[**1.42**] *Extent of local negative pressures.*

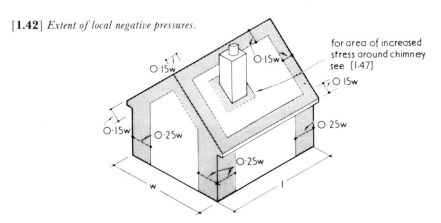

for area of increased stress around chimney see [1.47]

0.15w

0.15w

0.15w

0.15w

0.15w

0.25w

0.25w

0.25w

w

l

Dynamic pressure of the wind

The forces exerted by the wind on any part of a building may be taken as the product of the dynamic pressure, the area on which it acts, and the co-efficient referred to earlier to allow for the situation on the building.

When wind is brought to rest against an obstacle, all its kinetic energy is transformed into dynamic pressure (q) which can be calculated from the formula

$$q = \varrho \frac{V_s^2}{2}$$

where ϱ = air density
V_s = design wind speed

In SI units the expression becomes
$$q \ (N/m^2) = 0.613 \ V_s^2 \ (m/s)$$
To save calculation, a conversion chart is provided in the CP (Figure 2) from which the pressure q can be directly read off for any relative wind speed (both imperial and metric units are shown). For greater accuracy or convenience three tables are also provided giving values of q in SI units (N/m^2), metric technical units (kgf/m^2) and Imperial units (lbf/ft^2).

Wind velocity

To enable the pressure to be determined, it is first necessary to establish the appropriate wind velocity to which the building is likely to be subject. This is a complex business bringing in a series of variable factors.

The initial basis for the assessment is a wind speed contour map of the UK (figure 3 in the CP). Velocities are given in m/sec and relate to maximum 3 second gust speed likely to be exceeded on average only once in fifty years, measured at 10 m above ground in open level country. They vary from a minimum figure of 38 around the London area to 54/56 in the Orkneys and Hebrides. Generally, the pattern is one of increasing speeds to the north and west. As an example, an average figure of 46/48 occurs in the Border Country, the extreme west of Wales, Cornwall and roughly across the centre of Ulster. This basic wind speed figure is referred to as V.

It has to be adjusted for three factors which are described as:
s1   Local topographic influences.
s2   Surface roughness of the environment, gust duration appropriate to size and the height of the structure.
s3   The design life of the building.
The design wind speed (V_s) can then be calculated from: $V_s = V \times s1 \times s2 \times s3$.

S1 Topography

Height above sea level does not in itself affect wind speed but exposed hills rising well above their surroundings may cause accelerated wind, as also may some valleys so shaped as to cause funnelling of the wind. Conversely, in steep-sided enclosed valleys wind speed may be less than normal.

For all normal sites a factor of 1.0 is recommended, but in cases such as those quoted above higher or lower values within the range 1.1 to 0.9 may be appropriate. Caution is necessary when using a reducing factor. In extreme cases a value of 1.2 may possibly be justified. If doubt exists the Meterological Office may be consulted.

S2 Surface roughness, duration of gust, and height of building

This factor really combines three separate considerations which are grouped together simply because their effects can all be represented in a single table (table 3).

Surface roughness
Any strong wind speeds near to the ground are affected by ground roughness, which tends to reduce speed. Four categories are described:
1   Open country with no shelter (eg fens, airfields, moorland, farmland without hedges, coastal fringes, etc.). Mean level of obstruction taken as zero.
2   Open country with scattered wind breaks (eg most farmland and country estates, except well wooded parts). Mean level of obstruction assumed to be 2 m.
3   Country with many wind breaks (eg well wooded parkland and forest areas, small towns and suburbs). Generally, the top level of obstructions is assumed to be about 10 m. This category includes all built-up areas except those in category 4.
4   Surfaces with large and numerous obstructions (eg the centres of large towns and cities). The general roof height assumed to be about 25 m or more.
Where buildings are sited near to the edge of an area having a particular category, it may be necessary to assume that the adjacent lower category applies – the effect of surface roughness not being instantaneous. The principles are illustrated in diagram [1.43].

[**1.43**] *Change in surface roughness*

x is the shortest distance (in any direction)
Building considered as within Category 2, if x is less than the following
If building is above general level of obstruction $x = 1$ *Kilometre*
otherwise depends on ground coverage

    if not less than 10 *per cent* .... $x = 500$ m
    "   "   "   "   15 *per cent* .... $x = 250$ m
    "   "   "   "   30 *per cent* .... $x = 100$ m

Gust duration

The maximum wind speed assumed also depends on the length of the gust being considered. The shorter the gust period the higher will be the average speed over that period. With larger buildings a longer period can be assumed since it is unlikely that the maximum gust effect will be applied to the whole building at once. Three alternatives are given in table 3 to be applied as follows:

3-second gust for all glazing, cladding and roofing. For structural design of the whole building use a 5-second or 15-second gust according to the size, as shown in diagram [1.44]. These are known as Classes A, B and C respectively, as listed in table 3 of the CP.

Height

Table 3 also provides a series of values graduated according to the total height of the structure above ground level. When calculating the total overturning effect of the wind, a single wind strength can be assumed relating to the total height of the building. Alternatively, the building may be divided into several parts and advantage taken of the reduced effect on the lower sections. The principles are illustrated in diagram [1.45]. The same rule applies to pitched roofs.

[**1.45**] *The S 2 factor: subdivision of height.*

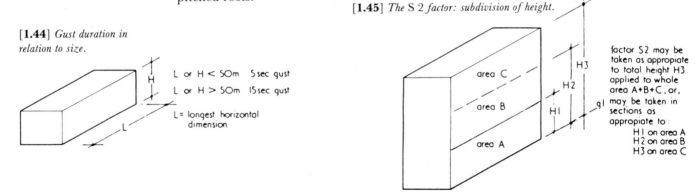

[**1.44**] *Gust duration in relation to size.*

L or H < 50m   5 sec gust
L or H > 50m   15 sec gust

L= longest horizontal dimension

factor S2 may be taken as appropiate to total height H3 applied to whole area A+B+C, or, may be taken in sections as appropiate to:
H1 on area A
H2 on area B
H3 on area C

Buildings close to a cliff or escarpment need special consideration and the CP provides rules for assessing an effective height to be used in calculations. The method varies according to the angle of the escarpment on which the building is situated, and the principles are illustrated in the diagram [1.46].

[**1.46**] *The S 2 factor. Height of buildings near cliffs or escarpments.*

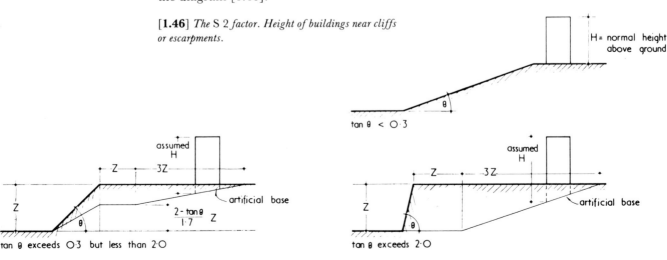

S3 Building life

The S3 factor is related to the probability that the basic wind speed will be exceeded in any particular length of time. The basic speeds shown on the map are maximum 3-second gust speeds likely to be exceeded only once in 50 years. This factor, however, is based on statistical concepts, and it can be shown mathematically that the probability (P) that a value greater than x (basic wind speed) will occur in any period of N years is governed by the formula:

$$P = 1 - (1 - \frac{1}{T})\,N$$

where T represents the return period (ie the period in which the basic wind speed is likely to be exceeded only once).

For a period of 50 years, which is the normal situation, the probability level is 0.63 and not 1.00 as might be expected.

The CP provides a simple chart which gives values for the factor S3 using four different probability levels and exposure periods from two years to 200 years (Fig. 1). It also states that S3 should be taken as 1.00, with certain exceptions which include temporary or short life structures and, conversely, structures where an abnormally long life is expected, or greater than normal safety is required. The matter is explained in greater detail in Appendix C which does suggest that a period of two years, giving an S3 value of 0.77 at the normal probability level of 0.63, would be acceptable for assessing wind loads during construction. The Approved Document itself, however, overrules this suggestion by a proviso that in no case shall the factor S3 be taken as less than 1'.

The other probability levels shown in Fig. 1 of the CP are unlikely to be much used. They are 0.1, 0.01 and 0.001. Appendix C gives an example of the use of level 0.01 giving S3 = 1.35 at 50 years. Although not evident from the diagram, this converts the once in 50 years wind to once in about 5000 years. Clearly, as records have only been kept for a fraction of that time, this must give rise to speculation as to the accuracy of statistical methods in such examples. Unless circumstances are exceptional, therefore, factor S3 will be taken as 1.00, which means it will have no effect on calculations.

This seems the least realistic part of the CP since statistics of this sort are always difficult to accept. Clearly, if it is accepted that during the normal life of a building the design wind speed will be exceeded once, there would seem little reason to worry if this happened more than once, in which case it is hard to understand why doubling the design life of a building to say a hundred years should have any real influence on the design's basis. Equally, although a structure may even be classed as temporary, it may still be subject to the maximum design wind speed during its short life.

Pressure co-efficients

As explained earlier, these are simply a means of expressing the variation in the normal dynamic pressure of the wind relating to various directions and situations. Tables 7 and 8 in the CP give details of external pressure co-efficients to be applied to walls, roofs and monopitches respectively. The abbreviation used for the term 'external pressure co-efficient' is 'Cpe'. This is to differentiate it from 'internal pressure co-efficient' for which the abbreviated term is 'Cpi'. Figures are given in the tables for three different height/width ratios and two alternative length/width ratios which should cover the majority of cases.

It is emphasised that all structures must be checked, with each face being considered in turn as the windward face.

The tables also give figures for high local pressure co-efficients which must be used for calculating the local loads on cladding, roofs, etc. in the appropriate situations but *not* for determining the total load on the building.

Local co-efficients

Areas around projections, such as chimney stacks or surface areas in passages through buildings and so on, should be given a local Cpe of −1.2. Parapets are also a case requiring special consideration because the wind pressures are considerably reduced below the average at the top of the windward face. The sketch [1.47] illustrates these points.

This is one of those factors which were first covered by BRS Digest 119, but not included in the 1970 edition of CP 3: part 2. They were later included in the 1972 edition of the Code so that reference to BRS Digest 119 is no longer necessary.

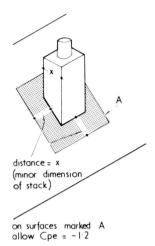

distance = x
(minor dimension
of stack)

on surfaces marked A
allow Cpe = -1·2

[**1.47**] *Local coefficients for projections, narrow openings and parapets. Note that reduced figures may be used for parapets.*

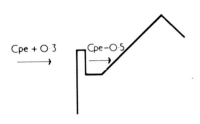

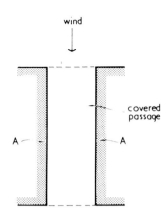

Internal pressures

The total force on any cladding element depends upon the difference between the internal and external pressures. Internal pressures depend on the permeability of each face of the building. This can be expressed as a percentage of opening in relation to the total area of the face. Even with all doors and windows shut, the gaps which occur around them provide a passage for air. When all doors and windows are shut, the permeability of the average office or domestic block is in the range 0.01 to 0.05 per cent. This is quite a low figure and one open window even in quite a large facade will increase the percentage dramatically. The position of openings in relation to wind direction will decide whether or not the internal pressure is positive or negative, with a correspondingly varying effect upon the loads sustained by the roof and cladding. A simple illustration of the principles involved is given in the sketch [1.48].

[**1.48**] *Internal pressures: general principles.*

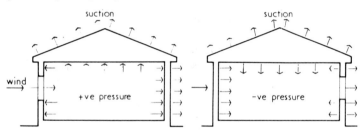

A. Opening on windward side. Positive internal pressure increases effect of external suction and decreases effect of external pressure.

B. Opening on leeward side. Negative internal pressure increases effect of external pressure and decreases effect of external suction.

Since facades where windows are provided may be subject to wind effects from any direction, it is necessary to allow for the most severe conditions. In the CP, such openings (windows, doors, and so on) are referred to as 'dominant openings' and rules are given for calculating the Cpi in relation to the size and position of such openings in comparison with the total normal permeability of the building. This, however, presumes that it is possible to know with reasonable accuracy where and to what extent a dominant opening will occur, and also to be able to assess accurately the total distributed permeability of the other faces of the building. It is possible to envisage circumstances where the design of a building is clearly controlled by a dominant opening (eg aircraft hangars, factories with large sliding doors, and so on). For normal occupied buildings, however, it would clearly be impossible to state how many windows or doors might be opened during a gale, and the CP therefore gives some general rules for guidance where specific information is not available.

There are two main conditions:

1   Where no dominant opening is likely to occur. The sketch indicates the principles to be followed: diagram [1.49].

2   Where a dominant opening will exist. If only a small possibility exists of a dominant opening during a storm, the Cpi should be taken as the more onerous of +0.2 or −0.3. If a

dominant opening is likely to occur during a storm, the principles to be followed are indicated in the sketch [1.49].

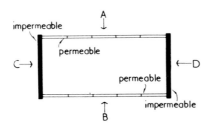

Wind direction A or B: cpi = + 0.2
Wind direction C or D: cpi = − 0.3

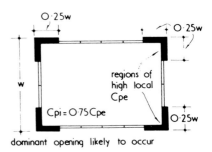

Where openings can occur only as shown, normal values of cpe to be used. If openings can occur in regions of high local cpe, then the higher value must be taken.

no dominant opening

[**1.49**] *Internal pressures: assumed cpi for various conditions.*

For all wind directions: cpi = − 0.3

Total load on structural elements

Having arrived at a value for the design wind speed (V_s) and, from this, having determined the appropriate dynamic pressure (q) and finally having settled the critical values for the external and internal pressure co-efficients (Cpe and Cpi), the total wind load (F) on any flat wall or roof panel of given area (A) is:

F = A.q. (Cpe − Cpi)

In cladding which is comprised of several layers (eg a roof with tiles, felt and boarding), the pressure between the layers will be at some intermediate level between the Cpe and Cpi. Care must be taken to ensure that the whole pressure difference is not brought to bear on some thin membrane not designed to resist it. In the same way, there may be a pressure gradient across the interior of a building which could impose a load on partitions.

To keep down the effect of Cpi on elements of structure, the internal pressure is sometimes controlled by deliberately introducing permeability. A simple example is indicated [1.50].

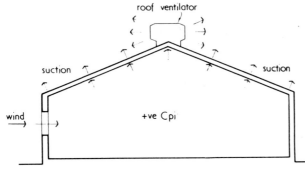

[**1.50**] *Deliberate control of internal pressure. Note: ventilator reduces positive cpi and hence upward load on roof.*

Total wind loads on the whole structure

The total load on a building is obtained by taking the vectorial summation of the loads on the individual surfaces. The principles are indicated in the sketch [1.51].

It is important to use only those loads which can occur simultaneously (ie for a given wind direction) and not the maxima used for the individual design of walls, roofs, etc. For simple calculations a single height figure is often taken, but with tall buildings designers will usually prefer to calculate using a series of height zones to avoid applying the maximum wind speed over the whole face of the building. In buildings of irregular outline this will always be necessary.

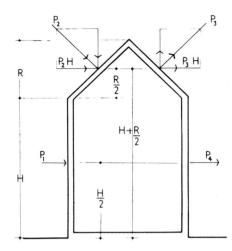

[**1.51**] *Summation of individual loads on surfaces.*
P_2H *and* P_3H *are the horizontal components of the roof*
wind loads which act normally to the slope.

Total overturning force

$$= \left[P_1 \times \frac{H}{2} \right] + \left[P_2H \times \left(H + \frac{R}{2} \right) \right] + \left[P_3H \times \left(H + \frac{R}{2} \right) \right] + \left[P_4 \times \frac{H}{2} \right]$$

plus the effect of the vertical components of P_2 *and* P_3 *and frictional drag if applicable*

Force coefficients

For simple structural shapes the CP has provided a simplified method of calculation. Instead of having to add together the various forces acting on individual parts using differing pressure coefficients, a single coefficient is provided to represent the combined effect on the whole structure. These are known as 'force coefficients' (Cf) and table 10 of the CP gives a series of these for rectangular buildings of varying plan shapes from square to long and narrow and varying height/breadth ratios. The range of shapes in table 10 varies from a square to a plan length/width ratio of 4:1 in five stages, with a height/breadth ratio from ½ up to 6:1 in five stages, which for winds in both directions (90° between) gives a total of 45 values for Cf, ranging from a minimum of 0.7 to a maximum of 1.6. The CP also states (paragraph 7.1) that these tables may be used for other buildings of similar shape, presumably by interpolation or, to a reasonable degree, by extrapolation.

One omission from the CP which was included in BRS Digest 119 is a note on the effect of small projections or recesses in otherwise rectangular plan forms. It states that small projections or recesses do not invalidate the use of force coefficients, providing these do not exceed 10 per cent of the floor area: diagram [1.52]. The Code states that values for buildings of other shapes will be published later as an addendum. In the meantime, the guidance given by BRS Digest 119 is presumably still valid. The same might be said for circular and polygonal buildings which are dealt with in table 6 of the Digest but omitted from the CP, presumably being the subject of further research.

[**1.52**] *Use of force coefficients in table 10; permitted variations from plain rectangle as recommended in BRS Digest 119.*

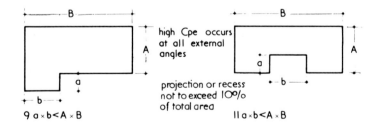

The general formula for the use of force coefficients is
F = Ae.q. Cf when
F is the force in the direction of the wind
Ae is the effective frontal area (projected area on a plane normal to the wind)
q is the dynamic pressure
Cf is the force coefficient in the direction of the wind.

Circular structures

The force coefficients for the special case of circular and polygonal structures (eg chimneys) are given in table 6 of BRS Digest 119. These vary according to shape, surface roughness, and height/diameter ratios. Simple circular structures of low height ratio offer the least resistance. They are not mentioned in CP 3 chapter V: part 2: 1970 other than to say that special investigations may be necessary.

Frictional drag

In most cases frictional drag may be ignored but, when the surface over which the wind blows is large in relation to the frontal area (eg single storey factories), the force created by frictional drag must be considered. The simple forumla given in BRS Digest 119 has been abandoned and there are now two formulae depending in whether the breadth (b) (dimension at right angles to the wind) is greater or less than the height (h). With rectangular buildings, the frictional drag need only be considered if the depth (d), ie the dimension in the direction of the wind, is more than four times the height or the breadth (d/h or d/b>4). In such cases the frictional drag (F') can be calculated as follows:

if $h \leqslant b$ $F' = Cf'qb\,(d-4h) + Cf'q2h\,(d-4h)$

but if $h \geqslant b$ $F' = Cf'qb\,(d-4h) + Cf'q2h\,(d-4b)$

The expression Cf' represents a coefficient of friction which is varied according to the surface across which the wind blows – that is the roof in the first formula and the side walls in the second. The values of Cf' are given as:

Cf' = 0.01 for smooth surfaces without corrugations.

Cf' = 0.02 for surfaces with corrugations across the wind direction.

Cf' = 0.04 for surfaces with ribs across the wind direction.

q is of course the normal dynamic pressure and b, d and h are breadth (across wind), depth (in direction of wind) and height: expressions used in tables 7, 8, 9 and 10 for pressure and force coefficients. The formulae could be slighly simplified to

$Cf'q\,(b+2h)\,(d-4h)$ when b exceeds h and

$Cf'q\,(b+2h)\,(d-4b)$ when h exceeds b.

As a prerequisite is that depth (d) must always be more than four times b or h, the expression $(d-4h)$ or $(d-4b)$ must always exceed unity; also, as b and d are multiplied (after adjustment) the final answer must be related to the plan area modified by the effect of the height, diagram [1.53].

Frictional drag is additional to any other forces calculated using force or pressure coefficients.

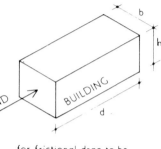

[**1.53**] *Frictional drag.*

for frictional drag to be considered d must exceed 4 times h or b

Loads during construction

Pressure coefficients which apply to completed buildings are not relevant during construction, when special conditions will apply. A typical example is the extremes of internal pressure which can arise when a building is partly clad. It is necessary to consider these possibilities and to arrange programmes to avoid dangerous conditions arising.

Another example is the case of a structure standing complete with frame and floors but without cladding, when critical loads can arise. The loads on such a structure can be calculated using coefficients as in the sketch [1.54].

In making these calculations, the Code states that it is permissible to assume a reduced S3 factor for the life of the building, based on the length of the site construction period, but with a minimum of two years. Using the graph in the CP, this would give an S3 factor of about 0.77 for a building in which the normal probability level was assumed. However, the Approved Document itself states that in no case shall the S3 factor be taken as less than 1.0 and, although not specifically stated, this presumably applies to temporary states during construction, as well as completed buildings.

[**1.54**] *Loads during construction: force coefficients.*

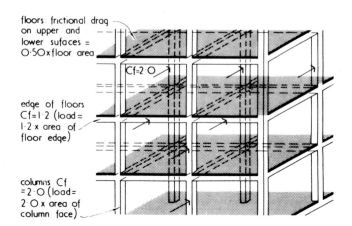

floors: frictional drag on upper and lower sufaces = O·5O x floor area

Cf=2·O

edge of floors Cf=1·2 (load= 1·2 x area of floor edge)

columns Cf =2·O (load= 2·O x area of column face)

The response of buildings to the wind — oscillation	Although not included in the Code, BRS Digest 119 deals briefly with such things as deflection due to wind and the oscillation of slender structures. Buildings generally are relatively stiff and trouble from excessive deflection has been rare. Recently, however, situations have been reached where blocks of flats of about thirty storeys have been subject to sway and wind vibration which, although not structurally dangerous, has been beyond the limit for residential occupancy.
	With slender structures, oscillation can arise when the natural frequency of the structure is less than the shedding frequency of the wind at maximum velocity. In such cases, structural damping or the use of devices to reduce aero-dynamic excitation is necessary. The CP merely states that such oscillations may require further investigation and observes that they may occur at wind velocities below the maximum.

Other codes and standards

Foundations — general	BS 8004: 1986
Structural work of reinforced, prestressed or plain concrete	BS 8110: Parts 1, 2 and 3: 1985 (now published), or CP 114: 1969 NOTES: 1 The reference to CP 110 will be deleted when BS 8110 is published. 2 The reference to CP 114 will be deleted two years after the date of publication of BS 8110.
Structural work of composite steel and concrete construction	CP 117: Part 1: 1965
Structural work of steel	BS 5950: Part 1: 1985, or BS 5950: Part 2: 1985 BS 5950: Part 4: 1982 BS 5950: Part 5: 1987 NOTE BS 5950 was published in August 1985. As, however, the BSI has not yet withdrawn BS 449: Part 2: 1969 the reference to this code is not being deleted at this stage.
Structural work of aluminium	CP 118: 1969 using one of the principal or supplementary aluminium alloys designated in Section 1.1 of that code, and for the purpose of Section 5.3 of that code, the structure should be classified as a safe-life structure.
Structural work of masonry	CP 111: 1970, or BS 5628: Part 1: 1978 BS 5628: Part 2: 1985 NOTE The reference to CP 111 will be deleted at the end of April 1987.
Structural work of timber	BS 5268: Part 2: 1984 BS 5268: Part 3: 1985 NOTE The Approved Document in support of Regulation 7 precludes the use of high alumina cement for structural work.

Note on British Standards

It can be observed that as new standards are published, the old ones are phased out, a two-year overlap being allowed for changeover. Apart from those referred to there are other new standards in the pipeline, but they are not mentioned unless an estimated publication date has been given.

Note also that the old procedure of classifying BSI documents as either British Standard Specifications (coded BS no.) or British Standard Codes of Practice (coded CP no.) has been abandoned and all are now given a BS number, regardless of content. Occasional reference may also be seen to DD numbers which stands for 'Draft for Development'.

Note on limit state design

Over the past two decades there has been a complete revision of the general approach to structural design in all media. This started in concrete with the proposed redrafting of CPs 114, 115 and 116 (reinforced, precast and prestressed concrete). Guidance became available in the recommendations of the European Concrete Committee published in 1964, which introduced the concept of 'limit states' as opposed to 'single failure' as design criteria.

In this concept, consideration is given to serviceability at all stages of structural behaviour: viz elastic, plastic, cracked and ultimate. Three limit states are normally considered: ultimate strength and the serviceability limit states of deflection and cracking under service loads. Design figures are used which make the chance of reaching the limit state of ultimate strength more remote than those for the two other criteria. The aim of limit state design is that the chance of each limit state being reached is substantially constant for all members in a structure, as appropriate to their situation. Thus is it unlikely the structure will become unfit for use. The method, as distinct from the earlier design load/elastic theory, employs a load factor rather than a stress safety factor. In elastic theory the loads used are the actual loads and the design stresses are the ultimate stresses divided by a factor of safety. In the load factor method, the loads are actual loads multiplied by a load factor, and the stresses are the actual ultimate design stresses. The use of both methods in the same design is prohibited. Lack of statistics has prevented a design method in *complete* accord with the probability theory, but the use of partial safety factors for both loads and stresses had enabled development of a design system which ensures acceptable probability that limit states will not be reached.

This led to the production of CP 110: 1972 which has been in general use ever since, although CP 114/115/116 have never been withdrawn and are still sometimes used. As may be seen above CP 110 itself is to be withdrawn when its revision, BS 8110: Parts 1, 2 and 3 is published. The CP 114 series will finally be withdrawn two years later.

Similar changes have been taking place in other fields, and the BSS on structural work of steel and masonry use limit state theory and partial safety factors. The new BS 5628 for timber does not.

A 3   DISPROPORTIONATE COLLAPSE

The regulation itself states:

	Requirement	Limits on application
	Disproportionate collapse	
Structure	A 3 The building shall be so constructed that in the event of an accident the structure will not be damaged to an extent disproportionate to the cause of the damage.	This requirement applies only to – (a) a building having five or more storeys (each basement level being counted as one storey); and (b) a public building the structure of which incorporates a clear span exceeding nine metres between supports.

The AD is very short, in the manner of Section 2, consisting simply of references to BSS plus a few directions. They are reproduced below:

Codes and Standards

The following Codes and Standards may be used in designing to meet the Requirement of Paragraph A 3 for a building having five or more storeys, provided the recommendations on ties, and the recommendations on the effect of misuse or accident are followed.

Structural work of reinforced, prestressed of plain concrete	BS 8110: Parts 1 and 2: 1985 (now published), or CP 110: Part 1: 1972 NOTE The reference to CP 110 will be deleted when BS 8110 is published.
Structural work of steel	BS 5950: Part 1: 1985 (now published). (The accident loading referred to in Clause 2.4.5.5 should be chosen having particular regard to the importance of the key element and the consequences of failure, and the key element should always be capable of withstanding a load of at least 34 kN/m^2 applied from any direction.)
Structural work of masonry	BS 5628: Part 1: 1978
Additional information	Structural failure of any member not designed as a protected key element or member, in any one storey, should not result in failure of the structure beyond the immediately adjacent storeys or beyond an area within those storeys of: (a) 70m^2, or (b) 15 per cent of the area of the storey whichever is less. Protected key elements or members are single structural elements on which large parts of the structure rely (ie supporting a floor or roof area of more than 70m^2 or 15 per cent of the area of the storey, whichever is less) and their design which should take their importance into account, and the least loadings they have to withstand are described in the Codes and Standards listed above.

It is interesting to note that although Regulation A 3 applies to both (a) buildings of 5 storeys or more *and* (b) public buildings incorporating a clear span of over 9 m, the codes and standards are recommended only for the first category (a). Regulations D 17/18 which A 3 replaces referred only to buildings over 5 storeys and this applied generally in BS publications too. There appear to be no specific guidelines for the type (b) buildings, apart from the general coverage of section 2 for all building types.

It will no doubt be of interest and assistance to the reader to understand the need for these special requirements, even though it is not possible, or necessary, to go into detail. They have a long history which really started with the partial collapse of a block of flats known as Ronan Point and which has been in and out of the news ever since.

As a result, a fifth amendment to the 1965 Regulations was published in 1970. This block, being system-built, of large storey-height panels, was proved to be highly susceptible to a gas explosion, which resulted in a house of cards type collapse. During the resulting enquiry it was realised that, although such structures were most susceptible to progressive collapse unless adequately tied in, other more normal types of structure could also be at risk. The amendment therefore applied to all buildings of 5 or more storeys, and proposed two possible methods to avoid collapse. The first required that the structure be designed so that if any single structural member were removed, the loads which it supported would be transferred to others, which had to be capable of sustaining such transferred loads (the transference of load

[**1.55**] *Limitation of structural failure.*

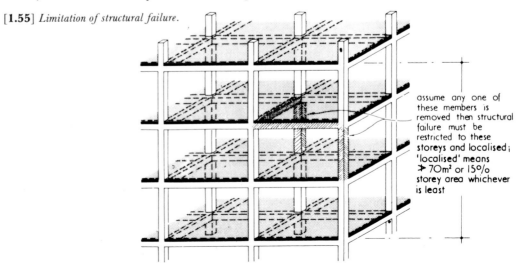

assume any one of these members is removed then structural failure must be restricted to these storeys and localised; 'localised' means ⊁70m² or 15% storey area whichever is least principle). The alternative was to make members which could not be removed strong enough to sustain the design load plus a possible accidental load (the key element principle).

The regulations specified a limit to the extent of any collapse after the removal of any one member not designed as a key element. The new AD does the same. The extent is illustrated in diagram [1.55].

The alternative basis required that the key elements, being members the removal of which would involve a larger collapse than that permitted above, must be designed to withstand a load of at least 34 kN/m² (originally 5 lbs/sq. in.) applied from any direction, in addition to the design loads. This load could be, and frequently would be, transmitted to the member by another element connected to it, which could be considerably greater than a load applied directly to the member itself. An obvious example is that of a floor slab supported by a beam, which would have to be designed to accept a load of 34 kN/m² over the whole floor area, not merely over the flange area of the member itself. This type of accidental load could be caused by an explosion similar to that at Ronan Point. There could however be other types of accidental loading such as a vehicle colliding with a column.

Because these requirements were concerned only with the risk of collapse, the regulations permitted a relaxation of the design imposed and wind loads to be used for this purpose only. This is now no longer needed, as these recommendations now form part of the general content of the BSS in which guidance is given on how to allow for accidental loads in the context of limit state design (see note at end of Section 2).

Regulation D 19 of the 1976 Regulations gave deemed-to-satisfy provisions for the design of these buildings in reinforced concrete. These included the use of CP 114/115/16 (with Addendum no 1: 1970) or the more recent CP 110: Part 1: 1972. The earlier CPs were based on traditional 'single failure' design criteria, and the Addendum referred to dealt specifically with large panel structures and the prevention of progressive collapse. It contained in particular recommendations regarding the provision of peripheral and internal ties, which are still valid. CP 110 covered the whole field of the earlier three codes, but embraced the new 'limit state' design philosophy. For this reason the two codes may never be used together.

References

British Standards and other documents referred to in the AD with page on which they are referred to in AD 'A'.

BS 12: 1978 *Specification for ordinary and rapid-hardening Portland cement* Amendment slip no 1: AMD 4259. £5·20 p. 48.

BS 187: 1978 *Specification for calcium silicate (sandlime and flintlime) bricks* £12·20 p. 39.

BS 449 *The use of structural steel in building* Part 2: 1969 *Metric units.* Amendment slip nos 1: AMD 416, 2: AMD 523, 3: AMD 661, 4: AMD 1135, 5: AMD 1787, 6: AMD 4576 Addendum no 1 (1975) to BS 449. Part 2: 1969 *The use of cold formed steel sections in building.* Amendment slip nos 1: AMD 1765, 2: AMD 1929. £22·80 p. 51.

BS 882: 1983 *Specification for aggregates from natural sources for concrete* £10·20 p. 48. Amendment slip no 1: AMD 5150

BS 1243: 1978 *Specification for metal ties for cavity wall construction* Amendment slip nos 1: AMD 3651, 2: AMD 4024. £7·00 p. 39.

BS 1297: 1970 *Grading and sizing of softwood flooring* £7·00 p. 5.

BS 3921: 1974 *Clay bricks and blocks* £22·80 p. 39.

BS 4471: 1987: *Sizes of sawn and pressed softwood*

BS 4011: 1966. *Recommendations for the co-ordination of dimensions in buildings. Co-ordinating sizes for building components and assemblies* Amendment slip no 1: AMD 1775. £5·20 p. 38.

BS 4471 *Specification for dimensions for softwood* Part 1: 1978 *Sizes of sawn and planed timber.* £7·00 p. 5.

BS 4978: 1975 *Timber grades for structural use* Amendment slip nos 1: AMD 1869, 2: AMD 2508, 3: AMD 2730, 4: AMD 2935, 5: AMD 4567. £16·20 p. 6.

BS 5268: *Code of practice for the structural use of timber* Part 2: 1984 *Code of practice for permissible stress design, materials and workmanship* Amendment slip no 1: AMD 4723, pp. 5, 6, 51. Part 3: 1985 *Code of practice for trussed rafter roofs* £29·20 pp. 4, 51.

BS 5328: 1981 *Methods for specifying concrete, including ready-mixed concrete* £16·20 p. 48. Amendment slips nos 1: AMD 4862, 2: AMD 4170

BS 5390: 1976 *Code of practice for stone masonry* Amendment slip no 1: AMD 4272. £22·80 p. 39.

BS 5628 *Code of practice for the structural use of masonry* Part 1 Amendment slip nos 1: AMD 2747,

2: AMD 3445, 3: AMD 4800. £22·80 pp. 34, 39, 46, 51, 52. Part 3: 1985 *Materials and components, design and workmanship* £29·20 p. 34, 39, 51.

Amendment slip no 1: AMD 4974

BS 5950 *The structural use of steelwork in building* Part 1: 1985: *Code of practice for design in simple and continuous construction; hot rolled sections*, pp. 51, 52. Part 2: 1985: *Specification for materials, fabrication and erection; hot rolled sections*, p. 51. Part 4: 1982 *Code of practice for design of floors with profiled steel sheeting* £16·20 p. 51.

Part 5: 1987: *Code of Practice for design in cold formed sections*

BS 6073 *Precast concrete masonry units* Part 1: 1981: *Specification for precast concrete masonry units* Amendment slip nos 1: AMD 3944, 2: AMD 4462. £12·20 p. 39.

Amendment slip no 1: AMD 4949.

BS 6649: 1985: *Clay and calcium silicate modular bricks*

BS 6750: 1986: *Specification for modular coordination in building*

BS 8004: 1986: *Foundations*

BS 6399 Part 1: 1984 *Code for dead and imposed loads* £12·20 p. 51, Amendment slip no 1: AMD 4949

BS 8110: 1985: *The structural use of concrete.* Part 1: *Code of practice for design, materials and workmanship*, pp. 51, 52. Part 2: *Recommendations for use in special circumstances*, p. 51, 52.

Part 3: *Design charts for singly reinforced beams, doubly reinforced beams and rectangular columns*

CP 3: Chapter V *Loading.* Part 2: 1972 *Wind loads* £29·20 pp. 39, 51

Amendment slips nos 1: AMD 4952, 2: AMD 5152, 3: AMD 5343

CP 110: *The structural use of concrete.* Part 1: 1972 *Design, materials and workmanship* Amendment slip nos 1: AMD 2289, 2: AMD 3451. £32·60 pp. 48, 51, 52. Part 2: 1972 *Design charts for singly reinforced beams, doubly reinforced beams and rectangular columns* £26·20 p. 51. Part 3: 1972 *Design charts for circular columns and prestressed beams* £26·20 p. 51.

CP 111: 1970 *Structural recommendations for load bearing walls* Amendment slip nos 1: AMD 744, 2: AMD 2031. £16·20 p. 51.

CP 114: 1969 *Structural use of reinforced concrete in buildings* Amendment slip nos 1: AMD 1241, 2: AMD 1552, 3: AMD 1923, 4: AMD 2304, 5: AMD 4780* p. 51.

* Applicable to reprint issues from 1977. £22·80.

CP 117 *Composite construction in structural steel and concrete* Part 1: 1965 *Simply supported beams in building* £10·20 p. 51.

CP 118: 1969 *The structural use of aluminium* Amendment slip no 1: AMD 1129. £26·20 p. 51.

CP 2004: 1972 *Foundations* Amendment slip no 1: AMD 1755. £32·60 p. 51.

DD 34: 1974 *Clay bricks with modular dimensions* £22·80 p. 39.

DD 59: 1978 *Calcium silicate bricks with modular dimensions* £7·00 p. 39.

BRE Digest 119 *Assessment of wind loads* HMSO. £1 from BRE p. 39.

BRE Digest 290. *Loads on roofs from snow drifting against vertical obstructions and in valleys* HMSO 1984. £1 from BRE p. 51.

GENERAL NOTE   BS 8110 was published in September 1985. This code is a version of CP 110: Parts 1, 2 and 3: 1972, which has now been withdrawn by the BSI and references to earlier codes should therefore be deleted. Codes CP 111: 1970 and CP 114: 1969 have been withdrawn by BSI but these should provide satisfactory guidance in some circumstances on means of complying with the requirements relating to structure. Reference should be made to paragraph 0.2 (c) of this document.

(B1) Mandatory Rules for Means of Escape in Case of Fire

Where requirement B 1 applies, conformity with this document is the *only* way to comply. This does not preclude the use of the usual relaxation procedure. The requirement itself is as follows:

Requirement	Limits on application

B 1 Means of escape
 	
(1) There shall be means of escape in case of fire from the building to a place of safety outside the building capable of being safely and effectively used at all material times.
 	
(2) This requirement may be met only by complying with the relevant requirements of the publication entitled 'The Building Regulations 1985 Mandatory rules for means of escape in case of fire' published by HMSO (1985 edition).
	1 This requirement applies only to:
	(a) a building which is erected and which –
	  (i) is or contains a dwelling house of three or more storeys,
	  (ii) contains a flat and is of three or more storeys,
	  (iii) is or contains an office, or
	  (iv) is or contains a shop;
	(b) a dwelling house which is extended or materially altered and will have three or more storeys, and
	(c) a building of three or more storeys, the use of which is materially changed to use as a dwelling house.
	2 The means of escape provided need only, in the case of a dwelling house or a building containing a flat, afford escape for people from the third storey and above and, in the case of a building containing an office or a shop, afford escape for people from the office or shop.

As may be seen from the above requirement applies to only four types of building if we take extensions, alteration or changes of use as part of the dwelling house category. The document itself provides no details, but relies entirely on requiring compliance with the recommendations of four British Standards, except for a special escape provision for loft conversions in two-storey houses. There follows an abbreviated statement of the four sections and appendices in the document, with attendant comment on the changes since the 1976 Regulations. Following this again, in accordance with the philosophy of this Guide, is a run-down on the 'state of play' with regard to the BSI programme for revision of means of escape documents, plus a necessarily brief description of their contents.

The document is a good example of how deceiving brevity can be. The substantive part comprises only two pages, yet requires reference to material running to well over 100.

Section 1   Dwelling houses

This applies to new dwellings of three or more storeys and any extensions or alterations to the same, including 3 storey house conversions from other types of buildings. They must comply with BS 5588: Section 1.1: 1984 (CP for single family dwelling houses), the relevant clauses being 2,4,5 (except 5.2), 6 and 7.3. This is virtually all of it except the general clauses (scope and use of the code) and the parts of clause 7 (Heating) which relate to ordinary heating systems.

These buildings were not included in Section II of Part E of the 1976 Regulations, although Regulation E 13(2) required certain provisions for stairways in 3 storey houses which seem to have been drawn from its predecessor CP3: Ch IV: 1948. Special arrangements are permitted for the addition of one or two habitable rooms in the roof space of 2 storey houses: see Appendix B.

Section 2   Flats

Applies to buildings of 3 or more storeys containing a flat on the third storey or above. They must comply with CP3: Ch IV: Part 1: 1971 *Flats and maisonettes in blocks over 2 storeys*. The relevant clauses are:

1.2   Definitions.
3   Planning recommendations.
4.2, 4.3, 4.4   Fire protection, doors and stairway enclosure.
5   Ancillary accommodation (except 5.6 Fuel storage).
6   Engineering services.

NOTE   Flats of one or two storeys were never in this code, but will be introduced in its revision (see later). This may possibly lead to them being brought within the scope of Building Regulations as regards escape in the future.

Section 3   Shops

Applies to any building comprising or containing a shop (shop is defined in the table of purpose groups in the Approved Document to B 2/3/4). They must comply with BS 5588: Part 2: 1985 (CP for shops). The relevant sections are:

One   (except clauses 1 and 3 – scope and use of the code)
Two, Three, Four, Five   (except 13.1 and 14.1 to 14.4 which relate to ordinary electrical and lighting systems).

This again is virtually all of it except section six which deals with special fire protection facilities (alarm, extinguishers etc) and provisions for fire brigade use. There is however one anomaly, namely that para 31 which concerns smoke control provisions, although relating in part to special provisions for fire fighting, also concerns ventilation of normal accommodation, escape stairs and lobbies and which must surely be relevant. The explanation may lie in the expectation that these means of ventilation, although generally available, will mainly be manipulated by the fire fighting service to control smoke movement during an emergency.

BS 5588: Part 2: 1985 is a revision of CP3: Ch IV: Part 2 which was the requirement in the 1976 Regulations.

Section 4   Offices

Applies to any building containing an office (office is defined in the table of purpose groups in the AD to B 2/3/4). They must comply with BS 5588: Part 3: 1983 (CP for offices) The relevant sections are:

One   (except clauses 1 and 3 – scope and use of the code)
Two, Three, Four, Five   (except 12.1 and 13.1 and 13.4 which deal with ordinary electrical installations and lighting and 22 which deals with data processing)

BS 5588: Part 3 is a revision of CP3: Ch IV: Part 3 used in the 1976 Regulations

The layout and general content of this document is very similar to Part 2 (see summary later). The same comments regarding ventilation apply as for shops except that the relevant paragraph number is 30.

Appendix A   Definitions

There is a short list: they are either self-evident or the same as those applying to Part B in general. Note also that in any reference to a building as having a certain number of storeys basements are not counted.

Appendix B   Loft conversions

Addition of new storey in loft spaces

This applies to the addition of not more than two habitable rooms in the roof space of two storey houses. Technically, such an alteration would convert the house into three storeys and hence bring it within the scope of Section 1, which would normally require a protected stairway. If the following recommendations are followed this is not necessary.

(*a*)   Existing doors to habitable rooms in the first storey to be made self-closing.

(*b*)   Existing doors in the ground storey to be made self-closing, and if the new storey has 2 habitable rooms, also fire-resisting.

(*c*)   Any glazing in doors to be wired glass.

(*d*)   If the new stair rises over an existing stair in the same enclosure the new room must be separated from the stair by fire-resisting self-closing doors and enclosure.

(*e*)   If the new stair rises from the stairwell through a room, it must be separated from the room and the rest of the house by fire resisting enclosure and there must be a fire-resisting self-closing door at the top or bottom.

(*f*)   If the new stair rises in a bedroom, that bedroom must be separated by fire-resisting construction from the rest of the house and there must be a fire-resisting enclosure and fire-resisting self-closing door at the top.

(*g*)   The room must have a window or skylight complying with the sketch [2.1]. NOTE   It is not made clear whether, if there are two rooms, this requirement applies to both. The details of the sketch are actually drawn from recommendations in BS 5588: Section 1.1 for inner rooms in two-storey houses.

[2.1] *NOTE   Opening positioned to allow rescue by ladder from ground.*

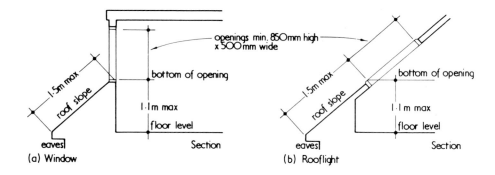

The following definitions apply to the above:

Habitable room includes a kitchen but not a bathroom

Self-closing includes the use of rising butts

Fire-resisting enclosures require a full ½ hour, but doors only 20 minutes integrity (No requirement for stability or insulation)

This ties in with the general requirements in Part B.

Comment

Requirement (*b*) above seems very all embracing. Taken literally (as it presumably must be) existing external doors and even larder or cupboard doors will need to be self-closing and possibly fire-resisting and it is hard to see the point of this.

The relevant British Standards

At the time of the 1976 Regulations these were all contained in CP3: Ch IV: Parts 1, 2 and 3, which dealt with fire precautions in flats, shops and offices respectively. Parts 2 and 3 have been revised and in accordance with current BSI practice are now published as BS 5588: Parts 2 and 3. The current state of play is as follows:

Subject	Previous code	Revised code
Dwelling houses	CP3: Ch IV: 1948	BS 5588: Section 1.1: 1984
Flats over 2 storeys	CP3: Ch IV: Part 1	Still in use.
Shops	CP3: Ch IV: Part 2	BS 5588: Part 2: 1985
Offices	CP3: Ch IV: Part 3	BS 5588: Part 3: 1983

CP3: Ch IV: Part 1 is to be re-issued as BS 5588: Section 1.2 and will include flats in blocks of 1 and 2 storeys which were previously included with dwelling houses. Other new parts are planned to include assembly buildings and shopping malls.

Points general to all the codes

The following briefly describes the principles on which all the codes relating to escape from fire are based.

Planning in relation to fire

The only sound basis for designing means of escape is to try to identify all possible sources of fire and predict the courses it might follow, in particular smoke and hot gases.
The risk of a fire starting in corridors, stairways etc, used only for access or escape, is negligible. The likely sources are in equipment, furniture, decorations or service plant and therefore likely to occur in furnished rooms, store rooms, kitchens etc. When a fire occurs in an enclosed space, hot gases rise to form a layer below the ceiling which deepens to fill the space below. Flames rise to the ceiling and are deflected down to accelerate the growth of the fire. A combustible ceiling can ignite and add to the fire. The generated gases become very toxic. In the absence of fire-resisting enclosure the fire will spread rapidly to other areas. A fire is thus a danger to all persons within a compartment. Risk to persons outside that compartment can also arise if fire is allowed to penetrate via openings in walls or into a shaft linking compartments.

Smoke
In the early stages the most important and first detected effects will be those of smoke and gases. These extend downwards from ceilings and at head height interfere with breathing, vision etc. To assist escape it is necessary to protect escape routes by self-closing doors and keep down the distance people have to travel to reach a protected stairway or exit.

Escape
Escape facilities must be sufficient to allow people to reach a safe area without delay. The place of ultimate safety is outside the building, but it is not always practical to evacuate a large building if a fire occurs anywhere within it. Occupants must however be able to reach a relatively safe place, leading ultimately to the outside. Exit capacities are recommended based generally on an evacuation time of 2½ minutes.

Disabled persons
The standards on shops and offices contain some advice on the problems of disabled persons who have access to upper floors. The numbers of such persons will not be predictable at the design stage, but it is envisaged that there will be few who will not be able to negotiate escape stairs with suitable assistance.
Although the use of lifts as a means of escape is ruled out for ambulant persons, they may possibly be used for wheelchair escapees who are in the charge of trained personnel. This is a matter for the building management and Appendix A of each document gives extensive advice on this. In the future the inclusion of a special lift might be considered and further research is in progress.

BS 5588: Section 1.1: 1984   Single family dwelling houses

Because of the small scale of the buildings the problem is different from that in large scale multi-occupation buildings, but the same general principles apply.

Fire development
Three possible situations can be identified:
(*a*)   A fire in an occupied room started by the occupant: usually immediately recognised and dealt with.
(*b*)   A fire in an unoccupied room which may spread and endanger other occupants before it is recognised.
(*c*)   A fire in a circulation space which presents the most severe danger, particularly to upper floor occupants.

Means of escape
Houses usually have only one stair. In two-storey houses means of escape from the upper floor is assumed to be possible via windows. In house of 3 storeys and above protection of the stairway is necessary. In houses of 4 or more storeys an alternative means of escape from the upper floors is necessary. Basement bedrooms should also have an alternative means of escape.
Recommendations for 3 storey houses and above include that no rooms *except* a kitchen, utility, bathroom, dressing room or wc on the first floor or above should be built as an inner room (ie access is via another room) except on the first floor if provided with a suitable window. Stairways should be protected as shown in diagram [2.2].

[*2.2*] *Stairways in houses with three or more storeys*
a   *Upper floors*
b   *Ground floor, one escape route only*
c   *Ground floor, two or more escape routes*

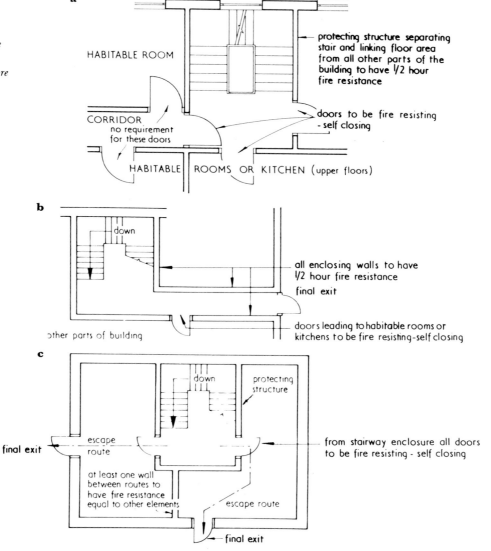

NOTES
1   *Building Regulations may require the protecting structure to have more than ½ hr fire resistance in some circumstances.*

2   *In houses of 4 or more storeys, an alternative escape route must be provided from each floor above the third storey.*

The BS also contains recommendations on glazing, fire-resisting doors and stairway design, all of which tie in with the general requirements of the Building Regulations.

Item 7.3, which is specifically mentioned as a relevant paragraph, makes recommendations regarding ducted heated systems in houses over 3 storeys which are mainly to the effect that any air passed into a protected stairway should be ducted back to the heater, not returned via transfer grilles.

CP3: Ch IV: Part 1: 1971
Flats and maisonettes

As stated earlier this has yet to be revised, and still uses the three stage definition of escape routes which has been abandoned in BS 5588: Parts 2 and 3 (see below). The following is a summary:

Stage 1
Within the individual dwelling, the most serious accidents occur in the room where the fire originates. Kitchens and living rooms present the greatest risk, especially after bedtime. Maisonettes are worse in this respect, but, even in flats, the risk is there, especially if doors of kitchens or living rooms are between the bedroom doors and the only entrance door from corridor or balcony. Planning should therefore be arranged so that this does not occur. Doors to all rooms, except bathrooms and wcs, should be self-closing and fire-resisting. The main entrance door should be similarly arranged and have the hotel-bedroom type of lock (self-fastening, operated by key from outside but by turn knob inside. The walls of the entrance lobby should have a prescribed minimum fire resistance and the travel distance from any bedroom door to the entrance should also have a prescribed limit. Where these arrangements cannot be met, an alternative exit (say *via* one of the bedrooms) should be provided. The same applies to maisonettes where the risk is greater, and it is often possible in planning these to provide an escape route from the upper floor to a public area (or from the lower floor, if the bedrooms are below the living area).

Stage 2
This concerns the safety of occupants using the horizontal escape route, once outside their own flat, leading to the Stage 3 or final exit. This route is usually identical with the normal approach and there are three common types:
1   An external balcony or deck,
2   Subsidiary stairs from the external deck,
3   Subsidiary stairs via an internal corridor.
The first suggests that it is the safest, but the risk of difficult conditions due to smoke and ice must not be forgotten; also, if there is only one stair, persons may need to pass the external wall, door, windows, etc. of the burning flat. This calls for minimum resistance periods for the wall and door, and also for limits to sill heights and window sizes. With two stairways this danger is eliminated as escapees simply go the other way (provided the entrance to the flat is not in a 'dead end').
The second system can be regarded as reasonably safe providing the subsidiary stair serves only one or two flats, is well ventilated at the top and NOT closed by a door at the bottom but set back sufficiently to keep steps free of snow or ice. Once, having reached the balcony, the same restrictions described above apply.
The third system, although at first sight seeming risky (claustrophobic), may often provide the best control. The corridor is of course protected to a degree from the smoke of a fire starting in one flat due to the use of self-closing fire-resisting entrance doors to all flats. However, any smoke which does penetrate (perhaps during the escape of persons in the affected flat) can be dealt with by a policy of containment involving the provision of smokestop doors at such intervals across the corridor that the distance from any flat entrance to a safe area (beyond such doors) is never too far for safety. Alternatively, a policy of dispersal by providing through ventilation of the corridor can be adopted. The risk of a fire actually starting in a corridor is remote. Another safety system is to provide a separate route for escape only, either by providing balconies or by providing stairs which lead up or down, from individual flats or pairs of flats, to a corridor on the adjacent floor.
If corridors provide the only escape route, it is essential that there are two staircases. But, if only one stair is provided, access to it must be from a place of safety – ie a ventilated lobby between corridor and stair, separated from both by smoke doors. This also applies for flats opening from 'dead legs' of corridors, even where there are two stairs. No flat door should ever discharge into a corridor beyond the smoke doors on the only route to the stairway.

Stage 3

This is concerned with the safety of occupants using the main vertical escape route, ie a stair-way leading from the corridor or balcony mentioned in Stage 2. (A lift is no use, for obvious reasons.) The objectives are: (i) to prevent smoke or fire entering at any point and blocking the escape of occupants in higher storeys; (ii) to ensure protection of the route from the bottom of the stairway to the open air. The latter point is sometimes missed, as it means that the ground storey must be differently planned from all upper storeys to avoid the risk of escape being cut off by a fire starting on the ground floor. Generally, it is much preferred for escape stairs to discharge directly into the open air without passing through any ground floor entrance or circulation space.

All main stairways should be totally enclosed by a protecting structure and approached only *via* self-closing fire-resisting doors. No store rooms, cupboards or other spaces containing inflammable material should open off them, although wash rooms and wcs are permissible as containing no fire risk. Even so, there must still be some risk of smoke penetration, so that, whenever possible, two stairs should be provided and smoke stop doors should be placed across the corridor between (in addition to those leading to the stairs), thus providing at least two doors between one of the stairs and the smoke-logged area. If only one stair is provided, there must be a ventilated lobby between it and the corridor, with doors at each end. An alternative arrangement is to allow all flat entrances to give access to a ventilated lobby from which an enclosed corridor leads to the stairway (so that, again, there are two fire doors and a ventilated space between flat exits and the stair). At ground level, two stair exits should never discharge into a common hall. Basements are particularly prone to become sources of fire, and main escape stairs should, therefore, never connect directly with basements. Complete separation is preferable but, if every unit has access to two stairways and one of them stops at ground level, it is reasonable to continue the second one to the basement, but only *via* a ventilated lobby with fire doors at each end.

[**2.3**] *Flats   3 stages on escape route*

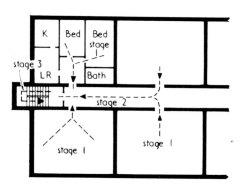

BS 5588: Part 2: 1985   Shops

In this replacement for CP3: Ch IV: Part 2 the three stages used before have been abandoned in favour of a simple division into horizontal travel and vertical travel.

The general points above apply, and in addition:

Internal subdivision

If compartments are formed as required by Regulations, evacuation procedures can be based on individual compartments, rather than on whole buildings. However arrangements involving open spatial (vertical) planning, such as where gallery floors overlook a central open space, may infringe upon Building Regulations and require early consultation with the control authorities. Generally, because of the large number of people involved, such arrange-ments are not recommended for buildings with more than a few storeys, and only then when a suitable smoke control system is provided. Open storey (horizontal) planning involving large open floor areas has the advantage of any incidents being immediately obvious, but also the risk of very rapid fire spread due to the nature of the goods on display. It is essential to ensure maximum visibility across sales areas to exit positions. (This is something which must depend to a large extent on the display arrangements adopted).

Shopping malls need special consideration – the provision of smoke control arrangements may allow exits onto malls to be treated as storey exits. Individual shops need fire resisting separation and large shops may need separation from the malls by back-up shop window walls and fire shutters.

Escape from public areas
The provisions depend on the number of people and the size and geometry of the building, which will between them determine the size and number of escape routes.

Horizontal routes
Maximum travel distances from any point to an exit are specified. These are given as direct distances (assuming no obstructions) and as travel distances (passing around obstructions). The latter are 50 per cent greater than the former. There should always be a minimum of two alternative routes, which are only considered as alternatives if separated by an angle of at least 45° or by fire-resisting construction. The principle actual recommendations are illustrated in diagram [2.4].
There are concessions for ground floors and rules regarding inner rooms. The width and number of escape routes is calculated from tables which give occupation space factors and clear widths required for the resulting number of occupants. The resulting sizes have to be arrived at by discounting one of the available exits in turn (assumed blocked by fire). Escape across flat roofs is not recommended, but may be allowed with certain precautions.

[**2.4**] *Shops*

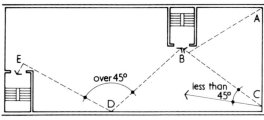

Direct distances

AB one route only max 12m
CB two routes less than 45° between max 12m
DB/DE alternative routes max 30m each

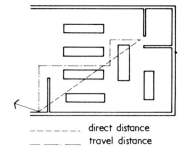

-------- direct distance
———— travel distance

Travel distances (around obstacles)
may be 18m and 45m

Vertical routes
Accommodation stairways (as distinct from protected stairs) and escalators are permitted but must be sited so that their location does not prejudice access to the escape stairs. (Author's comment – however as they must allow the passage of smoke between floors they must constitute some danger – presumably they are not permitted to penetrate floors designed as compartment floors).
Ignoring these there must be at least two protected stairways with additional stairs as required to meet the demands of travel distance. They should be sited to afford effective alternative routes (see diagram [2.4]) and away from any open connections between floors. Tables are provided to calculate the minimum widths of stairways, based on occupation figures as before. There are however two alternatives:
1   Assuming that the whole building will have to be evacuated (figures are given for up to 10 storeys served), and
2   Assuming effective compartmentation and the need to evacuate only two floors, in which case ventilated access lobbies should be provided between storeys and stairs.
Protected stairways should be enclosed in fire-resisting construction and should contain nothing other than sanitary accommodation. They must be accessible directly from a storey (not through any other stairway or ancillary accommodation). There are also rules regarding external openings in relation to any other external openings in adjacent structures.
Basement stairways should preferably serve the basement only, entered from the outside of the building, but in buildings having two or more stairways serving upper floors, one may be continued to the basement if separated by a protected lobby. Such lobbies are also required in buildings exceeding 18 m in height and between stairs and enclosed car parks or other areas of higher risk.

Final exits
These should not serve more than one stairway and give direct access to a place of safety. This is usually the open air but in some circumstances might be a mall, arcade, concourse or walkway if clearly defined.

Small shops

These are defined as comprising no more than a basement, ground and first storey, with no storey exceeding 280 m² and with accommodation for not exceeding 30 persons per storey (or 100 persons on the ground storey if having independent final exit).

There are reduced travel distances prescribed for egress from storeys via only one stairway. There are also special regulations permitting the use of open stairways in shops with a floor area not exceeding 90 m² per storey.

Construction

There are recommendations regarding fire resistance, shafts, doors, glazing etc, which are generally in line with Building Regulations.

Engineering services and ancillary accommodation

Spaces containing engineering installations and ancillary accommodation generally produce a greater fire risk than normal public areas and require special consideration. Standards are recommended for lighting for escape routes, heating and fuel storage, mechanical ventilation, lift motor rooms, refuse chambers, store rooms, car parks, staff restaurants and workshops.

BS 5588: Part 3: 1983   Offices

This replaces CP3: Ch IV: Part 3, and as in the case of shops above, the previous three-stage classification has been replaced by division into horizontal and vertical travel. In fact the whole document is similar to that on shops but the differences arising out of office use need to be explained.

Internal subdivision

The considerations are the same. As with shops open spacial planning (through several stories) requires special consideration. Usually however storeys will form separate compartments, but may themselves be open planned or cellular (subdivided into small rooms). Offices built for rental may be built as open planned to be later subdivided by tenants.

Escape from office areas

As before the provisions depend mainly on travel distances, combined with occupation figures. If the building is in multiple occupation this may affect the arrangements and require increased provisions.

Horizontal routes

The main principles are the same. The building will usually be planned using direct distances (open plan), but when subdivision is introduced, maximum travel distances also apply, as illustrated in diagrams [2.5, 2.6].

[**2.5**] *Cellular planning: travel distances.*

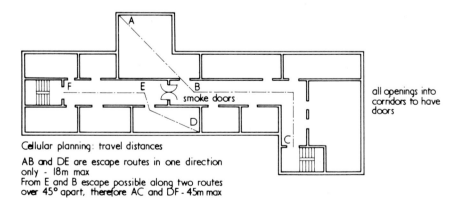

Cellular planning: travel distances

AB and DE are escape routes in one direction only - 18m max
From E and B escape possible along two routes over 45° apart, therefore AC and DF - 45m max

all openings into corridors to have doors

There should always be two alternative routes, but if part of the route is along a single path (eg dead ends) it must be strictly limited in length.

Exceptions to the escape route rule include storeys served by one stair only (see later), short distances (eg from room to corridor), inner rooms if certain safety provisions apply and

[**2.6**] *Open planning: direct distances.*

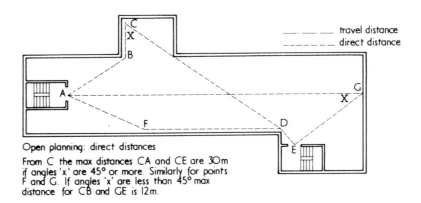

Open planning: direct distances
From C the max distances CA and CE are 30m
if angles 'x' are 45° or more. Similarly for points
F and G. If angles 'x' are less than 45° max
distance for CB and GE is 12m.

rooms used by less than 50 persons. The latter seems a somewhat over generous exception, but BSs do not usually err on the side of laxity. Widths and number of escape routes are arrived at as for shops. There are also a number of recommendations regarding corridors, principally that corridor partitions should be taken up to the ceiling, dead-end corridors enclosed with fire resisting construction and corridors joining alternative exits divided by doors into sections.

These are well illustrated in the BS.

Vertical routes
The rules on stairways are generally the same as for shops, and similar tables are provided to determine the number and widths. The location of stairways in open plan office buildings with a central service core may pose special problems as regards separation of alternative escape routes.

Buildings not over 3 storeys (or 11 m) in height may have a single stairway.

Final exits, construction, engineering services and ancillary accommodation
Recommendations are all as for shops.

Notes on other legislation

Under the Fire Precautions Act 1971, designated buildings for which a fire certificate is required must have suitable fire precautions which, in addition to other measures, include means of escape. Buildings currently designated include factories, offices, shops, railway premises, hotels and boarding houses. When Building Regulations apply the Fire Authority cannot normally insist on structural or other alterations being made as a condition of giving a certificate (this means in the cases of offices and shops at present).

The Health and Safety Executive have similar responsibilities for special risk premises such as nuclear installations, mine buildings and large chemical plants. Where these are involved the Local Authority or approved inspector should consult the local office of the H and SE.

Under the Housing Act 1985 Local Authorities must require means of escape from certain houses not forming a single household. The Housing (Means of Escape from Fire in Houses in Multiple Occupation) Order 1981 (SI 1981/1576) specifies houses of three or more storeys (not counting basements) with a total floor area exceeding 500 m².

Under Section 72 of the Building Act 1984 a Local Authority after consultation with the Fire Authority may require means of escape to be provided from certain buildings having a floor more than 20 ft above ground or floor level. These include the following:

(*a*)   Buildings let as flats or tenements.

(*b*)   Buildings used as an inn, boarding house, hospital, nursing home, boarding school, childrens' home or similar institution, or

(*c*)   Buildings used as a shop, restaurant or warehouse which have sleeping accommodation for employees on an upper floor.

This section does not apply where means of escape are required by Building Regulations.

For additional provisions relating to escape in case of fire in Inner London refer to the London Building Acts (Amendment) Act 1939 Part V.

References

The following British Standards are referred to in the Mandatory Rules:

BS 5588 *Fire precautions in the design and construction of buildings* Section 1.1 : 1984 *Code of practice for single family dwelling houses*. Part 2 : 1985 *Code of practice for shops*. Part 3 : 1985 *Code of practice for office buildings*. £22·80 (£11·40).

CP 3 *Code of basic data for the design of buildings* Chapter IV *Precautions against fire*. Part 1 : 1971 *Flats and maisonettes (in blocks over two storeys)* Amendment slip no 1: 1972 (AMD 851). Amendment slip no 2: 1973 (AMD 1077). Amendment slip no 3: 1976 (AMD 1889). Amendment slip no 4: 1978 (AMD 2708). £26·20 (£13·10).

Approved Document B (B2/3/4) Fire Spread

There are four requirements to Part B, but B 1, Means of Escape, has been dealt with elsewhere, in what is exceptionally a set of mandatory rules for which, unlike the ADs generally, there is no permissible alternative. The requirements are as follows:

	Requirement	Limits on application
	Internal fire spread (surfaces)	
Internal walls, ceilings	B 2. In order to inhibit the spread of fire within the building, surfaces of materials used on walls and ceilings –	
	(a) shall offer adequate resistance to the spread of flame over their surfaces; and	
	(b) shall have, if ignited, a rate of heat release which is reasonable in the circumstances.	
	Internal fire spread (structure)	
Structure	B 3. – (1) The building shall be so constructed that, in the event of fire, its stability will be maintained for a reasonable period.	
	(2) The building, or the building as extended, shall be sub-divided into compartments where this is necessary to inhibit the spread of fire within the building.	
	(3) Concealed spaces in the structure or fabric of the building, or the building as extended, shall be sealed and sub-divided where this is necessary to inhibit the unseen spread of fire and smoke.	
	(4) A wall common to two or more buildings shall offer adequate resistance to the spread of fire and smoke.	
	(5) For the purposes of sub-paragraph (4) a house in a terrace and a semi-detached house are each to be treated as being a separate building.	
	External fire spread	
External walls, roofs	B 4. – (1) The external walls of the building shall offer adequate resistance to the spread of fire over the walls and from one building to another, having regard to the height, use and position of the building.	
	(2) The roof of the building shall offer adequate resistance to the spread of fire over the roof and from one building to another, having regard to the use and position of the building.	

Quite why it has been found necessary to subdivide the requirements in this particular rather arbitrary way is not clear, and the structure of the Approved Document itself takes no account whatever of this arrangement. Taken together they do however provide a succinct statement of the methods to be used to inhibit fire spread in and between buildings, namely:

○   Restriction of surface spread.
○   Maintenance of stability.
○   Compartmentation and/or separation.
○   Restricting continuity of concealed spaces.
○   Prevention of fire spread from external walls and roofs.

0.4   These principles are expanded upon in an introduction. They will be familiar to most users of the existing Regulations, although never explicitly set out. The following is a brief summary:

Internal fire spread – surfaces

0.5/0.9   This can be prevented by using materials of low surface spread of flame characteristics and/or of low rate of heat produced. The provisions are mainly for walls and ceilings, but may also apply to surfaces in concealed spaces. They do not apply to floor or stair surfaces or fittings. Effectiveness is judged by BS test procedures.

Internal fire spread – structure

0.10/0.18   Premature failure, resulting in fire spread, can be prevented by giving elements a specified period of fire resistance, which includes 3 criteria:

○   Resistance to collapse – stability (load-bearing elements)
○   Resistance to penetration – integrity (fire separating elements)
○   Resistance to heat transfer – insulation (fire separating elements)

The provisions for fire-resistance apply mainly to 'elements of structure' which are defined in Appendix L (loadbearing members plus fire separation members). They do not include the lowest floor, a platform or elements supporting the roof (unless this acts as a floor). Also included are some other elements such as doors, casings and barriers.

In some cases such elements are to be made of 'materials of limited combustibility'. This is a new term which is defined in Appendix A and includes within itself totally non-combustible materials.

The term limited combustibility is for some reason used throughout, but A 13 makes it clear that for certain elements, basically the elements of structure, full non-combustibility is required.

Minimum periods of fire resistance are specified related to building use, height and size of building or compartment. Higher standards are required for basements due to the greater difficulty of dealing with fires there. When an element separates two buildings or compartments needing different standards the most onerous requirements are taken.

All three resistance criteria named above do not necessarily apply in every case: for example, structural frame members need only be judged on stability or doors on integrity; also they may need to resist fire from one, both or all directions. Appendix A details these requirements.

Compartmentation

0.19/0.26   The spread of fire can also be limited by dividing a building into separate compartments by using 'compartment walls and/or floors'. 'Separating walls' (between buildings) serve the same purpose and are always required. Compartmentation is required in multi-storey buildings (over certain size limits) and in single storey buildings with sleeping accommodation.

Buildings may be divided vertically into separate parts, allowing each part to be separately assessed, and in dealing with fire-resistance requirements reference to buildings is often followed by the term 'separated part' (see General Note preceeding Sections 1 to 6 later).

Limitation of compartment size below the maxima permitted may often be advantageous in order to reduce the fire-resistance requirements or set up separate purpose groups. Obviously some openings in compartment walls will be needed to allow communication, and these have to be suitably protected by fire-resisting doors, shutters etc. Some limited penetration of separating walls and compartment floors is also allowed, providing the penetrating elements are suitably fire-stopped (ie any gaps between such elements and the barrier itself are closed). Vertical links between compartments are dealt with by providing protected shafts.

Concealed spaces and fire stopping
0.27   These include roof voids and spaces above suspended ceilings as well as ordinary cavities. It is important to prevent these from allowing fire or smoke to by-pass barriers. There are rules to prevent this and to limit the size of extensive cavities.
In separating elements the need to seal every imperfection of fit by fire-stopping is stressed.

External fire spread
0.29/0.32   The risk of fire spreading from one building to another depends on the distance between them and the fire porosity of the wall, as well as the size of the fire. The distance between can only be regulated by relating the faces of a building to its own boundaries. The fire porosity depends on the size and number of openings (or unprotected areas), assuming the solid part of the wall has adequate resistance. The size of the fire may be limited by compartmentation. All three factors are inter-related and the provisions reflect this. Thus for example, the minimum distance from a boundary may be reduced by limiting the extent of the openings or the size of the compartments.
With roofs the risk is related to the size of the whole building, proximity to the boundary and type of construction.

Structural integrity of building as a whole
0.33   The level of performance can be met by following the guidelines in Approved Document A and in *Guidelines for the construction of fire-resisting structural elements*, HMSO 1982.

Varying the provisions
0.34   There will also be cases where the normal standard provisions will prove unreasonable difficult, or even impossible. With the new structure of the regulations it is possible for these to be varied without recourse to formal relaxation procedures as in the past. Whether or not such changes can be agreed will depend on the general situation. Factors which may be taken into account include the general construction, fire properties of materials, fire load and fire hazard, space separation from boundaries, means of escape, access for fire fighting and provision of safety features such as sprinklers or detection systems. Many of these are matters outside the jurisdiction of the Regulations, but may nevertheless be taken into account when deciding on possible variations.

Purpose groups
0.35/0.40   The provisions required depend, *inter alia*, on the use to which the building is to be put. There are now 9 purpose groups, replacing the previous 8, the extra one being due to the separation of what was Group III (other residential) into flats and the remainder of that group which includes hotels, hostels etc. Unfortunately, the groups are no longer numbered, so that it is not now possible to refer to a group or groups by simple numerical references. This may have slight advantage in avoiding misunderstanding, but involves a considerable loss of convenience, and it is to be hoped that it will be changed in due course.
The groups are divided under two main headings, residential and non-residential, and a complete list follows. They can be applied to a whole building or to a separate part or compartment. Where a building contains an ancillary use, the purpose group is to be taken for the whole from the main use, except that in the following cases, parts may be treated as having an ancillary purpose in their own right.
(*a*)   A flat or maisonette.
(*b*)   The storage area of a shop of over ⅓ the total.
(*c*)   Any other use if the area exceeds ⅕ the total.
Presumably this means without having to be separated or compartmented, since it is already stated that separate parts or compartments can have different purpose groups.
Certain large buildings may have a complex mix of purpose groups, in which case it will be necessary to study the impact of each part on the others, and special measures may be necessary (see para 6.45 regarding shopping complexes).
Table 0.1 of the Approved Document is included as it described the groups in detail. Any added notes are in italics.

Table 0.1   Designation of purpose groups

Purpose for which building or a compartment of a building is intended to be used	Purpose group
Residential group	
Private dwelling house which does not include a flat or a building containing flats	Dwelling house
A dwelling which is self-contained and is not a private dwellinghouse	Flat (includes a maisonette)
Hospital, home, school or other similar establishment used as living accommodation for, or for the treatment care or maintenance of, persons suffering from disabilities due to illness or old age or other physical or mental disability, or under the age of five years, where such persons sleep in the premises	Institutional
Hotel, boarding house, hostel and any other residential purpose not described above	Other residential
Non-residential group	
Public building[1] or a place of assembly of persons for social, recreational or business but not office shop or industrial	Assembly
Premises used for the purpose of administration, clerical work (including writing, book-keeping, sorting papers, filing, typing, duplicating, machine calculating, drawing and the editorial preparation of matter for publication), handling money or telephone and telegraph operating	Office
Premises used for the carrying on of a retail trade or business (including the sale to members of the public of food or drink for immediate consumption, retail sales by auction, the business of lending books or periodicals for the purpose of gain and the business of a barber or hairdresser),and premises to which members of the public are invited to resort for the purpose of delivering their goods for repair or other treatment, or of themselves carrying out repairs to or other treatment of goods	Shop
A factory within the meaning ascribed to that word by section 175 of the Factories Act 1961 (but not including slaughter houses and other premises referred to in paragraphs (d) and (c) of subsection (1) of that section[3]	Industrial
Place for storage, deposit or parking of goods and materials (including vehicles) and any other non-residential purpose not described above[2]	Other non-residential

NOTES

[1] Public building is defined in Building Regulation 2(2). [*These include a theatre, hall or other public place, a school not controlled by the Education Act 1980 or a place of worship*].

[2] A detached garage not more than 40 m² in area is included in the Dwelling house purpose group; as is a detached open carport of not more than 40 m², or a detached building which consists of a garage and open carport where neither the garage nor open carport exceeds 40 m² in area.

[3] The reference to paragraphs (d) and (c) of subsection (1) of section 175 of the Factories Act is in error and should be (d) and (e).

Arrangement

The expression 'making a meal of it' hardly does justice to this rewrite of the 1976 Part E, Section I. The 42 octavo pages of the original now occupy 80 A4 pages, and although a slightly larger print accounts for some of this, the total number of words, or equivalent in tables etc, amounts to about three times the previous quantity; a formidable expansion.

This is the result of a decision to present the bulk of the provisions in separate sections for each purpose group; although this has not in fact been carried through fully. Sections 1 to 5 deal separately with the four residential and assembly groups, whereas Section 6 takes together the other four groups. Apart from the fairly individual character of Section 1, dwelling houses, there would seem to be no better reason for separating the 4 groups covered by Sections 2 to 5 than for separating the four which are lumped together under Section 6 (offices, shops, industrial and storage) and which are widely disparate in character and fire resistance requirements. One almost gets the impression that the authors themselves grew tired of the tedious repetition, of which this arrangement produces a great deal.

There is the credit side that the designer of a particular building has the information he needs, uncluttered by the requirements for other purpose groups, but there is the loss of instant comparison between one class and another, which gave a picture of the overall purpose of the provisions and how they related to different types of building; not perhaps important to individual cases, but of value in discerning general trends and reasoning. This is something surely we all need to understand if we are not to work merely as automatons.

The other side of the coin is that the 6 Sections do not cover the whole field. Each deals with the same 9 separate elements, but these have to be backed up by Appendices, of which 6 deal with certain elements in general terms, plus 3 which deal with aspects of all of them. This effectively means that a great deal of cross-referencing is involved, with the user having constantly to turn from the section he is using to an appendix in order to deal with each element in turn.

It was for consideration, in producing this guide, whether it might be worth while dismantling this widely dispersed structure and reassembling it in more compact form. This could have had advantages for the user. To have done this however would have ruled out the possibility of direct cross-reference to the Approved Document and it was felt that this would cause too many problems.

The solution adopted therefore, to make the whole thing more digestible, is to maintain the same framework, but where the content is simply a repetition of that in previous sections, to say so and refer back to those. This is not quite as good as grouping them all together, but at least has the merit of showing which items are unchanged throughout.

The Approved Document has a contents page which is in itself, perforce, a mass of repetition. Without reprinting it, the following notes should give the reader an overall picture of the structure of the document. The six sections are as follows:

Section 1   Dwelling houses.
Section 2   Flats.
Section 3   Institutional.
Section 4   Other residential.
Section 5   Assembly.
Section 6   Offices, shops, industrial, other non-residential (mainly storage buildings).

Each section has the following parts:

OO	Load-bearing elements of structure.	NOTE
O	External walls.	O These parts each have an appendix devoted to them.
OO	Roof construction.	OO These parts are dealt with mainly in Appendix A.
O	Separating walls.	
O	Compartment walls and floors.	Some sections also have a note on varying the provisions.
O	Protected shafts.	
O	Concealed spaces and fire stopping.	
OO	Internal surfaces.	
	Stairways.	

There are the following appendices:

A   Performance of materials and structures
B   Concessions for plastics materials.

○   C   Separating walls.
○   D   Compartment walls and floors.
○   E   Protected shafts.
    F   Protection of openings.
○   G   Concealed spaces.
○   H   Fire-stopping.
○   J   External walls – space separation

In addition there are two general appendices dealing with methods of measurement and definitions (K and L).

Sections 1 to 6

Before dealing with individual sections, the following general notes are to assist the reader in comprehending the overall picture, and explain some conventions that have been adopted to avoid the constant repetition of ungainly expressions. They are numbered to facilitate reference back from elsewhere in the text.

1   Tables are not generally reproduced exactly as in the document; the information is the same, but where possible it has been condensed with, it is hoped, greater legibility.

2   Table numbers and diagram numbers are omitted in favour of a direct reference to the text code, to avoid possible misinterpretation (a distinct possibility as it stands). However tables which apply throughout have been numbered T.2, T.3 etc.

3   The term 'separated part' which means a part of a building completely separated by a vertical wall in one plane (ie a special type of compartment) only has significance in relation to the effective height or number of storeys, when determining fire resistance or the need for non-combustibility. Such parts can be treated separately for these purposes. In this Guide the term 'building' can be assumed to include a 'separated part of a building' whenever appropriate (ie in relation to height or number of storeys).

4   In the tables showing fire resistance periods the terms 'floor area of each storey' and 'cubic capacity of building' refer, where appropriate, to the area of each storey within, and cubic capacity of, a compartment. Compartmentation is therefore a means of keeping down the fire resistance requirements of large buildings. The notes explaining this below each table have been replaced by a simple reference to this note.

5   The notes referred to in 4 above do not appear below the tables for fire-resistance in dwelling houses and flats. This is because in dwelling houses there are no requirements for compartmentation other than above basements. In flats however the situation is somewhat complicated since the rules require that each flat should effectively be a separate compartment, yet the table includes size limits of 3000 m² (8500 m³) and 2000 m² (5500 m³) for buildings under or over 28 m high respectively. These are far above any possible limits for a single flat and yet well below those for a block of flats unles these were to be limited to approximately 20 flats in tall buildings. This is clearly not the case, so that the maximum size figures mentioned must refer to major compartment sizes, embracing a number of flats, probably in most cases a complete floor of a building. This was clear enough in E 4 and E 5 of the 1976 Regulations but seems to have been blurred in the rewrite.

6   Confusion can arise in reference to the number of storeys. A basement storey (generally one having a floor level more than 1.2 m below ground) is not counted when referring to a building of N number of storeys. Thus a building with only a ground storey and a basement is a one storey building. It is *not* a single-storey building, which is one with a ground storey only – no basement. Buildings which are not single storey buildings are normally referred to that way, ie 'not single storey', but occasionally the term 'multi-storey' is used. Whether this term includes buildings consisting only of a ground floor and a basement is not stated, but it must be presumed that it does. The term does not appear to have been used in the 1976 Regulations Part E.

7   The term 'boundary' in this part of the guide always refers to the 'relevant boundary', from which distances are measured and which is defined in Appendix J.

8   There are some unwieldy terms which require constant repetition. The most frequent of these is a new term 'materials of limited combustibility' (try saying this three times quickly before breakfast). It is defined in Appendix A 13/14 and includes within itself a special group known as non-combustible which represents a higher standard (although even this does not mean exactly what it says). A 13 makes clear that, for the main elements of construction this standard is required, the lower standard being permitted for such items as linings, roof coverings, cavity barriers and the like. Nevertheless the term 'materials of limited combustibility' is used throughout, so in this book the acronym MOLC has been

created. It has rather a fine onomatopoeic sound suggestive of something like papier-mâché, which might itself well come within the category thus abbreviated.

9   Where possible without losing clarity the content of the Approved Document has been abbreviated to avoid verbal indigestion. On the other hand where the Document simply inserts a cross-reference, this has been expanded upon to give the reader some idea of what is involved without having to search.

Section 1   Dwelling houses

Loadbearing elements of structure

1.2   Structural frames, beams, columns, load-bearing walls (internal and external), floors and galleries should have at least the fire resistance in the table below.

1.3   There are no requirements for structural frames, beams, columns in single or one storey buildings unless they support or form part of a wall which is required to be fire-resisting or support a gallery.

1.4   Some load-bearing elements have other functions (see later).

Table to 1.2 (dwelling houses)

Number of storeys	Fire resistance period in hours	
	Ground/upper storeys	Basement storey
Single storey	½	Not applicable
1, 2 or **3**	½	1*
4	1**	1
More than **4**	1	1½

* Reduced to ½ hr if basement area is not more than 50 m²
** Reduced to ½ hr for floors but not for compartment floors or floors contributing to the support of building as a whole (including beams).

NOTES
1   Basements not counted in number of storeys.
2   All separating walls are 1 hr min.
3   No size limits except 250 m² floor area per storey in 4 storey houses.
4   Any element must have at least the resistance of an element it supports.

External walls

1.5/1.6   They must meet the above provisions (even if non-loadbearing).

1.7   They must be of materials of limited combustibility (hereafter referred to as MOLC) if over 3 storey and less than 1 m from the relevant boundary, or over 15 m high in any case.

1.8   Internal surface materials may be combustible if not relied on to form part of the fire resistance and meet the provisions stated later.

1.9   External cladding materials may be combustible if not relied on to form part of the fire resistance and comply with the limitations in the table below (T2). It may also be limited by the space separation provisions of Appendix J.

Combustible insulating material is also permitted in cavity walls or hollow blocks: see Appendix G.

1.10   Any structure carrying or forming part of the wall which itself should be of MOLC must also be formed of MOLC.

1.11/1.12   The extent of any unprotected areas (which include openings *and* parts of walls which are not up to full standard) must be limited to that allowed by Appendix J.

NOTE   It is clear from A 13 that in this case, and that of all other major separating elements 'limited combustibility' means noncombustible: see table to A 13.

Table T2. Limitations on external cladding

Maximum height of building [m]	Distance of cladding from any point on the relevant boundary*		
	Less than 1 m	1 m or more	
15	Class 0	no provision	
over 15	Class 0	any cladding less than 15 m above the ground	timber at least 9 mm thick; or any material with an index of performance (I) not more than 20
		any cladding 15 m or more above the ground	Class 0

NOTES

For meaning of Class 0 and index of performance (I) *(See Appendix A)*

* The relevant boundary might be a notional boundary. *(See Appendix J)*

This table applies to all purpose groups

Roof constructions

1.14/1.17 The performance of these is classified by the methods in BS 476: Part 3: 1958 (see Appendix A). The required performance for two sizes of building is shown in the table (T 3) and this remains the same for all six sections (but see special note in Sections 1 and 6). There are some restrictions where roofs pass over separating walls (see C 2). Appendix A provides notional designations for some generic roof coverings and Appendix B exceptions where some plastic rooflights may be used, although not meeting the basic requirements. Rooflights must also comply with the provisions for internal surfaces.

Table T3. Limitations on roof construction

Description of building	Designation or covering of roof, or part of roof	Minimum distance from any point on a boundary			
		Less than 6 m	At least 6 m	At least 12 m	At least 22 m
1 building with a cubic capacity of not more than 1500 m³	AA, AB or AC	●	●	●	●
	BA, BB or BC	○	●	●	●
	AD, BD* CA, CB, CC or CD	○	●¹	●	●
	DA, DB, DC or DD*	○	○	○	●¹
	thatch or wood shingles	○	●¹	●	●
	glass or pvc⁴	●²	●	●	●
	no designation⁵*	○	●¹	●³	●³
2 building with a cubic capacity of more than 1500 m³	AA, AB or AC	●	●	●	●
	BA, BB or BC	○	●	●	●
	AD*	○	●¹	●	●
	BD, CA, CB, CC, CD† DA, DB, DC or DD	○	○	○	○
	thatch or wood shingles	○	○	○	○
	glass or pvc⁴	●²	●	●	●
	no designation⁵*	○	●¹	●³	●³

● Acceptable
○ Not acceptable

NOTES

* Including rooflights having a lower surface of at least Class 3 surface spread of flame. *(see Appendix B, Table B1)*
† Rooflights with these designations, which have a lower surface of at least Class 3 surface spread of flame, are permitted subject to the limitations given in Appendix B, Table B1.
¹ The area of the part of the roof should not be greater than 3 m² and it should be at least 1.5 m from any similar part, with the roof between the parts covered with a Material of Limited Combustibility *(see Appendix A, Table to A14)*

² Only for (a) a balcony, verandah, open carport, covered way or detached swimming pool, or
  (b) a garage, conservatory or outbuilding, with a floor area not greater than 40 m²
³ Twice the height of the building if this gives a greater distance.
⁴ Glass which cannot be designated; and rigid pvc as described in Appendix B, paragraph B5.
⁵ A covering which cannot be designated because of its low softening temperature. Glass if it can be designated is AA and does not need wire reinforcement.

NOTE   This table applies to all purpose groups but see special note re this section and Section 6.

SPECIAL NOTE   In this group terraced houses are to be treated as buildings of over 1500 m³ regardless of size. (See similar note in Section 6).

Separating walls

1.18/1.22   These are walls separating a house from any other building including another house. They must have the same fire resistance as for loadbearing elements and at least 1 hour in any case. They should be constructed of MOLC if they separate a 3 storey house from any other building, or any house from a building which has the same requirement.
Surface materials may be combustible if not required to contribute to fire resistance and comply with 1.39.
Any structure carrying or forming part of the wall must also be constructed of MOLC.
Any openings must be limited to those allowed by Apendix C and comply with Appendix F.

Compartment walls and floors

1.23/1.28   Floors over basements which exceed 100 m² in area in houses of 3 or more storeys must be compartment floors.
They must have the minimum fire resistance required for loadbearing elements, comply with Appendix D and be of MOLC. Internal surfaces which comply with 1.39 and any floor finish may be combustible if not relied on to contribute to fire resistance. Combustible fire protecting suspended ceilings may also be acceptable in some circumstances (see A 2).
Any structure forming part of or carrying a floor must also be constructed of MOLC.
Any stairway or shaft leading from the basement to another storey must be a protected shaft.
Any openings must be limited to those allowed by Appendix D and comply with Appendix F.
1.29   A wall between an attached or integral garage and a house must comply with diagram [3.1]. Note that the term '½ hour fire resisting door' in this case means 20 minutes integrity only: see A 2.

1.29 [**3.1**] *Separation between garage and dwelling house*

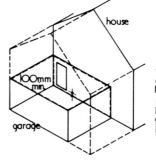

house

wall and any floor between garage and house to have 1/2 hour fire resistance. any opening in wall to be at least 100mm above garage floor level and to have a 1/2 hour fire resisting door

100mm min

garage

Protected shafts

1.30/1.36   These are required where vertical communication between compartments is necessary.
They must again have the minimum fire resistance for loadbearing elements and be of MOLC.
Surface materials may be combustible if complying with 1.39.

Any structure forming part of or carrying the enclosure must also be of MOLC.

Protected shafts must be constructed, ventilated and have uses limited so as to comply with Appendix E and protected as required by Appendix F. Paragraph 1.46 deals with the special case of stairways in houses of over 2 storeys.

Concealed spaces and fire-stopping

1.37/1.38   Concealed spaces must be sealed and divided by cavity barriers as required by Appendix G.

Joints between fire barrier elements (including cavity barriers) and openings through them for pipes etc must be fire-stopped as described in Appendix H.

Internal surfaces

1.39   The internal surfaces of wall or ceilings in rooms or circulation spaces (including protected shafts) must have the minimum classification given in the table, however:

1.40   The surfaces of ceilings below cavities, which are not divided by cavity barriers have different requirements. These may apply in the top storey of houses of 3 or more storeys: see G 5.

Table to 1.39   Minimum provisions for surfaces of walls and ceilings (dwelling houses)

Type of building	Small rooms (floor area no more than 4 m²)	Other rooms	Circulation spaces and protected shafts
1 or 2 storey house	Class 3	walls: Class 1* ceilings: Class 3	walls: Class 1 ceilings: Class 3
house with 3 or more storeys	Class 3	walls: Class 1* ceilings: Class 1†	Class 0†

NOTES

* Part of the walls may be of a lower class (Class 3 minimum) but in the area of the part (or the total area if there is more than one part) should not be more than one half of the floor area of the room and not more than 20 m².

† Rooflights in rooms and circulation spaces may be of a lower class (Class 3 minimum) if they meet the provisions in Appendix B, Table B3.

See addendum to Appendix A for effect of wall class relaxation.

1.41/1.43   Appendix A gives details of the classes 0, 1, 2, 3 and the tests required to establish these, also notional classifications for some common materials. Appendix B deals with concessions for plastics materials used in windows, rooflights and suspended ceilings. These cannot always be classified, but may be used within specific limitations (mainly of size). Generally roof lights must meet the provisions for roof construction as well as for internal surfaces.

Comment.

This is one of the places where the Guide tries to help by going beyond simply quoting BS reference numbers and test criteria, which if not understood are merely confusing. In Appendix A therefore will be found some notes on the objectives of various tests, how they are conducted and the significance of the reported results on which the Regulations are based.

Stairways

1.44   These, including landings, must be of MOLC if:

(*a*)   In houses of more than 4 storeys.

(*b*)   External and connecting ground floor with a floor or flat roof at more than 6 m above ground.

1.45   Combustible material may be used on the upper surface.

1.46   In houses over 2 storeys stairways may need to be enclosed to comply with B 1 *Means of escape.*

Section 2   Flats

In the Approved Document itself, all the items dealt with in Section 1 are dealt with again in the same way in this, and subsequent sections. As already stated it is not intended to follow this same procedure throughout, and where simple repetition is involved the reader will be referred to either Section 1 or if some changes have been made to whichever subsequent Section applies. Any differences will of course be meticulously pointed out and dealt with fully as necessary.

Load-bearing elements of structure

2.2/2.4   All as Section 1 except for revised table of fire resistance periods below.

Table to 2.2   Minimum periods of fire resistance (flats)

	Maximum dimensions			Minimum period [hours] for elements of structure in a	
Type of building	Height of building or of separated part [m]	Floor area of each storey [m²]	Cubic capacity of building [m³]	Ground or upper storey	Basement storey (including floor over)
Single storey (no basement)	no limit	3000	no limit	½*	not applicable
1 or 2 storey	no limit	500	no limit	½*	1
3 storey	no limit	250	no limit	1**	1
Any number of storeys	28	3000	no limit	1	1½††
	no limit	2000	no limit	1½††	2††

Modifications

Any element of structure should have at least the minimum period needed for any other element of structure which it carries or supports (whether that other element is loadbearing or not).

*   Increased to 1 hour for separating walls, and for any compartment wall and compartment floor between a flat and a part of the building used for non-residential purpose or a refuse storage container chamber.

**   Reduced to half an hour for any floor (which is not also a compartment floor) but not for any part of the floor which contributes to the support of the building as a whole, and not for any beam which supports the floor.

††   Reduced to 1 hour for any compartment wall between a flat and any other part of the same building if the wall –
(a) is non-loadbearing and does not form part of a protected shaft, and
(b) does not form part of the boundary with a different purpose group, where the minimum period of fire resistance for any element of structure in that other part exceeds 1 hour.

NOTES
1.   Refer to Appendix A, Table 1 to A2, for specific provisions of test.
2.   See general note on page 91.

External walls

2.5/2.13   All as Section 1.

Roof constructions

2.14/2.17   All as Section 1.

Separating walls

2.18   These are walls which separate attached buildings from each other. They must have at least the fire resistance given for loadbearing elements with a minimum of 1 hour and meet the provisions of Appendix C.

2.19   They should be of MOLC if the building is either:
(a)   Single storey and over 3000 m² floor area.
(b)   Over 2 storeys and with a floor area of 500 m² per storey or
(c)   The provisions of the other building require it.

2.20/2.22   The conditions respecting surfaces, supporting structure and openings are all as in Section 1.

Compartment walls and floors

2.23   The following must be compartment walls or floors. They must have at least the fire resistance of loadbearing elements and comply with Appendix D.
(*a*)   Any floor except within a maisonette separating a flat from any other part of the building.
(*b*)   Any wall separating a flat or maisonette from any other part of the building.
(*c*)   Any wall enclosing a refuse storage chamber.
(*d*)   Any wall or floor dividing off part of the building to be used for a mainly different purpose.
NOTE   (*a*) above means that floors separating circulation spaces from each other in flat blocks are now included, whereas in the 1976 regulations they were not. It follows that each floor must be a compartment and stairs must be protected shafts. This requirement was, however, previously covered for all but two storey blocks by the escape requirements in E 23.
2.24   The walls and floors illustrated in diagram [3.2] are to be constructed of MOLC.

2.24 [**3.2**] *Compartment walls and floors required to be constructed of materials of limited combustibility.*

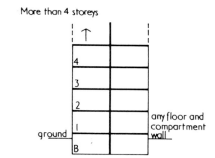

2.25   This also applies to walls in 2.23(d) above if they must have a fire resistance of 1 hour or more, but not if that requirement arises only because they are of the type in 2.23(b) or (c).
2.26   Surface materials for walls and ceilings which meet the requirements for 'internal surfaces' (see later) and floor finishes may be combustible if not relied on to contribute to the fire resistance of the wall or floor. Fire protecting suspended ceilings may also be combustible in some circumstances (see A 2).
2.27   If a wall or floor requires to be constructed of MOLC, any structure forming part of, or supporting them must also be constructed of MOLC.
2.28   Any stairway or other shaft passing from one compartment to another must meet the provisions for protected shafts (see below).
2.29   Any other openings in walls or floors must be limited to those in Appendix D and comply with Appendix F.

Protected shafts

2.30/2.35   All as in Section 1 except:
There is a rider in 2.32 dealing with internal surfaces which is not included in Section 1, but is in all subsequent sections. It arises from the definition of 'protecting structure'. This basically is the structure around a protected shaft, but part of this may consist of separating walls or compartment walls or floors which are not technically 'protecting structure'. For some reason in the old regulation E 10(4)(a) the relaxation permitting the use of combustible material in surface finishes omitted the proviso that these must not be relied on to contribute to fire resistance, which applied to all other fire-separating elements. It seems likely that this was an oversight but it has still been carried through in the new document. However for all practical purposes, surfaces on fire-separating elements which are required to be non-combustible, may be combustible within certain standard limitations, and this applies to protected shafts.

Concealed spaces and fire stopping

2.36/2.37   All as Section 1.

Internal surfaces

2.38/2.42   As for Section 1 except for new table (T4) below and:
2.39   If a ceiling is a type D fire protecting ceiling (see A 2) or is below a space not divided by cavity barriers (see G 5) different provisions apply. (These are two special cases, the first

being ceilings which are allowed to contribute to the overall fire resistance of a floor and the second to be used if it is not desired to use cavity barriers as required by G 4).

Table T4　Minimum provisions for surfaces of walls and ceilings

Small rooms (floor area not more than 4 m²)	Other rooms	Circulation spaces and protected shafts
Class 3	walls: Class 1* ceilings: Class 1†	Class 0†

NOTES
* Part of the walls may be of a lower class (Class 3 minimum but the area of the part (or the total area if there is more than one part) should not be more than one half of the floor ara of the room and not more than 20 m²

† Rooflights in rooms and circulation spaces may be of a lower class (Class 3 minimum), if they meet the provisions in Appendix B. Table to B3.

NOTE This tables applies throughout Sections 2 to 4.

Stairways

2.43　These (including landings) must be of MOLC unless within a masionette if:
(a)　Within a basement storey.
(b)　Within any storey of a building with 3 or more storeys.
(c)　External and connecting the ground floor to a floor or flat roof more than 6 m above the ground.
2.44　Combustible material may be used on upper surfaces.
2.45　In buildings of more than 2 storeys they may need to be enclosed to comply with Regulation B 1 – *Means of escape.*

SECTION 3　INSTITUTIONAL

These are hospitals, homes, schools etc where people sleep on the premises and require care or supervision.

Loadbearing elements of structure

3.2/3.4　All as Section 1 except for table as below.

Table to 3.2　Minimum periods of fire resistance (institutional)

Type of building	Maximum dimensions			Minimum period [hours] for elements of structure in a	
	Height of building or of separated part [m]	Floor area of each storey [m²]	Cubic capacity of building [m³]	Ground or upper storey	Basement storey (including floor over)
Single storey building	no limit	3000	no limit	½*	not applicable
Any other building	28	2000	no limit	1	1½
	over 28	2000	no limit	1½	2

Modifications
Any element of structure should have at least the minimum period needed for any other element of structure which it carries or supports (whether that other element is loadbearing or not).

* Increased to 1 hour for separating walls, and for any compartment wall between any part of the building used for institutional purposes and a part of the building used for non-residential purposes.
NOTE
1. See general note No. 4.

External walls	**3.5/3.6** They must meet the same fire resistance standards as loadbearing elements (even when not loadbearing) **3.7** They must be constructed of MOLC if the building is: (*a*) Over 15 m in height or (*b*) Less than 1 m from relevant boundary and multi-storey, or single storey and either compartmented or over 3000 m² floor area. NOTE A 'separated part' can be assessed individually (see general note 3). **3.8/3.13** The remaining provisions covering internal surfaces, external cladding, supporting structure and unprotected areas are the same as for Section 1.
Roof constructions	**3.14/3.17** All as for Section 1.
Separating walls	**3.18** These are walls which separate attached buildings from each other. They must have at least the fire resistance required for loadbearing elements, which a minimum of 1 hour, and meet the provisions of Appendix C. **3.19** They must be constructed of MOLC if either building is: (*a*) Single-storey with a floor area of over 3000 m², or (*b*) Multi-storey. **3.20/22** The conditions respecting surfaces, supporting structure and openings are the same as for Section 1.
Compartment walls and floors	**3.23** The following must be compartment walls or floors. They must have at least the fire resistance for loadbearing elements and comply with Appendix D. (*a*) Any floor. (*b*) Walls needed to divide the building into compartments not exceeding: 3000 m² in single storey buildings. 2000 m² in multi-storey buildings. (*c*) Any wall or floor dividing off part of the building to be used for a mainly different purpose. **3.24** They must be constructed of MOLC if required to have a fire resistance period of at least 1 hour, but this does not apply if the requirement arises only because of item (*c*) above. **3.25/3.28** The provisions regarding surfaces, supporting structure, stairways, shafts and openings are the same as in Section 2.
Protected shafts	**3.29/3.34** All as for Section 2.
Concealed spaces and fire stopping	**3.35/3.36** All as for Section 1.
Internal surfaces	**3.37/3.41** All as for Section 2.
Stairways	**3.42** These (including landings) must be constructed of MOLC if: (*a*) Internal or (*b*) External and connecting the ground floor with a floor or flat roof over 6 m above ground. **3.43** Combustible material may be used on upper surfaces.

Section 4   Other residential

In the 1976 Regulations this purpose group included flats, which have now been separated out in Section 2. This group is left with some of the characteristics from Section 2 and some from Section 3 Institutional.

Loadbearing elements of structure

4.2/4.4   All as in Section 1 except for modified table below.

Table to 4.2   Minimum periods of fire resistance (other residential)

	Maximum dimensions			Minimum period [hours] for elements of structure in a	
Type of building	Height of building or of separated part [m]	Floor area of each storey [m²]	Cubic capacity of building [m³]	Ground or upper storey	Basement storey (including floor over)
Single storey	no limit	3000	no limit	½*	not applicable
1 or 2 storey	no limit	500	no limit	½*	1
3 storey	no limit	250	no limit	1**	1
Any number of storeys	28	3000	8500	1	1½
	no limit	2000	5500	1½	2

Modifications
Any element of structure should have at least the minimum period needed for any other element of structure which it carries or supports (whether that other element is loadbearing or not).
*   Increased to 1 hour for separating walls, and for any compartment wall and compartment floor between any part of the building used for other residential purposes and a part of the building used for non-residential purposes.

**   Reduced to half an hour for any floor (which is not also a compartment floor) but not for any part of the floor which contributes to the support of the building as a whole, and not for any beam which supports the floor.
NOTE
1.   See general note No. 4 (p. 91).

External walls

4.5/4.6   These must meet the fire resistance standards for loadbearing elements (even if not loadbearing)
4.7   They must be constructed of MOLC if the building is:
(a)   Over 15 m in height or
(b)   Less than 1 m from the boundary and if single storey and either compartmented or over 3000 m² floor area or
(c)   Less than 1 m from the boundary and 3 or more storeys or if only 1 or 2 storeys has over 500 m² floor area per storey.
NOTE   A 'separated part' can be assessed individually.
4.8/4.13   The remaining provisions concerning internal surfaces, external cladding, supporting structure and unprotected areas are the same as for Section 1.

Roof constructions

4.14/4.17   All as for Section 1.

Separating walls

4.18   These are walls which separate attached buildings from each other. They must have at least the same fire resistance as loadbearing elements and meet the provisions of Appendix C.
4.19   They must be constructed of MOLC if the building is:

(*a*)   Single storey and compartmented or over 3000 m² floor area, or

(*b*)   Multi-storey and compartmented and having either 3 or more storeys or only 1 or 2 storeys with over 500 m² floor area per storey.

4.20/4.22   The conditions regarding surfaces, supporting structure and openings are as for Section 1.

Compartment walls and floors

4.23   The following must be constructed as compartment walls or floors, have at least the fire resistance required for loadbearing elements and comply with Appendix D.

(*a*)   Any floor over a basement storey exceeding 100 m² floor area.

(*b*)   If the building exceeds 28 m in height, any floor more than 9 m above the ground or over a basement.

(*c*)   Any wall or floor needed to divide the building into compartments not exceeding the sizes in the table.

(*d*)   Any wall or floor dividing off part of the building to be occupied for a mainly different purpose.

Table to 4.23   Maximum dimensions of building or compartment (other residential)

Type of building	Height of building [m]	Floor area of any storey in building or compartment [m²]	Cubic capacity of building or compartment [m³]
Single storey	no limit	3000	no limit
Multi-storey	not more than 28	3000	8500
	over 28*	2000	5500

NOTE
* Also refer to paragraph 4.23(b) which
   concerns the provision of compartment floors
   in any building exceeding 28 m in height.

4.24   They must be constructed of MOLC if required to have a fire resistance of 1 hour or more, but not if this arises only because of (*d*) above.

4.25/4.28   The provisions regarding surfaces, supporting structure, stairways, shafts and openings are the same as for Section 2.

Protected shafts

4.29/4.34   All as for Section 2.

Concealed spaces and fire-stopping

4.35/4.36   All as for Section 1.

Internal surfaces

4.37/4.41   All as for Section 2.

Stairways

4.42   These must be constructed of MOLC if:

(*a*)   Within a storey having elements of structure requiring a fire resistance of 1 hour or more.

(*b*)   External from the ground floor to a floor or flat roof over 6 m above the ground.

4.43   Combustible materials may be used on upper surfaces.

Section 5   Assembly

This was previously Group VII of the 1976 Regulations.

Loadbearing elements of structure

5.2/5.4   As for Section 1 except for modified table below.

Table to 5.2   Minimum periods of fire resistance (assembly)

| Type of building | Maximum dimensions | | | Minimum period [hours] for elements of structure in a | |
	Height of building or of separated part [m]	Floor area [m²]	Cubic capacity [m³]	Ground or upper storey	Basement storey (including floor over)
Single storey	no limit	3000	no limit	½*	not applicable
	no limit	no limit	no limit	1	not applicable
Any other	7.5	250	no limit	½*	1†
	7.5	500	no limit	½*	1
	15	no limit	3500	1**	1
	28	1000	7000	1	1½
	no limit	no limit	7000	1½	2

Modifications
Any element of structure should have at least the minimum period needed for any other element of structure which it carries or supports (whether that other element is loadbearing or not).
*   Increased to 1 hour for separating walls.
†   Reduce to half hour if the area of the basement is 50 m² or less (but not for separating walls).

**   Reduced to half an hour for any floor (which is not also a compartment floor) but not for any part of the floor which contributes to the support of the building as a whole, and not for any beam which supports the floor.
NOTE
1.   See general note No. 4 (p. 91).

External walls

5.5/5.6   These must meet the fire resistance standards for loadbearing elements (even if not loadbearing).
5.7   The must be constructed of MOLC if the building is:
(*a*)   Over 15 m in height or
(*b*)   Less than 1 m from the boundary and if single-storey either compartmented or over 3000 m² in floor area or
(*c*)   Less than 1 m from the boundary and if multi-storey, more than 7.5 m high or more than 250 m² floor area per storey.
NOTE   A 'separated part' of a building may be treated individually.
5.8/5.15   The remaining provisions covering internal surfaces, external cladding supporting structure and unprotected areas are the same in general as in Section 1. However there are some special provisions which apply to assembly buildings only which are contained in 5.11 and 5.14 and are as follows:
5.11 and **5.14**   If the building has more than 1 storey (galleries counted) any part of a wall not more than 7.5 m above the ground or above any roof or deck to which people have access may only have the unprotected areas indicated in diagram [3.3] and the external surfaces of such walls must meet the provisions shown in the diagram. In general these requirements add up to treating such walls as though they were on a boundary even though they are not, but the thinking behind it is not obvious (although it clearly has to do with protecting people inside from possible fire outside, rather than the other way round).

5.11 [**3.3**] *Outside walls: surfaces (assembly building of more than 1 storey)*

NOTES

1 *Unprotected areas in shaded part to be limited to:*
(a) doors, or
(b) other openings that would enable persons inside the building to be aware of any fire that might start outside the building.

2 *Surfaces of shaded part, including any glazed opening (but not any door or any frame for a door or glazing) to have:*
(a) if less than 1m from any point on the relevant (or notional) boundary: a Class 0 surface
(b) if 1m or more from the boundary; fire propagation index (I) not more than 12 and sub-index (I_1) not more than 6.

3 *Special provisions apply to fire resistance of shaded*

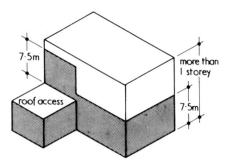

part if 1m or more from relevant boundary. (See Appendix A, Table to A2, item 4(b)). These mean that the wall is to be fire-resistant from the outside as well as from the inside with a maximum of 1 hr.

4 *The unshaded parts are to be treated normally.*

Roof constructions

5.16/5.19   All as for Section 1.

Separating walls

5.20   These are walls which separate attached buildings from each other. They must have at least the fire resistance required for loadbearing elements and meet the provisions of Appendix C.

5.21   They must be constructed of MOLC if either building is:

(*a*)   Single storey and compartmented or over 3000 m² floor area.

(*b*)   Multi-storey and either compartmented or more than 7.5 m high or more than 250 m² floor area per storey.

5.22/5.24   The provisions regarding surfaces, supporting structure and openings are as for Section 1.

Compartment walls and floors

5.25   The following must be constructed as compartment walls or floors, have at least the fire resistance required for loadbearing elements and comply with Appendix D.

(*a*)   If the building has a height of more than 28 m, any floor more than 9 m above the ground, or over a basement and

(*b*)   In buildings with 2 or more storeys (galleries counted) any wall or floor required to divide the building into compartments having a capacity of not more than 7000 m³ and

(*c*)   Any wall or floor dividing off part of the building used for a mainly different purpose.

5.26   They must be constructed of MOLC if required to have a fire resistance of 1 hour or more. However this does not apply to existing floors where the work comprises a material alteration and the building or 'separated part' when complete is not more than 15 m high.

5.27/5.30   The remaining provisions regarding stairways, surfaces, supporting structure, shafts and openings are as for Section 2.

Protected shafts

5.31/5.36   All as for Section 2.

Concealed spaces and fire-stopping

5.37/5.38   All as for Section 2.

Internal surfaces

5.39/5.43   All as for Section 2, except for the table, which has changes in the rules for small rooms (see below).

Stairways

5.44/5.45   All as for Section 4.

Table to 5.39   Minimum provisions for surfaces of walls and ceilings (assembly)

Small rooms (floor area not more than 30 m²)	Other rooms	Circulation spaces and protected shafts
Class 3	walls: Class 1* ceilings: Class 1†	Class 0†

NOTES
* Part of the walls may be of a lower class (Class 3 minimum) but the area of the part (or the total area if there is more than one part) should not be more than one half of the floor area of the room and not more than 60 m².

† Rooflights in rooms and circulation spaces may be of a lower class (Class 3 minimum) if they meet the provisions in Appendix B, Table to B3.

NOTE   This table also applies to Section 6.

Section 6   Offices, shops, industrial and other non-residential

These four remaining purpose groups are dealt with together.
They were groups IV, V, VI and VIII in the 1976 Regulations, Group VI being then known as 'Factory' and Group VIII as 'Storage and General'

Loadbearing elements of structure

6.2/6.4   All as Section 1 except for revised table below.

Table to 6.2   Minimum periods of fire resistance (offices, shops etc)

Purpose group and type of building	Maximum dimensions			Minimum period [hours] for elements of structure in a	
	Height of building or of separated part [m]	Floor area¹ [m²]	Cubic capacity¹ [m³]	Ground or upper storey	Basement storey (including floor over)
Office single storey	no limit	3000	no limit	½*	not applicable Z
	no limit	no limit	no limit	1	
not single storey	7.5	250	no limit	½*	1† X
	7.5	500	no limit	½*	1
	15	no limit	3500	1**	1
	28	5000	14000	1	1½
	no limit	no limit	no limit	1½	2
Shop single storey	no limit	2000	no limit	½**	not applicable Z
	no limit	3000	no limit	1	
	no limit	no limit	no limit	2	
not single storey	7.5	150	no limit	½*	1† X
	7.5	500	no limit	½*	1
	15	no limit	3500	1**	1
	28	1000	7000	1	2
	no limit	2000††	7000††	2	4
Industrial single storey	no limit	2000	no limit	½*	not applicable Z
	no limit	3000	no limit	1	
	no limit	no limit	no limit	2	

Table to 6.2 (continued)   Minimum periods of fire resistance (offices, shops etc)

Purpose group and type of building	Maximum dimensions			Minimum period [hours] for elements of structure in a	
	Height of building or of separated part [m]	Floor area[1] [m²]	Cubic capacity[1] [m³]	Ground or upper storey	Basement storey (including floor over)
not single storey	7.5	250	no limit	½*	1† X
	7.5	no limit	1700	½*	1
	15	no limit	4250	1**	1
	28	no limit	8500	1	2
	28	no limit	28000	2	4
	over 28	2000	5500	2	4
Other non-residential single storey	no limit	500	no limit	½*	not Z
	no limit	1000	no limit	1	applicable
	no limit	3000	no limit	2	
	no limit	no limit	no limit	4	
not single storey	7.5	150	no limit	½*	1† X
	7.5	300	no limit	½*	1
	15	no limit	1700	1**	1
	15	no limit	3500	1	2
	28	no limit	7000	2	4
	28	no limit	21000	4	4
	over 28	1000	no limit	4	4

Modifications

Any element of structure should have at least the minimum period needed for any other element of structure which it carries or supports (whether that other element is loadbearing or not).

* Increased to 1 hour for separating walls.
† Reduced to ½ hour if the area of the basement is 50 m² or less (but not for separating walls).
†† Where the building is fitted throughout with an automatic sprinkler system meeting the relevant recommendations of BS 5306: Part 2: 1979, these figures may be doubled.

X and Z – Building within limits of size shown on this line are referred to in paragraphs 6.7 and 6.19.

** Reduced to ½ hour for any floor (which is not also a compartment floor) but not for any part of the floor which contributes to the support of the building as a whole, and not for any beam which supports the floor.

NOTE
1. See general note 4 (p. 91).

External walls

6.5/6.6   These must meet the fire resisting standards for loadbearing elements (even if not loadbearing).

6.7   They must be constructed of MOLC if the building is:
(a)   More than 15 m in height or
(b)   If single storey, less than 1 m from the boundary and either compartmented or outside the limits of the lines marked Z in the table to 6.2, or
(c)   If multi-storey, less than 1 m from the boundary and outside the limits of the lines marked X in the table to 6.2.

NOTE   The lines marked X and Z are those stating the smallest size limitations for each group, for which only a half hour's fire resistance for elements above ground is required.

6.8/6.13   The remaining provisions covering internal surfaces, cladding, supporting structure and unprotected areas are as in Section 1.

Roof constructions

6.14/6.17   Generally as for other sections but see special note.

SPECIAL NOTE   All industrial and other non-residential buildings must be treated as buildings of over 1500 m³ capacity, whatever their size. This means that the second half of the table applies to all buildings in these groups.

Separating walls

6.18   These are walls which separate attached buildings from each other. They must have at least the fire resistance required for elements of structure and comply with Appendix C.

6.19   They must be constructed of MOLC if either building is:

(*a*)   Single-storey and compartmented, or outside the limits in the lines marked Z in the table to 6.2 or

(*b*)   Multi-storey and compartmented or outside the limits in the lines marked X in the table to 6.2.

6.20/6.22   The provisions regarding surfaces, supporting structure and openings are as for Section 1.

Compartment walls and floors

6.23   The following must be constructed as compartment walls and floors, have at least the fire resistance required for loadbearing elements and comply with Appendix D.

(*a*)   Any floor over a basement exceeding 100 m^2 in a shop.

(*b*)   If the building has a height of more than 28 m, any floor more than 9 m above ground or over a basement.

(*c*)   Any wall or floor needed to divide the building into compartments not exceeding the size limits in the table to 6.23.

(*d*)   Any wall or floor dividing off part of the building used mainly for a purpose different from the main purpose.

6.24   They must be constructed of MOLC if required to have a fire resistance of 1 hour or more, but this does not apply to existing floors in alteration work if the completed building is not more than 15 m high.

6.25/6.28   The remaining provisions for surfaces, supporting structure, stairways, shafts and openings are as for Section 1.

Table to 6.23   Maximum dimensions of building or compartment (offices, shops etc)

Use	Height of building [m]	Floor area of any storey in building or compartment [m^2]	Cubic capacity of building or compartment [m^3]
shop (not sprinklered)	no limit[1]	2000	7000
(sprinklered)[2]	no limit[1]	4000	14000
industrial	not more than 28	no limit	28000
	over 28[1]	2000	5500
other non-residential	no more than 28	no limit	21000
	over 28[1]	1000	no limit

NOTES

[1] However, see also paragraph 6.23 which concerns the provision of compartment floors in any building exceeding 28 m in height.

[2] Where the building is fitted throughout with an automatic sprinkler system meeting the relevant recommendations of BS 5306: Part 2: 1979.

[3] There are no limits for single storey buildings or offices.

Protected shafts

6.29/6.34   All as for Section 1.

Concealed spaces and fire-stopping

6.35/6.36   All as for Section 1.

Internal surfaces

6.27/6.41   All as for Section 5.

Stairways

6.42   These must be constructed of MOLC if:

(*a*)   within a storey containing elements of structure requiring a fire resistance of 1 hour or more, but excluding a stairway within a shop if not enclosed in a protected shaft.

(NOTE   These are what are known as accommodation stairways and are always additional to those required for fire escape purposes)

(*b*)   External and connecting the ground floor with a floor or flat roof more than 6 m above ground.

6.43   Combustible materials may be used on upper surfaces.

6.44   Note that stairways in buildings containing shops and offices may need to be enclosed and protected to meet the requirements of Regulation B 1 as laid down in the *Mandatory rules for means of escape from fire* Sections 3 and 4. These are mentioned specifically because these rules only apply to these two groups in Section 6. However the rule that requires all vertical communication between compartments to be in a protected shaft is of course universal: see compartment walls and floors.

Varying the provisions

The guidance notes referred to in the introduction on the possibility of varying the provisions in specific cases are quite lengthy. The factors which in general need to be taken into account are described in the introduction. A summary of the specific cases mentioned is given below.

Dwelling houses

1.47   There are concessions regarding means of escape requirements for 3 storey houses (Regulation B 1) where these arise as a result of a 2 storey house becoming 3 storey only because of a loft conversion, which adds not more than 2 habitable rooms in the roof. The provisions of this document require floors of 3-storey houses to have a full half hour's fire resistance, but floors in existing 2 storey houses may often provide only a modified half hour (stability 30 mins, integrity and insulation 15 mins). In such cases, providing the requirements for loft conversions set out in B 1, the DOE *Mandatory rules for means of escape in case of fire* are adhered to, it is considered reasonable to accept a modified half hour for the existing first floor where this only separates rooms from each other. If the new stairway rises over a floor in a room, this part of the floor should have a full half hour. Many existing floors fall short of the full half hour only because they have plain edged boarding. They can usually be brought up to standard by the addition of 3.2 mm hardboard: BRE Digest 208 gives further guidance.

Conversion to flats

2.46/2.49   When a house or other building is converted into flats it may be difficult to meet the normal provisions.

Three-storey buildings generally need 1 hour fire resistance for elements of structure. However if means of escape are good a full half hour standards may be acceptable in three-storey buildings, but not in buildings of 4 or more storeys where the full hour would normally be necessary.

In buildings over 4 storeys all compartment floors (ie every floor except within a maisonette) must be constructed of MOLC. Again if means of escape is good this might be relaxed.

Floors in institutional buildings

3.44/3.47   All such floors must normally be constructed of MOLC. Sometimes however, the use of timber floors is considered desirable to create a more homely atmosphere (eg in old peoples' homes). Such buildings usually have supervisory staff and therefore, if there is also good means of escape including fully protected stairways and 24 hours supervision, the use of timber floors and stairs may be accepted in 2 storey buildings (or 3 storeys if the top floor is staff only).

The same may be acceptable for existng buildings not more than 15 m high.

Shopping centres

6.45/6.48   Large modern shopping complexes, particularly where involving malls and covered service areas, clearly pose problems. In particular, maximum compartment sizes will be a difficulty, bearing in mind that it would in general not be practical to compartment a shop from the mall serving it.

It is possible to provide a satisfactory standard of safety without fully complying with this Approved Document. This involves the use of compensatory measures not necessarily within the orbit of Building Regulations. It has always been policy to consider such factors when dealing with relaxations. They might include:

(*a*)   Unified ownership and control.

(*b*)   Adequate means of escape and smoke control.

(c)   Sprinkler protection in areas with a fire load.

(d)   Fire alarm systems with automatic detection.

(e)   Access for fire fighting.

(f)   Maximum use of MOLC.

(g)   General minimum fire resistance of 2 hours (4 in basements).

(h)   Floors generally constructed as compartment floors.

(i)   Walls between units constructed as compartment walls.

(j)   Compartmentation of 'large' shop units from mall which could be by fire shutters (3700 m^2 is suggested as 'large' or 2000 m^2 each if there are two opposing large shops.)

There is further guidance in *Fire prevention guide No 1 – Fire precautions in town centre developments*, HMSO 1972 and BRE report *Smoke control methods in enclosed shopping complexes – A design summary*, HMSO 1979.

Steel portal frames

6.49/6.55   These are often used in single-storey buildings where there is no fire resistance requirement. However, they may be built into external walls near to boundaries which do require such resistance. Since portal frames act as a single element (due to rigid column/rafter joints) collapse of the rafters would affect the columns, so that they too may need to be fire-protected. This can be avoided if the column members are rigidly fixed to a base large enough to resist overturning, have brick or concrete protection, extending up to a protected ring beam, and there is some form of roof venting for early heat release (PVC rooflights equal to 10 per cent of floor area, evenly spaced, would do).

There is an alternative method which does not require roof venting: see the Approved Document 6.54.

Raised storage areas

6.56/6.60   Raised free-standing floors, possibly supported by racking, are frequently installed in single-storey industrial buildings. Whether these count as galleries (less than half the main floor area) or as additional floors, they would normally require the fire resistance specified for elements of structure.

In favourable circumstances a lesser period, or even an unclad steel structure, might be considered. There would have to be a low number of persons employed, no members of the public, layout to enable anyone on the floor to be easily aware of a fire below, and good escape routes.

A perforated floor, leaving gaps around the perimeter, or a smoke detector system, appropriately sited, could provide adequate early warning. The surface rating of the ceiling below the raised floor might also be lower than normal providing there is no need for an escaping person to escape under it.

Multi-storey car parks

6.61/6.62   Limited provision for compartmentation, fire resistances and space separation can be acceptable. This was recognised a long time ago, after the receipt of many representations by the then Minister of Housing and Local Government, to the effect that the normal requirements for storage buildings were too onerous for this type of building, MOHLG circular 17/68 set out the circumstances under which relaxation would normally be allowed. They are described below and illustrated, with the original imperial dimensions converted into rounded-off metric equivalents. It is these recommendations that are now described in the notes on varying the provisions in the Approved Document.

Conditions under which provisions might be relaxed

Car parks must be open sided at least partially with a lower floor level no more than 1.2 m below ground. If over 15 m high all elements of structure must have a minimum fire resistance period of one hour, but for buildings under 15 m high this is not essential. The points are illustrated in diagram [3.4].

The expression 'little fire resistance' used for buildings less than 15 m high can be taken to include unprotected structural steel of suitable size and weight. Unprotected steel does, of course, have some period of fire resistance, particularly in heavier sections. In case A quoted in the appendix to the circular, exposed steelwork was used with column weights ranging from 4.01 kg to 6.23 kg/m run and beam weights from 3.74 kg to 11.62 kg/m run. The fire resistance of this steel was estimated to be approximately ten minutes, but in view of the excellent means of escape and low fire risk this was thought to be adequate. To justify relaxation all construction must be of non-combustible materials and there are rules about separa-

6.61/62 [**3.4**] *General conditions for granting relaxations in multi-storey garages.*

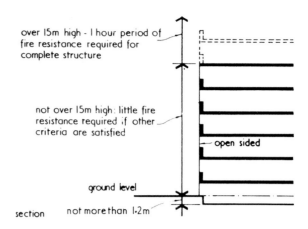

over 15m high - 1 hour period of fire resistance required for complete structure

not over 15m high: little fire resistance required if other criteria are satisfied

open sided

ground level

section   not more than 1·2m

tion from adjoining buildings and distances between the car park and other buildings on the same site and also in relation to boundaries and roads. These are illustrated in diagram [3.5].

[**3.5**] *Separation of multi-storey garages from adjoining buildings.*

NOTE   Adequate fire brigade access must be provided. If the separating distance is less than 9 m the rules in Appendix J must be applied. If this results in any deficiency in ventilation area this may be made up by mechanical means.

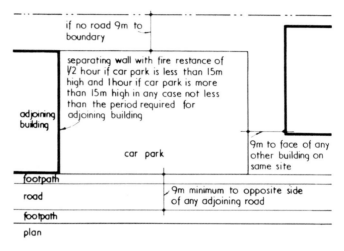

if no road 9m to boundary

separating wall with fire restance of ½ hour if car park is less than 15m high and 1 hour if car park is more than 15m high in any case not less than the period required for adjoining building

adjoining building

car park

9m to face of any other building on same site

footpath

road

9m minimum to opposite side of any adjoining road

footpath

plan

It is also a requirement that a certain minimum degree of cross-ventilation should be provided by means of permanent open space at least along the two longer sides of the building. The requirement is for a minimum open area at both sides of the building of 2½ per cent of the floor area. This is illustrated in diagram [3.6] and a further diagram illustrates the effect

6.61/6.62 [**3.6**] *Cross ventilation in multi-storey garages.*

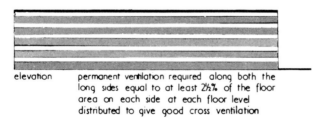

elevation   permanent ventilation required along both the long sides equal to at least 2½% of the floor area on each side at each floor level distributed to give good cross ventilation

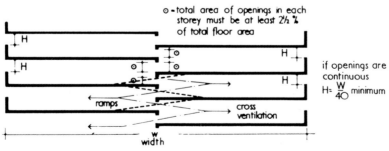

o = total area of openings in each storey must be at least 2½ % of total floor area

H

H

H

H

o

o

if openings are continuous

$H = \dfrac{W}{40}$ minimum

ramps

cross ventilation

W
width

cross section

NOTE   When openings at each side are continuous the height of opening H will be at least 2½ per cent of the overall width or W/40. For example if a building is 30 m wide height must be 750 mm minimum. If much above 60 m wide, the requirement might begin to affect the storey height as, after allowing for slab thickness, beams, barrier rails and so on, it might be difficult to achieve a height of more than 1500 mm of free space.

of the overall width of the building on the height of a continuous opening which would need to be left in each storey. Although not specifically mentioned it follows that there must be no internal walls that would obstruct the cross-ventilation of the building to any greater degree than the external walls. This will need to be carefully checked in the very common type of car park which operates on a split level principle. The free space in the centre of such a building at the change of level does tend to be obstructed by structural beams, and so on, which may occupy quite a large part of the total height available in any one storey; diagram [3.6]. Diagram [3.7] also illustrates the requirements with regard to means of escape.

6.61/62 [**3.7**] *Means of escape in multi-storey garages.*

Escape stair: there must be at least two

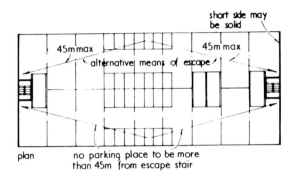

Canopies over petrol pumps
6.63/6.65 Some of these (under 30 m² area and more than 1 m from the boundary) are exempt, falling within Class VI of Schedule 3, but many larger ones could not meet the provisions for unprotected areas without being sited unreasonably distant from a boundary. Because of the high degree of ventilation, unless the canopy is immediately adjacent to a building on an adjoining site, these provisions can reasonably be disregarded.

Provision of sprinklers
6.66/6.67 The provisions do permit compartment sizes in some shops to be doubled if sprinklers are fitted (see Section 6).
They may also be considered as compensatory features in other circumstances where possible relaxation is being considered. For example, the compartment size in industrial buildings, or where space separation is deficient in the case of a shop or industrial building, in which case the relevant distance appropriate to residential, office or assembly buildings might be acceptable if sprinklers are fitted.

Appendix A Performance of materials and structures

General arrangement

This describes in detail how the standards required for various elements, which are laid down in Sections 1 to 6 can be provided. It deals with a number of aspects of the fire performance of materials and construction. It does something towards clarifying the somewhat mystical references to test results in the 1976 Regulations, but in other ways it is more difficult to assimilate. It covers:

A 2   Fire resistance of elements   previously E 1(5)
A 2   Fire protecting suspended ceilings   previously E 6
A 2   Notional periods of fire resistance   previously E 1(5) Sched 8
A 3   Notional designation of roof coverings   previously E 1(6) Sched 9
A 4/11 Wall and ceiling linings   previously E 15
A 13/14 Definition of 'materials of limited combustibility'.

The last item is a new term. It enlarges on the definition of non-combustible used in the old Regulations and defined in A 4(1).

It does not cover the use of plastics in ceilings, roofs and rooflights, previously partly included in E 15(4) and (5) and partly in E 16. All are now collected together in Appendix B.

Comment

A 2 Notional periods of fire resistance, gives just a few constructions for simple floors and walls of up to 1 hour fire resistance. The user is now expected to refer to other published material, of which there is a generous supply, and out of which the BRE report of 1982 is probably the most used. The examples that *are* shown are clearly only for small-scale domestic work. Schedule 8 provided a comprehensive selection of constructions for all types of walls, reinforced concrete frame members, steel frames, structural aluminium, timber and concrete floors.

A 3 Roof coverings by contrast provides exactly the same information as the old Schedule 9.

Fire resistance

A 1 The performance of an element, product or material can be demonstrated by either:

(*a*) Being shown by test to be capable.

(*b*) Having been assessed as meeting the performance (by some fire consultants or laboratories approved by an appropriate body, such as NAMAS, BRE etc)

(*c*) Conforming with one of the notional performance constructions in A 2

(*d*) Conforming with an appropriate specification in Part II of the BRE report *Guidelines for the construction of fire-resisting structural elements*, HMSO 1982.

A 2 The performance for elements of structure, doors etc. is determined by reference to the methods specified in BS 476: Parts 20 to 23: 1987 or to Part 8: 1972 in respect of items tested or assessed before 1 January 1988. Results of tests on proprietary materials and elements of structure are given in the following publications:

BRE Reports *Results of fire resistance tests on elements of building construction*, HMSO 1975 and volume 2, 1976.

Fire test results on building products: fire resistance, Fire Protection Association, London, 1983.

Fire protection for structural steel in buildings, Association of structural fire protection contractors and manufacturers, London, 1983.

Rules for the construction of firebreak doors and shutters, Fire officers' committee, Boreham Wood, 1985.

Information is also available from manufacturers' literature and trade associations. Any such references used should be verified and checked as being suitable for the application proposed; small differences in detail, such as joints or fixing methods, may significantly affect the rating.

There are three tables as follows:

Table 1 to A 2. Specific provisions of test for fire resistance of elements of structure etc.

The table gives details of the fire resistance requirements of elements in terms of the period of time and the direction from which the element must resist the fire. The period is usually that given for elements generally in Sections 1 to 6, but there are some specific exceptions.

The table itself is almost a repeat of Table 1 to Regulation E 1 of the 1976 Regulations, but is arranged in a different order. It has however an additional item dealing with divisions between protected shafts and lobbies and the item concerning structure surrounding stairways in houses of 3 or more storeys is omitted (this is now dealt with in Section 1 of B 1 *Means of escape*).

BS 476: Part 8: 1972, which defines the test procedures to be used, expresses its results as three periods, Stability (time before collapse), Integrity (passage of flame) and Insulation (passage of heat). Not all of these is required in every case. Structural members, for example need only stability, but fire separating members, such as compartment walls and floors, need all three. Walls generally need to be tested from both sides, but external walls which are not within 1 m of the boundary need testing from the inside only. Where tests from both sides are required, they are done separately.

To assist the reader to understand what is actually required, a brief description of BS 476: Part 8 is given below.

The table itself is a somewhat indigestible chunk of printed information so the requirements are expressed here in diagrammatic form [3.9]. Doors are not however a suitable subject for this form of treatment and so a note about these is added at the end.

A 2 [**3.8**] *Fire resistance requirement. Arrows indicate directions from which structure must resist fire.*
Numbers in brackets refer to items in Table 1 to A 2.

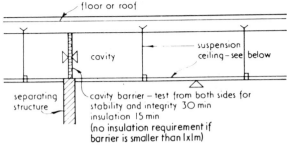

ceiling from below only 30 min for all three tests

Ceiling referred to in G 5 (enclosing a cavity beneath a floor or roof) (11) (see A 8(b)).
Cavity barrier large enough to include a square of 1 m sides.
NOTE   No sub-division of cavity is necessary if the ceiling:
(i)   extends throughout the compartment
(ii)   is not demountable
(iii)   has ½ hour fire resistance
(iv)   is imperforate (except permitted openings)
(v)   the upper surface is class 1
(vi)   the lower surface is technically non-combustible, (see A8(b)).

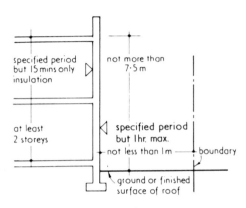

structure referred to in 5.11
external walls in certain assembly buildings

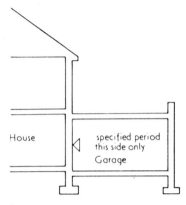

house   garage
wall between house and garage (8)

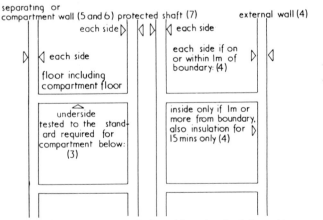

elements of structure are required to withstand tests of fire resistance to the standard required by EI(S) on one or both sides as indicated by arrows

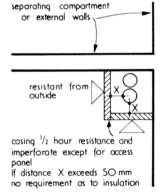

pipe casing referred to in Appx. F (10)

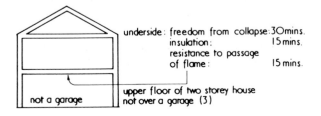

underside: freedom from collapse: 30 mins.
insulation: 15 mins.
resistance to passage of flame: 15 mins.
upper floor of two storey house not over a garage (3)

Doors (Item 9 of table)
The only requirement is for integrity (no period of stability or insulation is given). This is to comply with recently agreed international procedure, when it was decided to abandon the previous inclusion of stability. The integrity requirement is as follows:

1 In separating walls (except as in 5 below).	the required period with a minimum of 1 hour
2 Compartment walls (except as in 5 below).	the required period.
3 Protecting structure above ground in flats, other residential, assembly or office buildings.	30 mins.
4 Any other protecting structure.	½ the required period for the wall or 30 mins minimum.
5 Wall between a flat and a space in common use, door in a cavity barrier, between a house and a garage, and any other door not in 1 to 4 above.	20 mins.

Tests are to be from each side separately of a door and frame complete.

Table 2 to A 2   Floors with suspended ceilings
The fire resistance of a floor may be assisted by an applied ceiling. Suspended ceilings however may only be counted as contributing to fire resistance if they are of a certain type, and this depends on the type of floor (compartment or not) and the period required. Table 2 to A 2 below gives details of such ceilings.

Table 2 to A 2   Ceilings permitted to contribute to fire resistance

Height of building [m]	Type of floor	Provision for fire resistance of floor [hours]	Description of suspended ceiling
less than 15	not compartment	1 or less	Type A, B, C or D
	compartment	less than 1	
		1	Type B, C or D
15 or more	any	1 or less	Type C or D
no limit	any	more than 1	Type D

Ceiling type	Description	Ceiling type	Description
A	Surface of ceiling exposed to the cavity should be Class 0 or Class 1.	D	Ceiling should be a material of limited combustibility and be jointless (ie not contain access panels). Supports and fixings should be non-combustible. Any insulation above the ceiling should be of a material of limited combustibility.
B	Surface of ceiling exposed to the cavity should be Class 0. Supports and fixings should be non-combustible.		
C	Surface of ceiling exposed to the cavity should be Class 0. Ceiling should be jointless (ie not contain access panels). Supports and fixings should be non-combustible.		

Table 3 to A 2   Notional periods of fire resistance of some common constructions
This very restricted schedule is reproduced here. The previous guide devoted 10 pages to illustrating the constructions described in Schedule 8 of the 1976 Regulations for providing fire protection to the various elements. To assist the reader a brief summary of BRE 1982 report is given below, together with most of the note on Schedule 8 from the last Guide: still very useful if the reservations stated are observed.

Table 3 to A 2   Notional periods of fire resistance of some common constructions

These constructions are a selection from the current edition of the BRE report *Guidelines for the construction of fire resisting structural elements*. (HMSO 1982)

A large number of constructions other than those shown are capable of providing the fire resistance looked for. For example, various mineral based insulating boards can be used. Because their performance varies and is dependent on their thickness, it is not possible to give specific thicknesses in this Table. However, manufacturers will normally be able to say what thickness would be needed to achieve the particular performance.

Floors: timber joist

Modified half hour (stability 30 minutes) (integrity 15 minutes) (insulation 15 minutes)	1	any structurally suitable flooring: floor joists at least 37 mm wide ceiling (a) 12.5 mm plasterboard* with joints taped and filled and backed by timber, or (b) 9.5 mm plasterboard* with 10 mm lightweight gypsum plaster finish
	2	at least 15 mm t&g boarding or sheets of plywood or wood chipboard, floor joists at least 37 mm wide ceiling (a) 12.5 mm plasterboard* with joints taped and filled, or (b) 9.5 mm plasterboard* with at least 5 mm neat gypsum plaster finish
Half hour	3	at least 15 mm t&g boarding or sheets of plywood or wood chipboard, floor joists at least 37 mm wide ceiling 12.5 mm plasterboard* with at least 5 mm neat gypsum plaster finish
	4	at least 21 mm t&g boarding or sheets of plywood or wood chipboard, floor joists at least 37 mm wide ceiling 12.5 mm plasterboard* with joints taped and filled
1 hour	5	at least 15 mm t&g plywood or wood chipboard, floor joists at least 50 mm wide ceiling not less than 30 mm plasterboard* with joists staggered and exposed joints taped and filled

Table 3 to A 2   Notional periods of fire resistance of some common constructions

Floors: concrete

1 hour	6	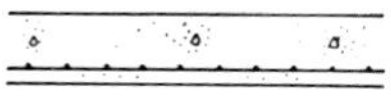	reinforced concrete floor not less than 95 mm thick, with not less than 20 mm cover on the lowest reinforcement

Walls: internal

half hour loadbearing	7	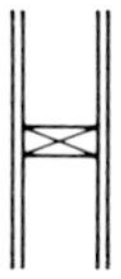	framing members at least 44 mm wide† and spaced at not more than 600 mm apart, with lining (both sides) of 12.5 mm plasterboard* with all joints taped and filled
	8	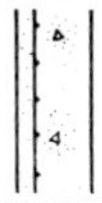	100 mm reinforced concrete wall** with minimum cover to reinforcement of 25 mm
1 hour loadbearing	9	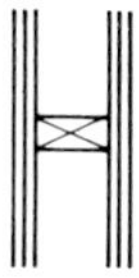	framing members at least 44 mm wide† and spaced at not more than 600 mm apart, with lining (both sides) at least 25 mm plasterboard* in 2 layers with joints staggered and exposed joints taped and filled
	10		solid masonry wall (with or without plaster finish) at least 90 mm thick (75 mm if non-loadbearing) Note: for masonry cavity walls, the fire resistance may be taken as that for a single wall of the same construction, whichever leaf is exposed to fire
	11	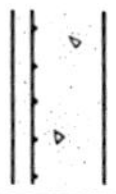	120 mm reinforced concrete wall** with at least 25 mm cover to the reinforcement

Walls: external

modified half hour (stability 30 minutes) (integrity 30 minutes) (insulation 15 minutes) loadbearing wall 1 m or more from relevant boundary	12	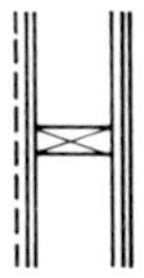	any external weathering system with at least 8 mm plywood sheathing, framing members at least 37 mm wide and spaced not more than 600 mm apart internal lining: 12.5 mm plasterboard* with at least 10 mm lightweight gypsum plaster finish
half hour loadbearing wall less than 1 m from the relevant boundary	13	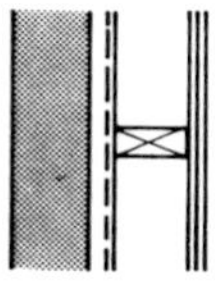	100 mm brickwork or blockwork external face (with, or without, a plywood backing); framing members at least 37 mm wide and spaced not more than 600 mm apart internal lining: 12.5 mm plasterboard* with at least 10 mm lightweight gypsum plaster finish

Table 3 to A 2   Notional periods of fire resistance of some common constructions

| 1 hour | 14 | solid masonry wall (with or without plaster finish) at least 90 mm thick (75 mm if non-loadbearing) |
| loadbearing wall less than 1 m from the relevant boundary | | |

Note: for masonry cavity walls, the fire resistance may be taken as that for a single wall of the same construction, whichever leaf is exposed to fire

NOTES

* Whatever the lining material, it is important to use a method of fixing that the manufacturer says would be needed to achieve the particular performance. For example, if the lining is plasterboard the fixings should be at 150 mm centres as follows (where two layers are being used each should be fixed separately):
9.5 mm thickness – 30 mm galvanised nails
12.5 mm thickness – 40 mm galvanised nails
19 mm–25 mm thickness – 60 mm galvanised nails

† Thinner framing members, such as 37 mm may be suitable depending on the loading conditions.

** A thinner wall may be suitable depending on the density of the concrete and the amount of reinforcement *(see Guidelines for the construction of fire resisting structural elements* (HMSO 1982) *)*

BRE Report   Guidelines for the construction of fire-resisting elements 1982

This report was intended to fill a need for 'simple generic descriptions of fire resisting elements' to supplement the wealth of information available in the form of test reports from the Fire Research Station and other testing laboratories. These are largely reports on proprietary materials or systems submitted for testing by manufacturers.

The BRS report contains 14 tables covering the main building elements. These are not intended to be exhaustive. It also contains much useful information on the principles involved in providing fire protection and the properties of suitable materials. In particular it stresses that there is no simple way of expressing the fire resistance of any particular material in relation to its thickness that would be universally applicable, so that each individual case must be assessed separately.

It may be for this reason that Approved Document B does not contain anything like the old Schedule 8, which was based on the results of tests carried out by the Fire Research Station. Nevertheless, Schedule 8 has been very useful as a general guide to what is possible and its recommendations were clearly not far from the mark in most cases, although, as with most things, further research will have shown up some need for changes. After careful consideration it has therefore been decided to include here the pages from the last Guide covering Schedule 8 with a warning as to limitations on its use (see later).

The tables in the report take into account the results of recent research and in particular the following:

1   The updating of information on reinforced concrete protection.

2   Further study of protection for a range of steelwork sizes.

The protection needed by steelwork depends on what is known as the P/A ratio (perimeter divided by the area of the section) and this varies for every individual beam or column size.

3   Work on loadbearing timber stud and joist construction. These were never included in Schedule 8, but some examples are included in table 4 and 6 of the Report.

Schedule 8 to the 1976 Regulations

As stated above the Guide material is reproduced here simply as an aid to designers. A check has been made with the BRE Report and other sources and in general the constructions specified in Schedule 8 still hold good. They also give far more information on a much wider range of methods and materials than the Report.

They should however only be used as a guide to normal practice and individual requirements should always be checked with manufacturers or other sources. The following detail points are also made:

1   In cavity walls the resistance may be taken as being that of a single leaf of the same construction.

2   In loadbearing cavity walls it is generally the inner leaf that takes the load. It is this leaf therefore whose stability will determine the fire resistance of the wall.

3   If the inner leaf is of framed composite construction and *also* loadbearing the fire resistance of the wall may be very poor, even if there is an outer skin of brickwork, because the structure will fail in stability (see item 13 in Table 3 to A 2).

4   If the inner skin is not loadbearing it may be the outer skin which determines the overall fire resistance. (NOTE   There are no loadbearing framed walls in Schedule 8).

5   External walls more than 1 m from a boundary are required to resist fire from the inside only and need only 15 minutes insulation regardless of the overall resistance period required. Hence they are dealt with separately (see Part Ic, Schedule 8).

6   There are major differences in the concrete structure recommendations in the BRE Report. Parts II and III of Schedule 8 have therefore been omitted and a summary of Table 8 and 9 of the report included. These are for unprotected concrete only and do not show the effects of extra protection such as lightweight plaster.

7   Notes have been added to some items which seemed a bit unrealistic. Although they were in Schedule 8 it is possible they were in error.

8   Steel frames in composite walls and partitions have been illustrated as angles although they might more frequently have been pressed steel sections.

9   Sprayed asbestos is no longer used, but other similar materials are available, not necessarily requiring the same thickness.

10   The steel protection is based on a minimum weight of section but see note (2) to the BRS Report above.

11   Thicknesses are given for ordinary gypsum/sand plaster, but the BRS report suggest that these might not be adequate and should be read as references to lightweight plaster which is clearly a better material for fire protection purposes where insulation is a prime factor.

(*Reg* E 1(5) *Schedule* 8 *part* I-A [**3.9**] *Fire resistance of masonry wall constructions. The diagram and chart show the thickness of masonry which provide a given period of fire resistance.*

NOTE   In this and the following charts the right-hand ends of the bars indicate the minimum thickness T for each fire resistance period.

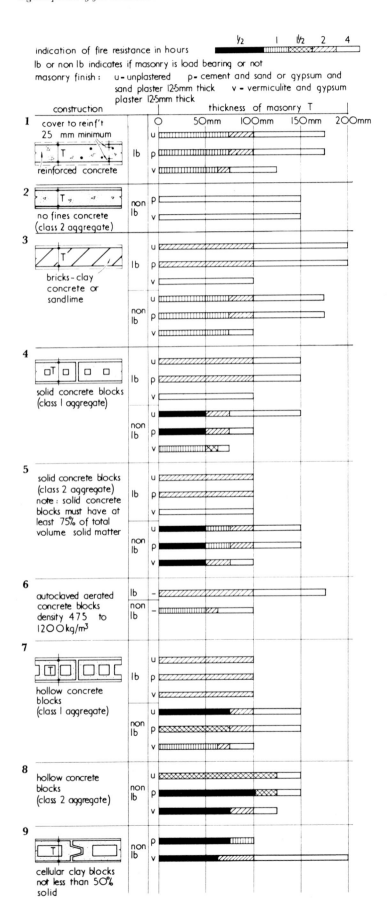

(*Reg* E 1(5) *Schedule* 8 *part* I-A [**3.9**] (*continued*)
*Fire resistance of masonry wall constructions. The
diagram and chart show the thickness of masonry
which provide a given period of fire resistance.*

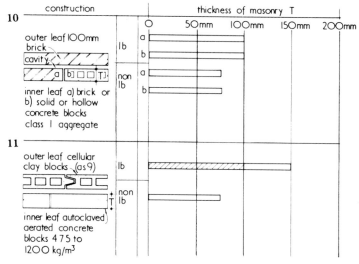

(*Reg* E 1(5) *Schedule* 8 *part* I-B [**3.9**] (*continued*)
*Fire resistance of framed, composite non-loadbearing
wall constructions.*
NOTE   The outside of the wall is always at the top.

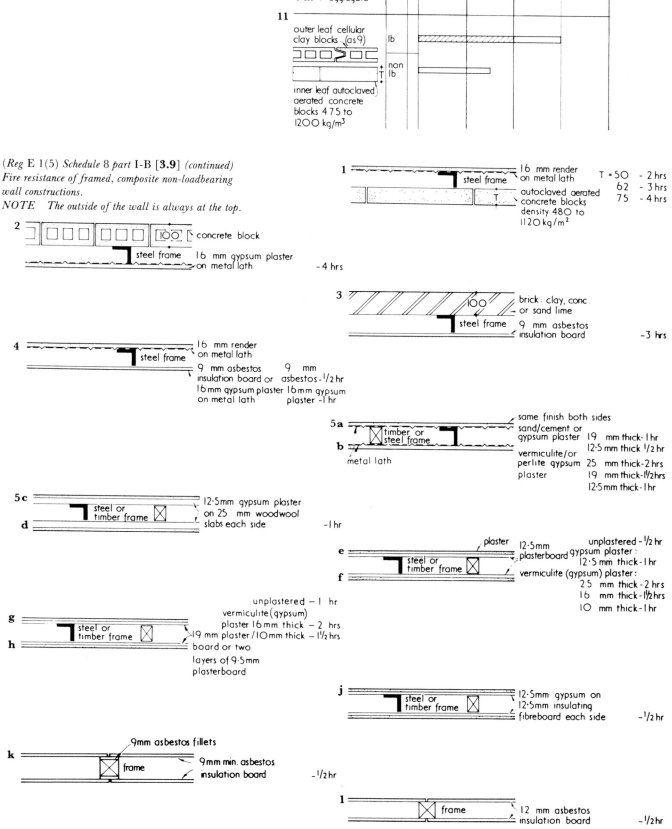

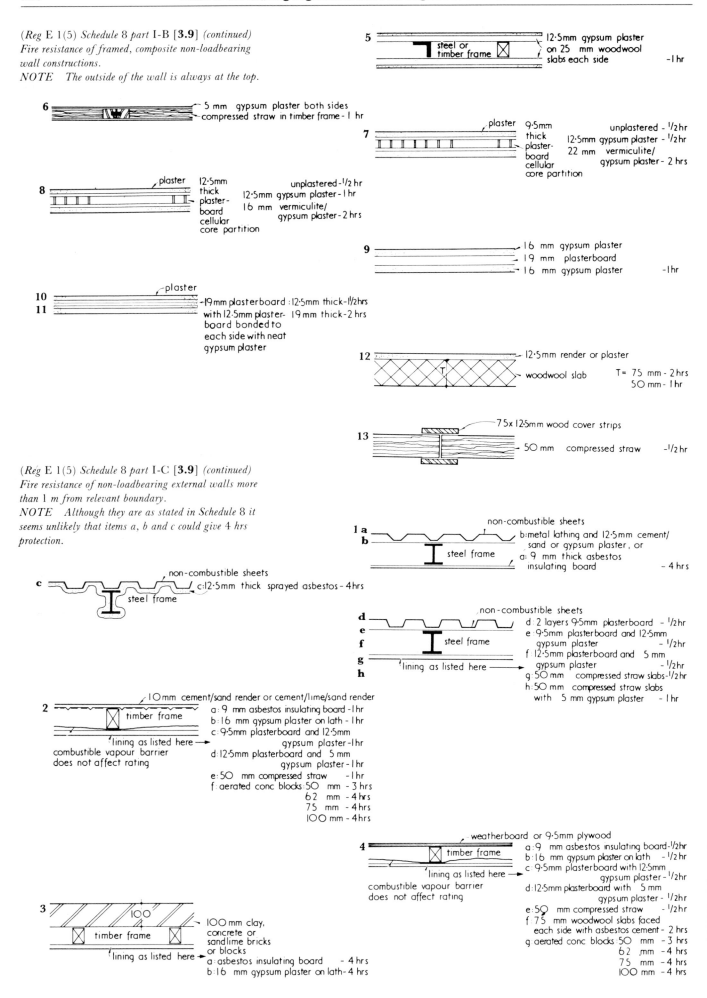

*(Reg E 1(5) Schedule 8 part I-B [**3.9**] (continued)*
Fire resistance of framed, composite non-loadbearing
wall constructions.
NOTE   The outside of the wall is always at the top.

5 steel or timber frame — 12·5mm gypsum plaster on 25 mm woodwool slabs each side — 1 hr

6 5 mm gypsum plaster both sides — compressed straw in timber frame - 1 hr

7 plaster — 9·5mm thick plasterboard cellular core partition — unplastered - 1/2hr / 12·5mm gypsum plaster - 1/2hr / 22 mm vermiculite/gypsum plaster - 2 hrs

8 plaster — 12·5mm thick plasterboard cellular core partition — unplastered - 1/2 hr / 12·5mm gypsum plaster - 1 hr / 16 mm vermiculite/gypsum plaster - 2 hrs

9 16 mm gypsum plaster / 19 mm plasterboard / 16 mm gypsum plaster — 1 hr

10
11 plaster — 19mm plasterboard : 12·5mm thick - 1 1/2hrs with 12·5mm plaster- 19 mm thick - 2 hrs board bonded to each side with neat gypsum plaster

12 12·5mm render or plaster / woodwool slab T = 75 mm - 2 hrs / 50 mm - 1 hr

13 75 x 12·5mm wood cover strips / 50 mm compressed straw — 1/2 hr

*(Reg E 1(5) Schedule 8 part I-C [**3.9**] (continued)*
Fire resistance of non-loadbearing external walls more
than 1 m from relevant boundary.
NOTE   Although they are as stated in Schedule 8 it
seems unlikely that items a, b and c could give 4 hrs
protection.

1 a
b non-combustible sheets / steel frame — b:metal lathing and 12·5mm cement/sand or gypsum plaster, or / a: 9 mm thick asbestos insulating board — 4 hrs

c non-combustible sheets / steel frame — c:12·5mm thick sprayed asbestos - 4 hrs

d
e
f
g
h non-combustible sheets / steel frame / lining as listed here — d: 2 layers 9·5mm plasterboard - 1/2hr / e: 9·5mm plasterboard and 12·5mm gypsum plaster - 1/2hr / f: 12·5mm plasterboard and 5 mm gypsum plaster - 1/2hr / g: 50 mm compressed straw slabs - 1/2hr / h: 50 mm compressed straw slabs with 5 mm gypsum plaster - 1 hr

2 10mm cement/sand render or cement/lime/sand render / timber frame / lining as listed here / combustible vapour barrier does not affect rating — a: 9 mm asbestos insulating board -1 hr / b: 16 mm gypsum plaster on lath - 1 hr / c: 9·5mm plasterboard and 12·5mm gypsum plaster -1 hr / d: 12·5mm plasterboard and 5 mm gypsum plaster -1 hr / e: 50 mm compressed straw - 1 hr / f: aerated conc blocks: 50 mm - 3 hrs / 62 mm - 4 hrs / 75 mm - 4 hrs / 100 mm - 4 hrs

4 weatherboard or 9·5mm plywood / timber frame / lining as listed here / combustible vapour barrier does not affect rating — a: 9 mm asbestos insulating board - 1/2hr / b: 16 mm gypsum plaster on lath - 1/2hr / c: 9·5mm plasterboard with 12·5mm gypsum plaster - 1/2hr / d: 12·5mm plasterboard with 5 mm gypsum plaster - 1/2hr / e: 50 mm compressed straw - 1/2hr / f: 75 mm woodwool slabs faced each side with asbestos cement - 2 hrs / g: aerated conc blocks: 50 mm - 3 hrs / 62 mm - 4 hrs / 75 mm - 4 hrs / 100 mm - 4 hrs

3 100 / timber frame / lining as listed here — 100 mm clay, concrete or sandlime bricks or blocks / a: asbestos insulating board - 4 hrs / b: 16 mm gypsum plaster on lath - 4 hrs

Table 8 to BRE Report 1982 [**3.10**] *Reinforced concrete columns.*

Type	Dimension see sketch (D)	Min. dimension for resistance of (hrs)				
		½	1	1½	2	4
1 *Fully exposed*	Size	150	200	250	300	450
	Cover	20	25	30	35	35
2 *50% exposed*	Size	125	160	200	200	350
	Cover	20	25	25	25	35
3 *One face exposed*	Size	100	120	140	160	240
	Cover	20	25	25	25	25

Minimum dimension. Walls to have fire resistance at least equal to the column and extend at least 600 mm each side without openings.

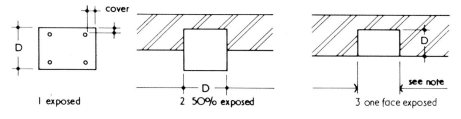

Table 9 to BRE Report 1982 [**3.11**] *Reinforced concrete beams*

Type		Min. dimension for resistance of (hrs)				
		½	1	1½	2	4
Reinforced	*Width*	80	120	150	200	280
Simply supported	*Cover*	20	30	40	50	80
Reinforced	*Width*	80	80	120	150	240
Continuous	*Cover*	20	20	35	50	70
Prestressed	*Width*	100	120	150	200	280
Simply supported	*Cover*	25	40	55	70	90
Prestressed	*Width*	80	100	120	150	240
Continuous	*Cover*	20	30	40	55	80

NOTE   Supplementary reinforcement is required when the cover to the outermost tendons (prestressed concrete) exceeds 40 mm.

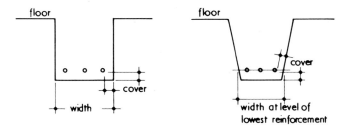

(Reg E 1(5) Schedule 8 part V-Λ subsection (Λ)) **[3.12]** *Fire resistance of encased stanchions of structural steel (weight not less than 45kg/m) with solid protection*

NOTE   If concrete is taken as loadbearing, reinforcement must be in accordance with BS 449:

part 2: 1969 (as read with the Supplement No 1 (PD 3343) to BS 449: part 1: 1970 and Addendum No 1 (April 1975) to BS 449: part 2: 1969).

NOTE   Figures for minimum thickness (T) for sprayed asbestos cement apply only to U.C.S. of serial size 203×203mm in BS 4: part 1: 1972.

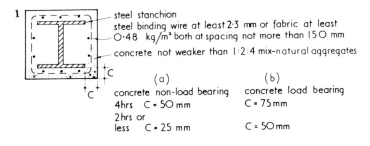

1   steel stanchion
steel binding wire at least 2·3 mm or fabric at least 0·48 kg/m² both at spacing not more than 150 mm

concrete not weaker than 1:2:4 mix-natural aggregates

(a)	(b)
concrete non-load bearing	concrete load bearing
4hrs C = 50 mm	C = 75 mm
2hrs or less C = 25 mm	C = 50 mm

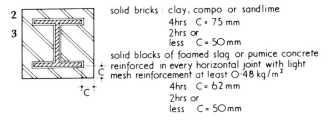

2
3

solid bricks : clay, compo or sandlime
      4hrs   C = 75 mm
      2hrs or less   C = 50 mm
solid blocks of foamed slag or pumice concrete reinforced in every horizontal joint with light mesh reinforcement at least 0·48 kg/m²
      4hrs   C = 62 mm
      2hrs or less   C = 50 mm

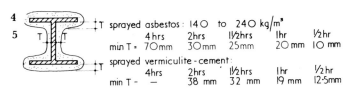

4
5

sprayed asbestos : 140 to 240 kg/m³

	4hrs	2hrs	1½hrs	1hr	½hr
min T =	70mm	30mm	25mm	20 mm	10 mm

sprayed vermiculite - cement :

	4hrs	2hrs	1½hrs	1hr	½hr
min T -	—	38 mm	32 mm	19 mm	12·5mm

(Reg E 1(5) Schedule 8 part V-Λ subsection (B)) **[3.12]** *(continued) Fire resistance of steel stanchions (weight not less than 45kg/m) with hollow protection.*
NOTES   All hollow protection to be effectively sealed at each floor level.

Where plaster forms the main insulation and is more than 25 mm thick, light mesh reinforcement should be incorporated 12.5 mm to 19 mm below the surface unless special corner beads are used.

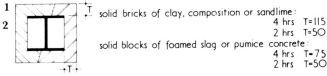

1
2

solid bricks of clay, composition or sandlime :
      4 hrs   T = 115
      2 hrs   T = 50
solid blocks of foamed slag or pumice concrete :
      4 hrs   T = 75
      2 hrs   T = 50

light mesh reinforcement in every horizontal joint

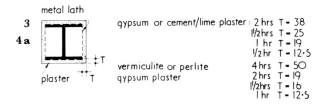

metal lath
3
4a
plaster

gypsum or cement/lime plaster :   2 hrs   T = 38
                1½hrs   T = 25
                1 hr   T = 19
                ½hr   T = 12·5
vermiculite or perlite gypsum plaster
                4hrs   T = 50
                2hrs   T = 19
                1½hrs   T = 16
                1 hr   T = 12·5

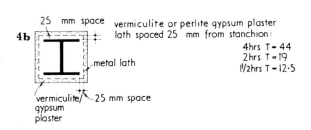

4b

vermiculite or perlite gypsum plaster
lath spaced 25 mm from stanchion :
                4hrs   T = 44
                2hrs   T = 19
                1½hrs   T = 12·5

metal lath

25 mm space
vermiculite gypsum plaster
25 mm space

(Reg E 1(5) *Schedule* 8 *part* V-A *subsection* (B))
[3.12] *(continued) Fire resistance of steel stanchions (weight not less than 45kg/m) with hollow protection.*
NOTES *All hollow protection to be effectively sealed at each floor level.*
Where plaster forms the main insulation and is more than 25 mm thick, light mesh reinforcement should be incorporated 12.5 mm to 19 mm below the surface unless special corner beads are used.

NOTE Figures for minimum thickness (T) for sprayed asbestos cement apply only to U.C.S. of serial size 203×203mm in BS 4: part 1: 1972.

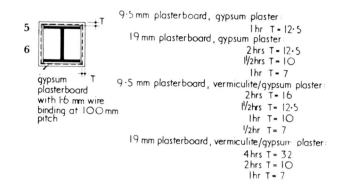

5
6

9·5 mm plasterboard, gypsum plaster:
1 hr T = 12·5
19 mm plasterboard, gypsum plaster:
2 hrs T = 12·5
1½ hrs T = 10
1 hr T = 7
9·5 mm plasterboard, vermiculite/gypsum plaster:
2 hrs T = 16
1½ hrs T = 12·5
1 hr T = 10
½ hr T = 7
19 mm plasterboard, vermiculite/gypsum plaster:
4 hrs T = 32
2 hrs T = 10
1 hr T = 7

gypsum plasterboard with 1·6 mm wire binding at 100 mm pitch

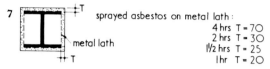

7

sprayed asbestos on metal lath:
4 hrs T = 70
2 hrs T = 30
1½ hrs T = 25
1 hr T = 20

metal lath

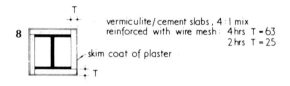

8

vermiculite/cement slabs, 4:1 mix
reinforced with wire mesh: 4 hrs T = 63
2 hrs T = 25

skim coat of plaster

9

asbestos insulating boards (density 510 to 880 kg/m³)
screwed to asbestos battens:
2 hrs T = 25
1½ hrs T = 19
1 hr T = 12
½ hr T = 9

50 x 25 mm asbestos battens

(Reg E 1(5) *Schedule* 8 *part* V-B *subsections* (A) *and* (B)) **[3.12]** *(continued) Subsection* (A). *Fire resistance of encased steel beams (weight not less than 30kg/m) with solid protection.*

NOTE Figures for minimum thickness (T) for sprayed asbestos cement apply only to U.B.S. of serial size 254×146mm in BS 4: part 1: 1972.

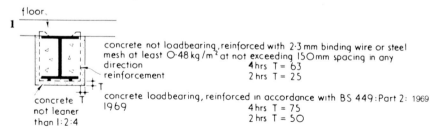

1

floor

concrete not loadbearing, reinforced with 2·3 mm binding wire or steel mesh at least 0·48 kg/m² at not exceeding 150 mm spacing in any direction
4 hrs T = 63
2 hrs T = 25

reinforcement

concrete not leaner than 1:2:4

concrete loadbearing, reinforced in accordance with BS 449:Part 2: 1969
4 hrs T = 75
2 hrs T = 50

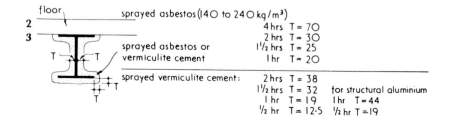

2
3

floor

sprayed asbestos (140 to 240 kg/m³)
4 hrs T = 70
2 hrs T = 30
1½ hrs T = 25
1 hr T = 20

sprayed asbestos or vermiculite cement

sprayed vermiculite cement:
2 hrs T = 38
1½ hrs T = 32   for structural aluminium
1 hr T = 19   1 hr T = 44
½ hr T = 12·5   ½ hr T = 19

(Reg E 1(5) Schedule 8 part V-B subsections (A) and (B)) [3.12] (continued) Subsection (B). Fire resistance of encased steel beams (weight not less than 30kg/m) with hollow protection. Where plaster forms the main insulation and is more than 25 mm thick, light mesh reinforcement should be incorporated 12.5 mm to 19 mm below the surface unless special corner beads are used.

NOTE   Figures for minimum thickness (T) for sprayed asbestos cement apply only to U.B.S. of serial size 254×146mm in BS 4: part 1: 1972.

NOTE   Part VI, structural aluminium, is seldom used. The range of insulating materials which are considered suitable is also a good deal smaller than those which may be used for steel and, as might be expected, aluminium requires a greater thickness for the same duty. Instead of adding a separate Part VI, therefore, the figures are placed alongside the appropriate specifications for steel.

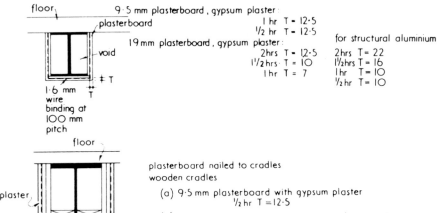

2

9.5 mm plasterboard, gypsum plaster:
1 hr T = 12.5
½ hr T = 12.5

19 mm plasterboard, gypsum plaster:
2 hrs T = 12.5
1½ hrs T = 10
1 hr T = 7

for structural aluminium
2 hrs T = 22
1½ hrs T = 16
1 hr T = 10
½ hr T = 10

3

plasterboard nailed to cradles
wooden cradles

(a) 9.5 mm plasterboard with gypsum plaster
½ hr T = 12.5

(b) 9.5 mm plasterboard with vermiculite/gypsum plaster
2 hrs T = 16
1½ hrs T = 12.5
1 hr T = 10
½ hr T = 7

(c) 19 mm plasterboard with vermiculite/gypsum plaster
4 hrs T = 32
2 hrs T = 10
1 hr T = 7

(d) 19 mm plasterboard with vermiculite/gypsum plaster
2 hrs T = 12.5

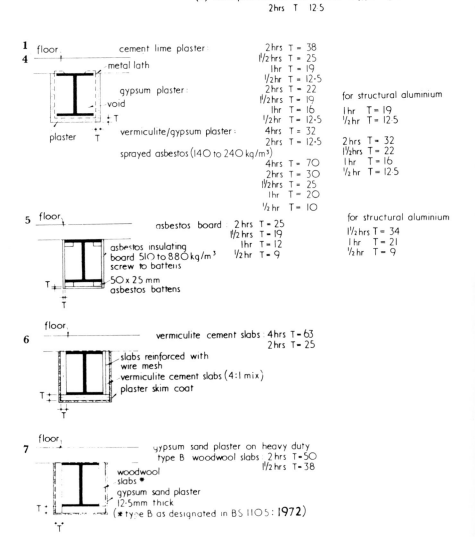

1
4

cement lime plaster:
2 hrs T = 38
1½ hrs T = 25
1 hr T = 19
½ hr T = 12.5

gypsum plaster:
2 hrs T = 22
1½ hrs T = 19
1 hr T = 16
½ hr T = 12.5

vermiculite/gypsum plaster:
4 hrs T = 32
2 hrs T = 12.5

sprayed asbestos (140 to 240 kg/m³)
4 hrs T = 70
2 hrs T = 30
1½ hrs T = 25
1 hr T = 20
½ hr T = 10

for structural aluminium
1 hr T = 19
½ hr T = 12.5

2 hrs T = 32
1½ hrs T = 22
1 hr T = 16
½ hr T = 12.5

5

asbestos board: 2 hrs T = 25
1½ hrs T = 19
1 hr T = 12
½ hr T = 9

asbestos insulating board 510 to 880 kg/m³ screw to battens

50 x 25 mm asbestos battens

for structural aluminium
1½ hrs T = 34
1 hr T = 21
½ hr T = 9

6

vermiculite cement slabs: 4 hrs T = 63
2 hrs T = 25

slabs reinforced with wire mesh
vermiculite cement slabs (4:1 mix)
plaster skim coat

7

gypsum sand plaster on heavy duty type B woodwool slabs: 2 hrs T = 50
1½ hrs T = 38

woodwool slabs *
gypsum sand plaster 12.5mm thick
(* type B as designated in BS 1105: 1972)

*(Reg E 1(5) Schedule 8 part VII [**3.13**]) Fire resistance of timber floors.*

NOTE   The term 'modified ½ hour' relates to item No 10 in Table 1 to regulation E 1 which permits reduced standards as regards passage of heat and flame (but not as regards collapse) for upper floors in purpose group I (small residential).

Construction	Rating	value of thickness T with		
		plain edge boarding on joists at least 38 mm wide **A**	16 mm t and g boarding on joists at least 38 mm wide **B**	21 mm t and g boarding on joists at least 50mm wide x175mm deep **C**
floor boards, joists / plaster / timber lath	modified ½ hr	16	16	—
	½ hr	—	—	16
plasterboard / timber lath and 16 mm min plaster	½ hr	12.5	9.5	—
metal lath / plaster	gypsum ½ hr	16	16	16
	gypsum 1 hr	—	22	—
	vermiculite ½ hr	12.5	12.5	—
	vermiculite 1 hr	—	12.5	—
sprayed asbestos to BS 3590 1970	½ hr	—	—	12.5
	1 hr	—	—	19
one layer plasterboard	modified ½ hr	12.5	9.5	9.5
plaster / 9.5 mm plasterboard	gypsum ½ hr	—	12.5	12.5
	gypsum modified ½ hr	12.5	—	—
	vermiculite 1 hr	—	12.5	12.5
plaster / 12.5mm plasterboard	gypsum ½ hr	12.5	5.0	4.5
2 layers plasterboard	modified ½ hr	19	—	—
	½ hr	25	22	19

(Reg E 1(5) *Schedule* 8 *part* VII [**3.13**]*)*
(continued) Fire resistance of timber floors.
NOTE   The term 'modified ½ hour' relates to item
No 7 in Table 1 to regulation E 1 which permits
reduced standards as regards passage of heat and flame
(but not as regards collapse) for upper floors in
purpose group I *(small residential).*

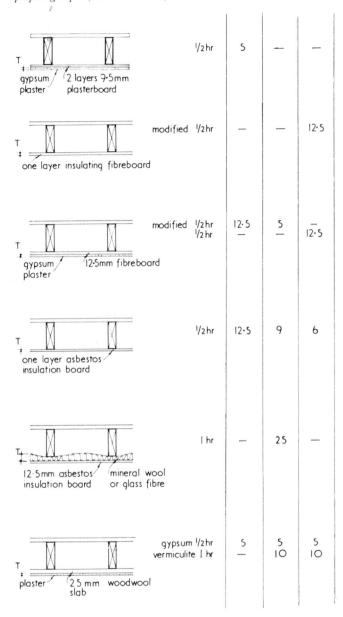

(Reg E 1(5) *Schedule* 8 *part* VIII [**3.13**]*)*
(continued) Fire resistance of concrete floors.
The diagrams and chart show thicknesses of solid
material for various types of floor construction to give
different periods of fire resistance
NOTE   The thicknesses of screeds can be included
but voids do not count.

NOTE   The right hand ends of bars indicate the
minimum thickness 'T' for each fire resistance period.

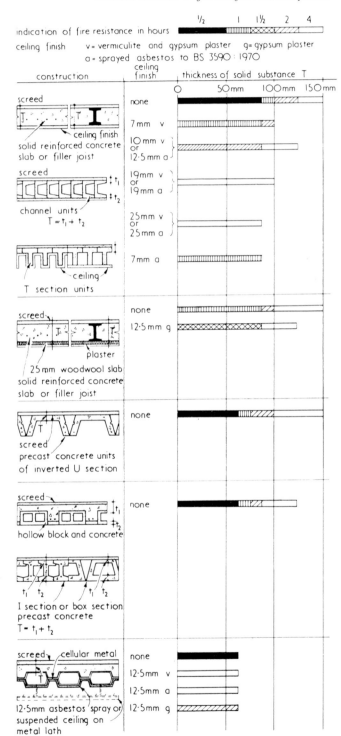

NOTE   The thickness of t and g boarding referred to
at the top of the 2nd and 3rd columns is minimum
'finished' thickness, corresponding to 'nominal'
thickness of about 20 mm and 25 mm respectively.
Part VII *also gives an alternative of 'an equivalent*
thickness of wood chipboard' but gives no guidance as
to how this should be determined. It will presumably
depend to some extent on the grade of chipboard used.

BS 476: Part 8: 1972   Fire tests on building materials

This contains the procedures to be adopted to determine the fire resistance of elements of construction as required by Building Regulations.

Generally the tests are made by exposing a sample to heat from a furnace which builds up temperature to a specified extent over a period of time (maximum 360 mins). The sample must be as representative as possible of actual construction including such joints and openings as will be present. It must also be conditioned, loaded and restrained at ends and sides to simulate site conditions.

Three criteria are determined:

Stability   Generally the time to collapse or serious deformation. (Note   Reloading is carried out 24 hours after the heating period).

Integrity   The development of cracks through which hot gases could pass, tested by using dry cotton wool pads up to 30 mm from the unexposed surface.

Insulation   By measuring the temperature of the unexposed face at frequent intervals. The mean temperature rise must not exceed 140°C. The test results are usually given as three figures being the period to failure under each of the three criteria eg stability 120, integrity 120, insulation 15, but with some elements not all the criteria are relevant. The Standard goes on to describe test methods for a variety of elements as follows.

1   Walls and partitions

These may be tested from one or both sides according to their possible exposure on site. The sample may include built in beams or columns or a door. The smallest sample must be 2.5 m × 2.5 m. The overall fire resistance is stated as the shortest of the three test criteria.

2   Floors and flat roofs

Ceiling finishes or suspended ceilings intended to contribute to the fire resistance must be included in the sample. The minimum size of the sample is 2.5 m wide by 4.0 m span and it must be loaded to reproduce the same maximum stresses as on site. The same restraint conditions are also to be simulated but if this is not possible it shall be simply supported. The furnace is situated below the sample. The same criteria are observed, but the sample is assumed to have failed in stability when deflection exceeds $1/30$.

3   Columns

The minimum height exposed is to be 3 m. Site conditions are to be simulated: eg if the column is to be part of a wall it shall be protected on the face(s) which will be protected by the wall. It must be loaded and restrained appropriately. It is exposed to heat from all radial directions and only the stability requirement is tested.

4   Beams

The sample is to be at least 4 m in length and to have a 75 mm concrete deck slab on top. It is exposed to the furnace on three sides unless intended to be protected by a suspended ceiling (see below).

It is judged on the time to failure in stability only and this is deemed to occur if the deflection exceeds $1/30$.

5   Suspended ceilings

The test is intended to assess the ability of such ceilings to protect structural steelwork supporting a floor slab and can also if need be, include the contribution made by the ceiling to the fire resistance of the supported floor.

The specimen has to be 2.5 m × 4.0 m minimum. The beams can be of solid or open web type weighing not less than 30 kg/m and covered by a lightweight aggregate concrete slab 130 mm thick. The support system must be as intended on site and any openings for vents, light fittings, etc, are to be included as well as the connected ducting. The assembly may be loaded or not, depending in whether deflection is likely to affect integrity.

Failure is presumed to occur when one or more panels become dislodged or the beam temperature exceeds a specified figure or deflection exceeds $1/30$.

Door and shutter assemblies

Minimum specimen size is 2.5 m × 2.5 m to represent the actual wall which will contain the door. The door must include all furniture and gaps between door and frame must be as expected in service and not less than 3 mm.

The door is tested from the side which will be exposed on site or if required to resist fire from both sides two samples are tested separately. The usual observations are made during the test and after cooling the ability of the door to be opened is checked.

The fire resistance is reported in accordance with the full three criteria but in some cases (if the door is glazed) the last one may be expressed as insulation = 0.

Glazing

This is tested in a similar way to door assemblies located in a construction to represent site conditions. Only the stability and integrity are tested, the latter by placing a maximum size on cracks (6 mm wide × 150 mm long).

A 3   Roofs

The standards required are given for each type of building in Sections 1 to 6 and are expressed in terms of designations determined by the test procedure specified in BS 476: Part 3: 1958. This is not the latest version, but the current version, published in 1975, is undergoing revision, and it appears that this is the reason why it has not so far been adopted. The test is designed to check the performance of the roof from the outside only. (NOTE   The latest version was not used in the 1976 Regulations either, although it must have been available at the time they were published). A note on BS 476: Part 3 is included below.

BS 476: Part 3: 1958 and 1975

In the 1958 standard two groups of letters, A to D, are used to express the results. The first letter represents penetration resistance and the second resistance to surface spread of flame. They are measured in separate tests.

The test is performed by applying a moving flame for 1 minute over a specified size of sample which is being subjected to radiant heat from a furnace designed to represent the exposure of a roof 7.5 m above ground to a fire in a building 13.5 m away, having a facade 15 m × 15 m with 50 per cent window opening. The test lasts 60 minutes following a 1 minute preliminary ignition test.

The designations are as follows:

First letter: penetration time

A   Not less than 1 hour.

B   Not less than 30 minutes.

C   Less than 30 minutes.

D   During the preliminary flame test.

Second letter: spread of flame

A   None.

B   Not more than 21 in (533.4 mm).

C   More than 21 in (533.4 mm).

D   Continues to burn for five minutes after withdrawl of test flame, or spreads more than 15 in (381 mm) during the preliminary test.

These designations are not used in the 1975 document and both criteria are determined by one test. The results are expressed by the letter X if the sample fails the preliminary ignition test, or P if it passes, followed by a number indicating the time before penetration occurred eg P60 means it did not occur in less than an hour. The extent of surface ignition (previously called spread of flame) is given in actual figures in the report, but no codified classification system is used.

The results are the mean of 3 samples and the equipment is arranged to simulate the slope of the roof on which the construction will be used. The sample may include a rooflight for which test results can also be given.

Notional designations

The table to A 3 supplies notional designations for some generic roof coverings. These are almost identical with those in Schedule 9 of the 1976 Regulations and are illustrated in diagrams [3.14, 3.15, 3.16, 3.17].

A 3 [**3.14**] *Part* I *pitched roofs covered with slates or tiles.*

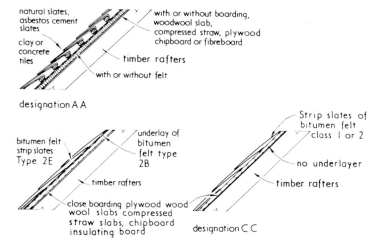

natural slates, asbestos cement slates

clay or concrete tiles

with or without boarding, woodwool slab, compressed straw, plywood chipboard or fibreboard

timber rafters

with or without felt

designation A A

bitumen felt strip slates Type 2E

underlay of bitumen felt type 2B

timber rafters

close boarding plywood wood wool slabs compressed straw slabs, chipboard insulating board

designation B B

Strip slates of bitumen felt class 1 or 2

no underlayer

timber rafters

designation C C

A 3 [**3.15**] *Part* II *pitched roofs covered with self-supporting sheets.*

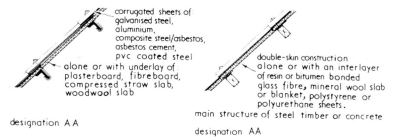

corrugated sheets of galvanised steel, aluminium, composite steel/asbestos, asbestos cement, pvc coated steel

alone or with underlay of plasterboard, fibreboard, compressed straw slab, woodwool slab

designation A A

double-skin construction alone or with an interlayer of resin or bitumen bonded glass fibre, mineral wool slab or blanket, polystyrene or polyurethane sheets.

main structure of steel timber or concrete

designation A A

Part IV (B) *pitched roofs covered with bitumen felt.*

A 3 [**3.16**] *Part* III *pitched or flat roofs covered with fully supported material.*

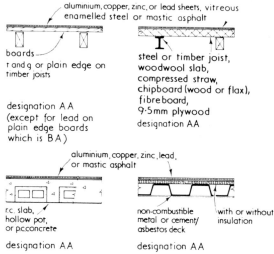

aluminium, copper, zinc, or lead sheets, vitreous enamelled steel or mastic asphalt

boards t and q or plain edge on timber joists

designation A A (except for lead on plain edge boards which is B A)

steel or timber joist, woodwool slab, compressed straw, chipboard (wood or flax), fibreboard, 9·5mm plywood designation A A

aluminium, copper, zinc, lead, or mastic asphalt

r.c. slab, hollow pot, or p.c.concrete

designation A A

non-combustible metal or cement/ asbestos deck

with or without insulation

designation A A

Part IV (A) *Flat roofs covered with bitumen felt. Any bitumen felt roofing applied to the deck-construction described below in the schedule for part* IV (B) *and having one of the following surface finishes may be deemed to be designated AA.*

1 Bitumen bedded stone chippings at least 12.5 mm deep
2 Bitumen bedded tiles of non-combustible material
3 Sand-cement screed
4 Macadam
NOTE   All references to bitumen felt roofing (or to bitumen felt strip slates in Part 1) are in relation to BS 747: 1977 (see below).

A 3 [3.17]   Notional designations of roof constructions. Part IV (B) roofs covered with bitumen felt

Details of Felt		Details of Deck		
Upper layers	Under layer (or layers)	Plywood 6 mm Wood flax Chipboard 12.5 mm T & G board 16 mm PE boards 19 mm (finished)	Compressed straw slab, screeded wood wool. Asbestos cement, aluminium or steel single or cavity deck (with or without fibreboard overlay)	Concrete or clay pot
1. Type 1E	Type 1B, min weight 1.3 Kg/m²	CC	AC	AB
2. Type 2E	Type 1B, min weight 1.3 Kg/m²	BB	AB	AB
3. Type 2E	Type 2B	AB	AB	AB
4. Type 3E	Type 3B or G	BC	AB*	AB
5. Single layer Type 1E		CC	AC*	AC

* NOTE   Compressed straw slabs with type 4 finishes are AC. Aluminium deck with type 5 finishes are CC. Two or three layer specifications are to be built up in accordance with CP 114: Part 3: 1970.

Note on BS 747: 1977 Specification for roofing felts

The Types specified in the table include 1E, 2E, 3E in conjunction with underlayers 1B, 2B, 3B or 3G.

The numbers 1, 2, 3, 4 indicate the base material as follows:

1 Mineral fibre, 2 Asbestos fibre, 3 Glass fibre, 4 Sheathing felt.

The letters indicate the type and hence the use as follows:

B   Fine granule faced both sides

E   Fine granule faced one side, mineral granules other side

F   Reinforced with hessian

G/H   Venting base layers.

Type B are normal underlayers including a top layer to be faced with chippings.

Type E are for finishing layers on sloping roofs

Type F are for sarking and vapour barriers below insulation

Types G/H are for bottom layers on roofs where partial bonding is required for ventilation.

Types 4A and B (not mentioned in the table) are dimensionally stable for underlayers below mastic asphalt and sarking below sheet metal roofs.

Wall and ceiling linings

A 4 to **A 7**   The incidence of flame spread over walls and ceilings is controlled by using materials which meet given performances under BS test procedures.

BS 476 is by now a creature of many parts each dealing with a different aspect of fire spread. Six of these parts are used in Appendix A. Parts 8 and 3 deal with fire resistance of elements and roofs and have already been described.

Parts 7 and 6 are used in this section (A 4 to A 12).

Parts 4 and 11 are used in the next section dealing with the combustibility of materials (A 13/A 14).

BS 476: Part 7 deals with surface spread of flame and defines 4 classes. Class 1, 2, 3 and 4 Class 4 is not used in Building Regulations. There is however an additional class 0 and the specification of this requires reference to fire propagation indices defined by test procedures laid down in BS 476: Part 6. The test procedures used in both these standards are described later.

A 8   Class 0 which restricts both the spread of flame across, and the heat released from a surface is defined as:

(*a*)   Composed throughout of materials of limited combustibility or

(*b*)   A class 1 material with a fire propagation index I of not more than 12 and sub-index i_1 of not more than 6.

A 9   The face of a thermoplastic material should only be taken as class 0 if it either:

(*a*)   Is fully bonded to a substrate which is not thermoplastic and the composite material complies with A 8(*b*) above or

(*b*)   It complies with A 8(*b*) above and forms the lining to a class 0 non-thermoplastic surface (for example, a lining material attached to a plaster wall surface).

A 11/12   Thermoplastic means a material with a softening point not higher than 120°C when tested to BS 2782 Method 102C: 1970 or 145°C when tested to BS 2782: Part 1: Method 120A: 1976: see later. There are concessions for these materials if they cannot be tested for surface spread of flame because of their low softening point: see Appendix B.

A 10   The ratings of some widely used materials or products is given in the Table to A 10 which is reproduced over.

Table to A 10   Typical ratings of some generic materials or products*

Classification	Material
Class 0 (this includes Class 1 materials)	1 any material of limited combustibility. cored products listed in Table to A 14 must meet the test requirements given in paragraph A 8(b). 2 brickwork, blockwork, concrete and ceramic tiles. 3 plasterboard (painted or not) with or without an air gap or fibrous or cellular insulating material behind. 4 wood wool slabs. 5 mineral fibre tiles or sheets with cement or resin binding.
Class 3**	6 timber or plywood with density more than 400 kg/m^3 painted or unpainted. 7 wood particle board or hardboard, either treated or painted.

NOTES

* Plastics materials are not included in this table because of their range of performance which is dependent on their formulation. Details of ratings to BS 476. Parts 6 and 7 are given in the documents referred to below.

** Timber products listed under Class 3 can be brought up to Class 1 with appropriate proprietary treatments.

The results of tests on proprietary materials may be found in:
BRE Report – *Results of surface spread of flame tests on building products*, HMSO 1976.
Fire test results on building products: surface spread of flame, Fire Protection Association, revised 1981, or manufacturers' or trade association literature.
Similar test results for fire propagation can be obtained from the same sources.

Addendum to Appendix A   Internal Surfaces

The actual requirements regarding the class of internal surfaces permitted vary according to building type and are included in Sections 1 to 6. This inhibits the making of any general comments or comparisons as in the previous guide to the 1976 Regulations. As it was felt that an overall picture, with examples, would still be useful an extract from that guide is reproduced here. The table below is now in effect a condensation of the tables in Sections 1 to 6 and clearly demonstrates what an ungainly beast Part B has become in its present form.

Requirements   Surfaces of walls and ceilings

Residential purpose group	Small rooms (max 4m^2)	Other rooms	Circulation and protected shafts
I house of not more than 2 storeys)	3	1	1
II (institutional)	1	0	0
III (Flats, other residential and houses over 2 storeys)	3	1	0
All other groups	*(max 30 m^2)*		
IV to VIII	3	1	0

NOTE
Ceilings in group I may be class 3 throughout and in group II may be class 1 in other rooms (bigger than 4m^2)

Relaxations (walls)
Some areas of wall surface (but not of ceiling surface) may be of a lower standard than that shown in the table provided that they are not less than class 3 and do not exceed:

(a)   Half the floor area of the room.

(b)   20 m^2 in groups I, II and III.

(c)   60 m^2 in groups IV to VIII.

These areas of wall are inclusive of any glazing, but additional to the unglazed areas of doors, frames (including window frames), fireplace surrounds, fitted furniture or trim (architraves, skirtings and so on).

It may be noted that in small rooms the requirement is only class 3 in any case, so that the relaxation is really necessary only in the larger rooms, except for group II (institutional buildings) where the relaxation with regard to small rooms would permit a maximum of 2 m^2 of class 3 wall lining.

In rooms generally the arithmetic shows that in small domestic sizes the relaxation would permit an area roughly equal to one wall to be lined with class 3 material, whereas in larger public rooms of limited height, where the floor to wall ratio is much greater, roughly half the perimeter of the room could be so treated. Two examples are illustrated in [3.18].

Sections 1 to 6 [**3.18**]
Relaxations to restrictions of surface spread of flame requirement (walls).

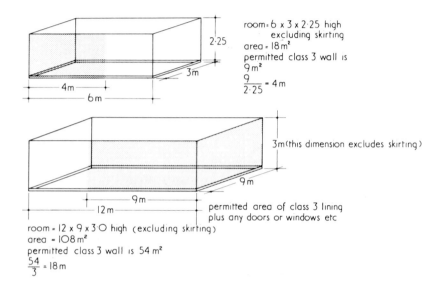

BS 476: Part 7: 1971

This test is designed for the classification of the surfaces of walls and ceilings as regards their tendency to support the spread of flame across them. The test is applied to a sample consisting of an assembly of materials as they will be used in practice. Six sample are tested each 230 mm × 900 mm x not more than 50 mm thick. The sample is mounted *at right angles* to a radiant panel of specified output and a gas flame applied to the lower corner next to the panel. The flame spread is measured for 10 minutes along a line 75 mm above the bottom edge and in particular after 1½ and 10 minutes.

The classifications are as follows:

Class	Flame spread after (mm)	
	1½ mins	*10 mins*
1	165	165
2	215	455
3	265	710
4	exceeding class 3 limits	

The results must be achieved by all six specimens except for a small tolerance on one specimen only.

BS 476: Part 6: 1968 and 1981   Tests for fire propagation of products

This specifies a method of test for a flat material, composite or assembly. The result is expressed as a fire propagation index to provide a comparative measure of its contribution to the growth of a fire. It is intended for the assessment of wall and ceiling linings. The test is carried out by subjecting three samples to heat from a combination of gas and electric sources and measuring the rise in temperature of the emanating gases over specific periods of time. This shows the contribution of heat made by the material being tested.

The final result is expressed as a fire propagation index which is an average of the three samples tested, and also a combination of the recorded results taken during the first 3 minutes, the next 7 minutes and the next 10 minutes (20 minutes in all). The combined index is denoted as I and the sub-indices (of which it is a mean) as i_1 i_2 and i_3. (Note up to 5 samples may be tested to obtain 3 valid results).

NOTE   Any reference used to substantiate the surface spread of flame rating must be checked to ensure it is applicable to the construction used. Small detail differences such as to thickness, substrate, fixings, adhesive etc may have significant effect on the rating.

Materials of limited combustibility

A 13/14   This is a new term used for the first time in the new Regulations. It is based on the use of BS 476: Part 11: 1982 which in effect assesses the amount of combustible material within a largely noncombustible product, and is really a more sophisticated version of BS 476: Part 4: 1970 which was, and is still used for defining the term non-combustible.

The term 'materials of limited combustibility' is used throughout Sections 1 to 6 and the Appendices: it has here been shortened to MOLC. It is explained in A 13 however that this term includes within itself a special category defined as 'non-combustible.' Only these materials may be used where there is a specific requirement for non-combustibility. This includes all principal elements of structure and a few other items which are listed in the table to A 13 below.

The table to A 14 lists the situations which require only limited combustibility. This being so it is difficult to see why the unwieldy term represented by MOLC is always used even though what is really meant is non-combustible. It seems to be a quite unnecessarily devious approach.

The two tables are included below and contain an exact definition of the two categories. Also included are some explanatory notes on Parts 4 and 11 of BS 476.

Table to A 13   Use of non-combustible materials

Use	*Material*
1 solid construction forming External walls, Separating walls, Compartment walls, Compartment floors and Protecting structure where there is provision in Section 1 to 6 for them to be constructed of materials of limited combustibility.	(a), (b), (c) or (d)
2 frames of hollow elements of structure referred to above	
3 loadbearing elements of structure forming part of, or which carry, any element of structure referred to in 1 or 2 above.	
4 supports and fixing of any suspended ceiling meeting the provisions given in the Table to A 2 (Types B, C and D).	
5 refuse chutes referred to in Appendix D, paragraph D6.	
6 flues meeting the requirements shown in Appendix F, Para F 19.	

NOTES

(a) Any material which when tested to BS 476: Part 11 does not flame and there is no rise in temperature on either the centre (specimen) or furnace thermocouples.

(b) Totally inorganic materials such as concrete, fired clay, ceramics, metals, plaster and masonry containing not more than 1 per cent by weight or volume of organic material. (Use in buildings of combustible metals such as magnesium/aluminium alloys should be assessed in each individual case).

(c) Concrete bricks or blocks meeting BS 6073: Part 1: 1981.

(d) Products classified as non-combustible under BS 476: Part 4: 1970.

Table to A 14   Use of materials of limited combustibility

Use		Material
1	insulating linings to hollow elements of structure referred to under item 2 in the Table to A 13.	(a), (b) or (c)
2	insulating linings to elements of structure referred to under item 3 in Table to A 13.	
3	class 0 materials meeting the provisions in paragraph A 8(a).	
4	roof coverings meeting the provisions:	
	(a) given in Note 1 of the tables for Limitations on roof construction in Sections 1 to 6.	
	(b) given in Appendix B, Table to B 3.	
	(c) shown in Appendix C, diagram to C 2.	
	(d) shown in Appendix G, diagram to G 7.	
5	roof slabs meeting the provisions shown in Appendix C, diagram to C 2(b).	
6	cavity barriers meeting the provisions of Appendix G, paragraph G 8.	
7	stairways where there is provision in Sections 1 to 6 for them to be constructed of materials of limited combustibility.	
8	Ceiling tiles/panels of any fire protecting suspended ceiling meeting the provisions given in Table 2 to A 2. (p. 116).	
9	insulation used in the cavity of hollow elements of structure referred to in 1 above, or behind linings referred to in 2 above.	(a), (b), (c) or (d)
10	insulation above any suspended ceiling meeting the provisions given in Table 2 to A 2 (Type D).	

NOTES

(a) Any non-combustible material listed in Table to A 13.

(b) Any material of density 300 kg/m^3 or more, which when tested to BS 476: Part 11, does not flame and the rise in temperature on the furnace thermocouple is not more than 20°C.

(c) Any material with a non-combustible core of 8 mm thick or more, having combustible facings (on one or both sides) not more than 0.5 mm thick. (Where a flame spread rating is specified, these materials must also meet the appropriate test requirements).

(d) Any material of density less than 300 kg/m^3, when when tested to BS 476: Part II, does not flame for more than 10 seconds and the rise in temperature on the centre (specimen) thermocouple is not more than 35°C and on the furnace thermocouple is not more than 25°C.

BS 476: Part 4: 1970 Non-combustibility tests

The test is made by heating a sample in a furnace and materials classified as non-combustible are those which make little or no thermal contribution to the furnace and do not produce a flame (parameters are specified). Three samples are tested. The test can be applied to coated materials.

The sample is tested over a period of 20 minutes in a furnace temperature of 750°C (±10).

BS 476: Part 11: 1982 Assessing the heat emission from building materials

This is the first of a new series for evaluating the behaviour of buildings materials in a fire. It gives a way of expressing results, but does not specify acceptance criteria, which depend upon the intended conditions of use (the Approved Document states the criteria required). It is designed for assessing simple materials, natural or artifically mixed, but not for combinations such as laminates. The test is made on a small cylinder of the material, placed in a cylindrical furnace with provision for measuring the temperature in the centre of the sample. The period of the test is generally until a stable temperature situation has been reached or 120 minutes maximum.

Three criteria are reported which are the mean of five tested specimens:

1	The total of periods of sustained flaming (exceeding 5 seconds each).
2	The rise in furnace temperature (as a result of heat contributed by the sample).
3	The rise in the temperature in the sample.

Limitations on these figures are used for classifying notional noncombustibility in Appendix A.

Appendix B   Concessions for plastics materials

The authors of this Appendix have taken certain provisions from 3 of the old Regulations and put them together. This really make good sense since they are all concerned with concessions for plastics.

The provisions were contained in Regulations E 15(4) Surface flame spread on ceilings, E 16 Exceptions permitting the use of plastics materials and E 17(6) Roofs – use of glass or plastics.

It is set out as follows:

B 1   Plastics materials having lower surface spread classifications than required by Sections 1 to 6 may be used for windows, rooflights and suspended ceilings in certain circumstances which are set out in B 2, 3 and 4.

The types of plastics which may be used are classified in accordance with tests in BS 2782. The requirements are given in B 5, 6 and 7 and to assist the reader a description of the BS tests is given at the end.

B 2   Windows to rooms may be glazed with a single layer of rigid PVC sheet described in B 5. NOTE   As there is no mention of circulation spaces, only rooms, it must be presumed that windows in such spaces must have glass in them.

B 3   Rooflights of plastics materials may be used in the circumstances described in the table to B 3.

B 3 [**3.19**] *Conditions allowing closer spacing for rooflights (See 2(c) (d) in table).*

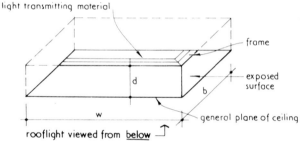

The exposed surface (except for the roof light frame) must be of a class no lower than that of the surrounding ceiling and dimension d not less than ¼ b or w which ever is the greater

Table to B 3   Concessions for rooflights of plastic materials

Material, or minimum surface spread of frame on lower side	Space which rooflight serves	Limitations			For rooflight with external surface of		
		Maximum area of each rooflight [m²]	Rooflight area as percentage of floor area of space in which rooflight situated [%]	Separation of rooflight by material of limited combustibility [m]	Rigid pvc as paragraph B5	AD, BD, CA, CB, CC, CD or no designation*	DA, DB, DC or DD
					Minimum distance from any point on the boundary [m]		
1 Rigid pvc as paragraph B5	any space (except a protected shaft)	no limit	no limit	no limit	6†	not applicable	not applicable
2 Class 3	(a) balcony, verandah, carport, covered way or loading bay which has at least one longer side wholly or permanently open, or detached swimming pool.	no limit	no limit	no limit	not applicable	6	22

Table to B 3   Concessions for rooflights of plastic materials

Material, or minimum surface spread of frame on lower side	Space which rooflight serves	*Limitations*			For rooflight with external surface of		
		Maximum area of each rooflight [m²]	Rooflight area as percentage of floor area of space in which rooflight situated [%]	Separation of rooflight by material of limited combustibility [m]	Rigid pvc as paragraph B5	AD, BD, CA, CB, CC, CD or no designation*	DA, DB, DC or DD
					Minimum distance from any point on the boundary [m]		
	(b) garage, conservatory or outbuilding with a maximum floor area of 40 m²	no limit	no limit	no limit	not applicable	6	22
	(c) circulation space** (d) room in a** Residential Assembly, Office or Shop purpose group	5	no limit	2.8 minimum (if rooflight complies with limits in Diagram to B 3. 3.5 minimum (if not)	not applicable	6	22
	(e) room in an** industrial or other non-residential purpose group	5	20 per cent maximum (evenly distributed)	1.8 minimum	not applicable	6	22

NOTES

*   A material which cannot be designated because of its low softening temperature.

†   No limit in the case of any space described in column (2), item 2(a) or (b).

**   Single skin material only

Rooflights with external designations shown in the last two columns must be separated from other similar lights by material of limited combustibility.

B 4   Suspended ceilings in rooms and circulation spaces may have one or more panels of PVC as defined in B 6 or other plastics as defined in B 7. The permitted sizings and spacings for each type are illustrated in the diagrams [3.20, 3.21].

B 4 [**3.20**] *Concessions permitting the use of ceiling panels of plastic material as* B 7.

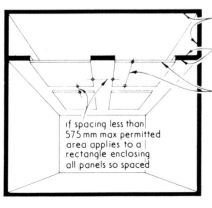

surfaces of enclosing space above ceiling and upper and lower surfaces of normal ceiling construction to be of a class not lower than required by Sections 1 to 6

no side to exceed 5 m in length

for max permitted area of panels see table below

thickness (or aggregate thickness if more than one sheet) not to exceed 3 mm

if spacing less than 575 mm max permitted area applies to a rectangle enclosing all panels so spaced

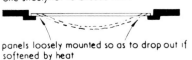

panels loosely mounted so as to drop out if softened by heat

	Room	Circulation space
Maximum area	4m²	2m²
Maximum percentage of floor area		
Residential and Assembly groups	30	15
Other buildings	50	15

B 4 [**3.21**] *Concessions permitting the use of ceiling panels of plastic material as* B 6.

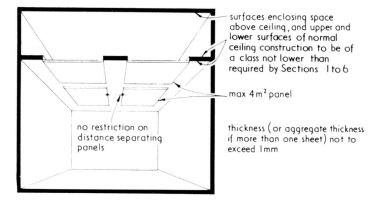

surfaces enclosing space above ceiling, and upper and lower surfaces of normal ceiling construction to be of a class not lower than required by Sections 1 to 6

max 4 m² panel

no restriction on distance separating panels

thickness (or aggregate thickness if more than one sheet) not to exceed 1 mm

Types of plastic materials

The terms used in this Appendix can be confusing with regard to just what is meant by thermoplastics, plastics, non-thermoplastics etc. The exact composition of these materials is not however important to the designer so that in this guide they are often simply referred to as plastics, of which PVC is one type.

B 5   Rigid PVC if tested to BS 2782: Method 508A: 1970: the test flame should not reach the first mark and the duration of flaming or afterglow should not exceed 5 seconds after removal of the burner.

B 6   PVC if tested to:

(*a*)   BS 2782: Method 508C: 1970, or BS 2782: Part 1: Method 140D: 1980, the distance of travel of the flame should not be more than 75 mm, or

(*b*)   BS 2782: Method 508D: 1970, or BS 2782: Part 1: Method 140E: 1982 –

   (i)   the specimen should not flame or glow for more than 5 seconds,

   (ii)   any material dropped from the specimen should not continue to burn after reaching the base of test apparatus,

   (iii)   charring or scorching should not extend over more than 20% of the area of the underside of the specimen, and

   (iv)   the length of the charred or scorched edge on the underside of the specimen should not be more than 50 mm.

Other plastics

B 7   If a specimen with a thickness of 3 mm is tested to BS 2782: Method 508A: 1970, the rate of burning should not be more than 50 mm a minute.

BS 2782   Methods of testing plastics

The whole of BS 2782 consists of methods of testing plastics for various properties. They are very numerous, 150 at least, but the Regulations are concerned only with those dealing with thermal properties (generally Part 1). These have numbers starting with 1. The inclusion of Method 508A is because it was originally allocated to Part 5 of the 1970 edition *Miscellaneous methods* and has not so far been reissued with a 1 prefix.

The 1970 edition was issued as a bound volume containing collected material from the period 1965–68. It had 5 parts. In 1975 a new general instruction and foreword was issued followed by a series of methods issued separately which now largely replace the 1970 issue which has been largely withdrawn, although some of the methods are still referred to in the AD as alternatives to the latest Part 1 numbers.

Methods 120A to 120E 1976

These are designed to determine the softening point of thermoplastic materials (NOTE   Appendix A also refers to Method 102C 1970 although this has been superseded. This continued reference to outdated methods is frequently found and is clearly to avoid existing materials which have already passed a test having to be retested every time a test method is changed).

The method employs a loaded rod placed on a sample which is slowly heated up in a liquid and the temperature recorded when the tip has penetrated a certain distance into the sample (1 mm in 120A and 0.1 mm in 102C). Two or more samples are taken until a result not more than 2°C apart is achieved and the mean taken.

Methods D and E use quicker heating up times and are less accurate.

Method 140D 1980
Replaces 508C: 1970. It is used to determine the flammability of thin flexible PVC sheet. The sample is a long strip stretched over a semi-circular frame. One end is exposed to a precise amount of burning ethanol and the distance over which the sample has burned is measured. Six pieces are tested.

Method 140E: 1982
Replaces 508D: 1970. Used for testing light bulk materials (eg polystyrene) in pieces up to 50 mm thick. The sample 150 mm square is mounted at 45° above a cup containing a specified quantity of ethanol which is then ignited. After the flame dies out the period of time for which the sample glows or flames is recorded. Also recorded is whether any material dropping onto the base continues to burn, the percentage of the area of the underside that is charred and the length of any charring which reaches any edge of the sample.

Method 508A: 1970
As yet there has been no replacement for this test for flammability, but an amendment was issued in 1974 (AMD 1524).
The specimen is 150 mm long × 13 mm wide. Two marks are made 25 mm from each end (100 mm apart). A specified intensity of flame is applied to one end for 10 seconds and the time is taken after that for the flame to travel 100 m past the first mark is recorded. From this the rate of burning in mm per minute is calculated. If the flame does not reach the first mark this is recorded and also the duration of any flame or afterglow after the removal of the burner.

Appendix C   Separating walls

C 1   Separating walls required by Sections 1 to 6 must:
(*a*)   Form a complete vertical barrier between buildings including roof spaces and basements, if any.
(*b*)   Have the appropriate fire resistance with a minimum of 1 hour
(*c*)   Be constructed of MOLC where required by Sections 1 to 6.
C 2   At a junction with a roof the wall should be taken above the roof or alternatively the roof construction should resist fire spread. The diagram shows three acceptable methods of achieving this, one of which is of universal application, the other two relating to specific types of building.
C 3   Junctions with external walls should be bonded or fire-stopped (see diagram [3.23]).

C 2 [**3.22**] *Separating wall penetrating roof.*

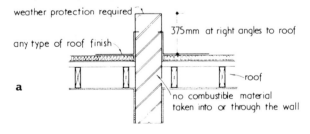

C 3 [**3.23**] *Junction of separating wall with external wall.*

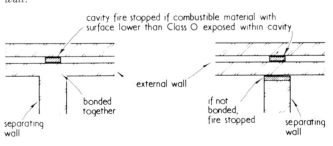

C 4   Combustible material should not be taken through or across the ends or top of the wall so as to impair its resistance to the spread of fire. The diagram to C 2 however [3.24], illustrates the circumstances where some combustible material may be carried over.

C 2 [**3.24**] *Alternative methods of treating junction of separating wall with roof:*
b   *applicable to all buildings;*
c   *when both buildings are residential, office or assembly buildings*
d   *when both buildings are houses up to three storeys*

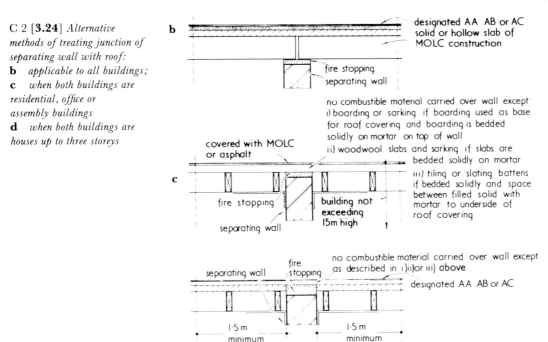

C 5   There should be no openings in a separating wall except as illustrated in diagram [3.25].

C 5 [**3.25**] *Permissible openings in separating wall.*

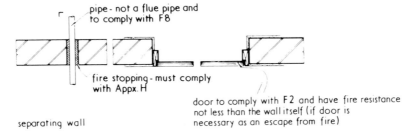

Appendix D   Compartment walls and floors

D 1   Compartment walls and floors required by Sections 1 to 6 must:
(*a*)   Form a complete barrier to fire between compartments.
(*b*)   Have the appropriate fire resistance.
(*c*)   If the fire resistance required is 1 hour or more, be constructed of MOLC where needed by Sections 1 to 6.
D 2   A compartment wall used to form a 'separated part' of a building (see general notes at beginning) must extend the full height of the building in one continuous vertical plane. The effect of this arrangement is illustrated in diagram [3.26].

D 2 [**3.26**] *Compartment wall forming 'separated part'.*

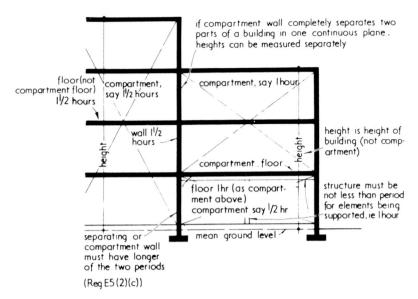

D 3   At a junction with a roof the rules are the same as for separating walls (see diagram to C 2 [3.24]).

D 4   Where compartment walls or floors meet other compartment walls, external walls, separating walls or protecting structure they must be bonded or fire-stopped.

D 5   Combustible materials carried through or across the top or ends of compartment walls or floors must not impair the fire resistance of the barrier. Combustible material in roofs carried over the top is permitted in the same circumstances as in C 4.

Timber beams, joists, purlins or rafters may be carried through a masonry or concrete wall if the necessary openings are as small as possible and fire-stopped. Trusses carried across compartment walls must be designed so that collapse due to fire in one compartment does not cause collapse in another.

D 6   The only openings permitted through compartment walls or floors in addition to such as are required to accommodate a protected shaft are those illustrated in diagrams [3.27, 3.28]. More detailed information is available in Appendix F.

D 6 [**3.27**] *Openings through compartment walls or floors.*

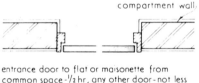

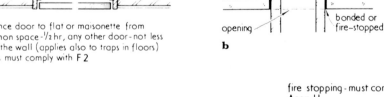

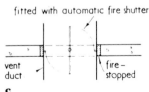

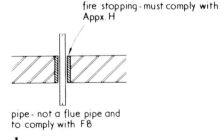

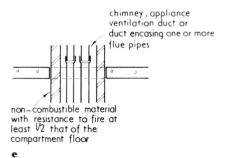

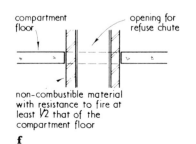

D 6 [**3.28**] *Chimneys and ducts passing through or forming part of a compartment wall or floor.*

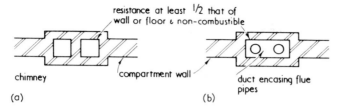

chimney

(a)

resistance at least ¹/2 that of wall or floor & non-combustible

compartment wall

duct encasing flue pipes

(b)

Appendix E   Protected shafts

E 1   Protected shafts required to comply with Sections 1 to 6 must:

(*a*)   Form a complete barrier to fire spread between the compartments which they connect.

(*b*)   Have the appropriate fire resistance required by Sections 1 to 6.

(*c*)   If the fire resistance required is 1 hour or more be constructed of MOLC where required by Sections 1 to 6.

Where they are not enclosed by other elements protected shafts are contained within protecting structure. Just what and what is not defined as 'protecting structure' is explained in diagram [3.29].

E 2   Where a protected shaft for which the fire resistance required does not exceed 1 hour is approached by way of a corridor or lobby the division between the lobby and the shaft may be glazing with ½ hour fire resistance (stability and integrity only) if the lobby enclosure also has ½ hour fire resistance. This is illustrated in a diagram taken from the Approved Document [3.30]. The theory behind this is no doubt, that taking the screen and the lobby/corridor walls together, there is still a total of 1 hour's resistance between the shaft and any possible fire source. The origin of this concession is not clear because it does not appear to be contained in the 1976 Regulations.

E 1 [**3.29**] *Definition of enclosing surfaces of protected shafts which are referred to as 'protecting structure'.*

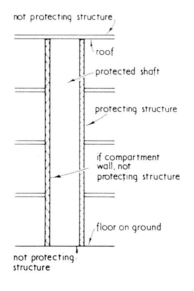

not protecting structure

roof

protected shaft

protecting structure

if compartment wall, not protecting structure

floor on ground

not protecting structure

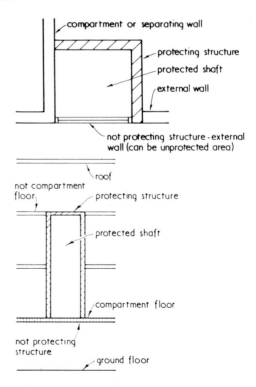

compartment or separating wall

protecting structure

protected shaft

external wall

not protecting structure - external wall (can be unprotected area)

roof

not compartment floor

protecting structure

protected shaft

compartment floor

not protecting structure

ground floor

E 2 [**3.30**] *Glazed screen separating protected shaft from lobby or corridor.*

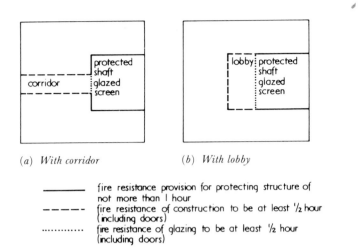

(a) *With corridor*   (b) *With lobby*

—————   fire resistance provision for protecting structure of not more than 1 hour
– – – –   fire resistance of construction to be at least ½ hour (including doors)
············   fire resistance of glazing to be at least ½ hour (including doors)

E 3   A protected shaft is defined as a stairway, lift, escalator, chute, duct or other shaft which enables persons, things and air to pass from one compartment to another. This can include pipes and ducts and sanitary accommodation may also be contained within protecting structure.

This is presumably because they are places of low fire risk.

E 4   There are rules as to the presence of pipes and vent ducts. These are shown in diagram [3.31]. In addition any pipe in a shaft carrying natural gas must be of screwed steel or all-welded steel to comply with the Gas Safety Regulations, SI 1972 No. 1178.

E 5/E 6   A shaft carrying a lift or a gas pipe must be adequately ventilated to the outside air (see diagram [3.31]).

E 7   Certain openings are permitted in protecting structure and these are also illustrated in diagram [3.31]. Some of the information shown here is actually contained in Appendix F (having been separated out from regulations E 8/9 and 10 of the 1976 edition) which deals with openings generally. The wisdom of such a separation is somewhat doubtful since it is just another case where cross reference is needed. Where a shaft is enclosed by other than protecting structure (compartment walls, separating walls etc) the openings in them are controlled by the rules for these elements.

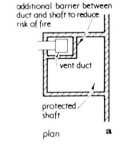

additional barrier between duct and shaft to reduce risk of fire

vent duct

protected shaft

plan   **a**

E 7 [**3.31**] *Diagrams illustrating permitted openings etc in protected shafts:*

a   *shaft containing vent duct, and other items;*
b   *lift shaft;*
c   *stairway.*

NOTE   Fire resisting doors to comply with Appendix F. If in flats, other residential, assembly or office building and above ground, they must provide ½ hour

fire resistance. In other cases they must provide half the resistance of the containing wall and never less than ½ hour. For lift doors see Appendix F.

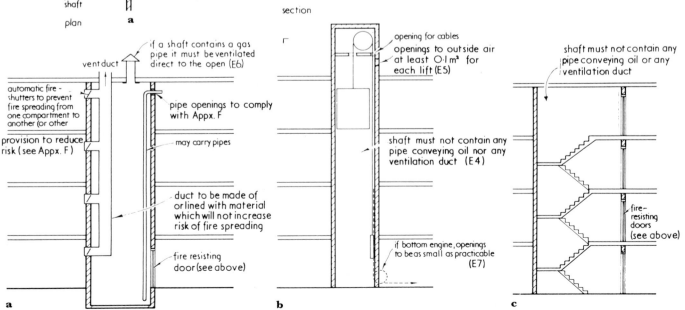

section

a

vent duct

automatic fire-shutters to prevent fire spreading from one compartment to another (or other

provision to reduce risk (see Appx. F)

if a shaft contains a gas pipe it must be ventilated direct to the open (E6)

pipe openings to comply with Appx. F

may carry pipes

duct to be made of or lined with material which will not increase risk of fire spreading

fire resisting door (see above)

b

opening for cables
openings to outside air at least 0·1 m² for each lift (E5)

shaft must not contain any pipe conveying oil nor any ventilation duct (E4)

if bottom engine, openings to be as small as practicable (E7)

c

shaft must not contain any pipe conveying oil or any ventilation duct

fire-resisting doors (see above)

Appendix F   Protection of openings

This appendix describes the precautions to be taken to protect any necessary openings in the various fire barriers.
They include openings for:
Doors
Pipes
Ventilation ducts
Flues etc.

Doors

F 2   All such doors must have the fire resistance stated in Appendix A, but if two doors are fitted in the same opening it is adequate if the required period can be obtained by both together.

F 3   All must be fitted with an automatic self-closing device capable of closing the door from any angle and against any latch which is fitted. However, in certain circumstances doors without self-closing devices may be fitted to protected shafts which only contain a lift. The exact situation is explained in a diagram taken from the Approved Document itself, diagram [3.32].

F 3 [**3.32**] *Protected shafts (alternative provisions for doors to a lift shaft)*

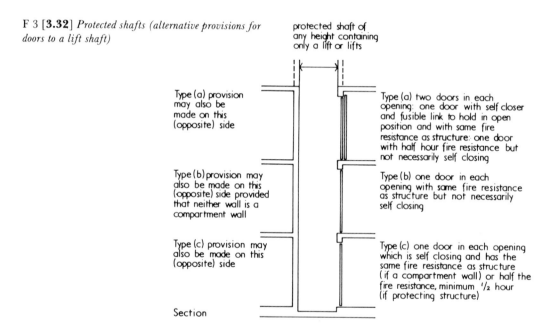

protected shaft of any height containing only a lift or lifts

Type (a) provision may also be made on this (opposite) side

Type (a) two doors in each opening: one door with self closer and fusible link to hold in open position and with same fire resistance as structure: one door with half hour fire resistance but not necessarily self closing

Type (b) provision may also be made on this (opposite) side provided that neither wall is a compartment wall

Type (b) one door in each opening with same fire resistance as structure but not necessarily self closing

Type (c) provision may also be made on this (opposite) side

Type (c) one door in each opening which is self closing and has the same fire resistance as structure (if a compartment wall) or half the fire resistance, minimum ½ hour (if protecting structure)

Section

F 4   If self closing devices are considered a hindrance to normal usage the door may be held back by either:
(*a*)   A fusible link (except as in F 6(*b*)) or
(*b*)   If the doors can be opened manually, by electro-magnetic or electromechanical devices susceptible to smoke.

F 5   Hinges must be of a material with a melting point not below 800°C (such as steel). Other types may be used where the assembly has been verified by test.

F 6   Doors on escape routes must be:
(*a*)   Capable of being easily opened by hand.
(*b*)   Held open only by an electro-magnetic or electro-mechanical device susceptible to smoke.

F 7   Where two fire resisting doors are fitted in the same opening on an escape route, one may have an automatic self-closing device and be held open by a fusible link if the other can be opened by hand and has at least a ½ hour fire resistance (see diagram [3.33]). This seems a little strange as one would have thought that the door which is held by a fusible link should also be capable of being opened by hand in case it has already closed with some frantic escapee on the wrong side.

This is a considerable simplification of the old regulation E 11 which contained a number of rules about door swings in some domestic situations and in protecting structure. Also omitted are the definitions of 'automatic self-closing device' and 'electromagnetic and electro-mechanical devices'. On reading further however these are to be found within the list of definitions in Appendix L at the end. It seems a strange aberration to put these away from the only place where they have any relevance, which shows once again that avoidance of the need for cross-reference was not one of the authors' objectives. For convenience they are included here.

'Automatic self-closing device' does not include rising butt hinges unless the door is:

(*a*)   To a flat or maisonette, or

(*b*)   In a cavity barrier, or

(*c*)   Between a dwelling house and its garage.

'Electro-magnetic or electro-mechanical device susceptible to smoke' means a device which will allow a door held open by it to close automatically in the event of each and any one of the following:

(*a*)   Detection of smoke by automatic apparatus suitable in the nature, quality and location, and

(*b*)   Operation of a hand operated switch fitted in a suitable position, and

(*c*)   Failure of electricity supply to the device, apparatus or switch, and

(*d*)   Operation of the fire alarm system if any.

F 7 [**3.33**] *Doors on escape routes.*

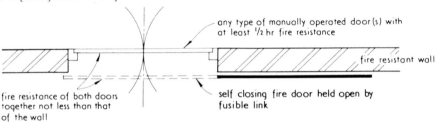

Pipes   **F 8**   Pipes may penetrate certain fire barriers in the circumstances illustrated in diagram [3.34].

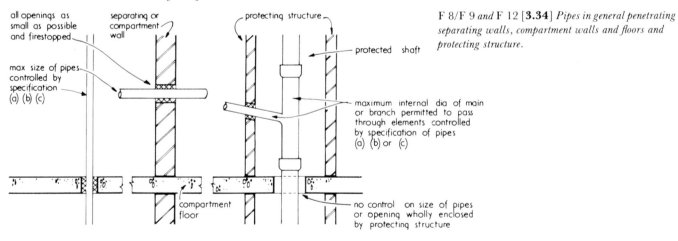

F 8/F 9 *and* F 12 [**3.34**] *Pipes in general penetrating separating walls, compartment walls and floors and protecting structure.*

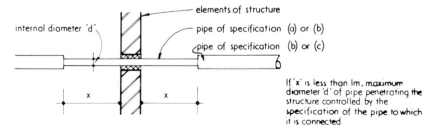

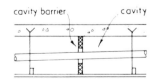

F 12 Change of pipe specification

F 9 In such cases either:

(*a*)   A proprietary system should be used which has been shown by test to maintain the fire resistance of the barrier or

(*b*)   The nominal internal diameter should not exceed that in the table below, the openings should be as small as possible and fire-stopped.

(NOTE   Alternative (*a*) has been added since the 1976 Regulations).

Table to F 9   Maximum nominal internal diameter of pipes

	Pipe material and maximum nominal internal diameter [mm]		
Situation	*Non-combustible material[1] (a)*	*Lead, aluminium or aluminium alloy, asbestos-cement or upvc[2] (b)*	*Any other material (c)*
1 structure (but not a Separating Wall) enclosing a Protected Shaft which is not a stairway or lift shaft.	160	110	40
2 Separating Wall between dwelling houses, or Compartment Wall or Compartment Floor between flats.	160	160 (stack pipe)[3] 110 (branch pipe)[3]	40
3 any other situation	160	40	40

NOTES

[1] A non-combustible material (such as cast iron or steel) which if exposed to a temperature of 800°C will not soften nor fracture to the extent that flame or hot gases will pass through the wall of the pipe.

[2] upvc pipes complying with BS 4514: 1983 upvc pipe complying with BS 5255: 1976

[3] Pipes forming part of an above ground drainage system and enclosed as shown in Diagram to F 10.

F 10   There are concessions for pipes which form part of an above ground drainage system in houses, flats and maisonettes only. These are also illustrated by diagram [3.35].

F 10 [**3.35**] *Pipes in casings forming part of above ground drainage systems in houses, flats or maisonettes.*

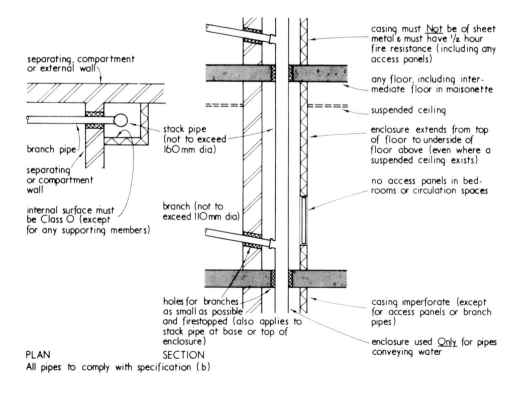

separating, compartment or external wall

branch pipe

separating or compartment wall

internal surface must be Class O (except for any supporting members)

stack pipe (not to exceed 160 mm dia)

branch (not to exceed 110 mm dia)

holes for branches as small as possible and firestopped (also applies to stack pipe at base or top of enclosure)

casing must Not be of sheet metal & must have ½ hour fire resistance (including any access panels)

any floor, including intermediate floor in maisonette

suspended ceiling

enclosure extends from top of floor to underside of floor above (even where a suspended ceiling exists)

no access panels in bedrooms or circulation spaces

casing imperforate (except for access panels or branch pipes)

enclosure used Only for pipes conveying water

PLAN   SECTION

All pipes to comply with specification (b)

F 11/12   These concern the assessment of the permitted maximum diameter where pipes penetrating a structure are connected to a pipe of lower specification. The effect is that if the joint is within 1 m of the structure surface, the rule for the lower specification must be used: see diagram to F 8 [3.34]. Also if a pipe of specification (*b*) is sleeved by a pipe of specification (*a*) the diameter for the sleeve may be used (i.e. 160 mm). This is illustrated by the diagram from the Approved Document [3.36]. It requires that the sleeve should be in contact with the pipe but it is difficult to see how such a close fit could be achieved in practice, and the diagram itself seems to suggest that some sort of packing would be needed, although this is not stated. This is a new rule not contained in the old E 12.

F 11 [**3.36**] *Sleeving of pipes.*

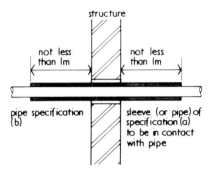

Ventilating ducts

F 13   Where ventilating ducts pass from one compartment to another the following precautions must be taken, principally to avoid smoke being conducted by them.

F 14   The precautions required depend on whether the ducts pass directly through compartment walls or floors or are contained within a protected shaft: See diagram to E 7.

F 15   In the first case (not in a shaft) the duct should be fitted with automatic fire shutters where it passes through a fire barrier and the opening is to be as small as possible and fire-stopped.

F 16   In the second case (within a protected shaft) it should be:

(*a*)   Fitted with automatic fire shutters at all inlets to and outlets from the shaft, unless some other provision (such as a shunt duct) is made to reduce the risk of fire spreading and

(*b*)   Constructed or lined with material which will reduce as far as possible the risk of fire spreading. Quite why it is put in this way is not clear – why not simply say made of MOLC?

F 17   Where the vent duct is in a protected shaft used for other purposes it should be enclosed to reduce the risk if fire passing between the duct and the rest of the shaft. Note however that vent ducts are not allowed in shafts containing lifts or stairways.

F 18   If the vent duct forms part of an air recirculating system additional precautions are necessary as follows:

One or more optical smoke detectors which respond to the scattering or absorbtion of light by smoke particles in a light beam should be fitted in the ductwork and be capable of changing the operation of the system so as to direct air to the outside of the building if the smoke reaches an optical density of 0.5dB/m.

NOTE   The above were previously contained in Regulation E 9, compartment walls and floors and E 10, protected shafts and are illustrated in the diagram to Appendix E [3.31].

Flues etc.

F 19   This is labelled F 18 in the Approved Document but this is clearly a misprint. It concerns flues, appliance ventilation ducts and ducts encasing one or more flue pipes passing through or forming part of a compartment wall or floor (one would imagine that the 'passing through' will relate only to the floor and the 'forming part of' to a wall).

These must be enclosed by structure of non-combustible material having at least ½ the fire resistance required for the wall or floor. Refer to the diagram to D 6 [3.28].

Appendix G Concealed spaces

G 1   This relates to cavities of various widths from the usual 50 mm in masonry walls to over 1 m above suspended ceilings and including roof spaces. To restrict the unseen spread of smoke etc they should be:

(*a*)   Closed around their edges.

(*b*)   Interrupted where they would otherwise bypass an abutting fire barrier.

(*c*)   Sub-divided where they exceed given maximum dimensions.

G 2   Cavity barriers may be formed by construction provided for another purpose if this meets the requirements of G 8.

Closing edges and sealing by-pass routes

G 3   The edges of cavities must be closed around any openings in the wall floor or any element containing a cavity, also to separate any cavity in one element from a cavity in an adjoining element. These situations are illustrated in the diagrams below [3.37]. This does not apply to a cavity in an external wall in certain circumstances [3.38]. (It is interesting to note that in such cases the rule does not require cavities to be closed at the sides or bottoms of openings).

G 3 [**3.37**] *Closure of certain cavities.*

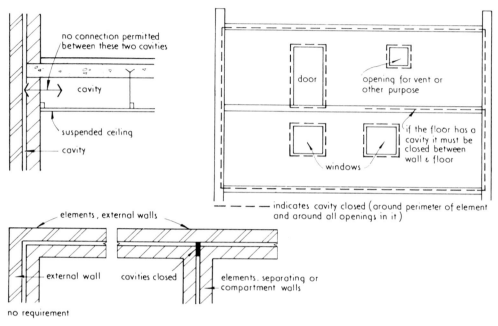

G 3 [**3.38**] *Exceptions relating to cavities in certain walls.*

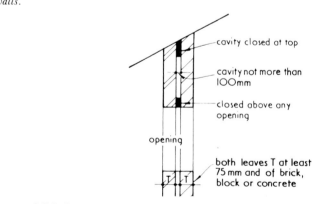

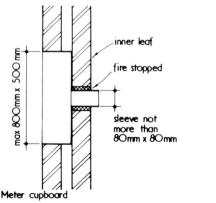

G 4   Cavities, including roof spaces, must be closed where any fire barrier element (wall, floor, ceiling, roof etc) abuts the cavity (including the frame of a fire-resisting door). This is illustrated in diagram [3.39] below.

G 4 [**3.39**] *Cavity barriers in abutting elements.*

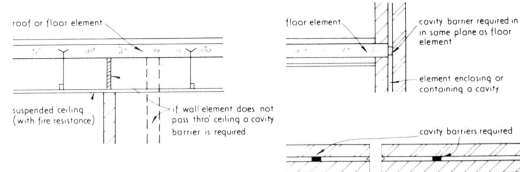

NOTE   This regulation applies to all elements required to have fire resistance, except where this requirement is solely because a wall is loadbearing (but see also G 5).

G 5   This does not apply in

(*a*)   External cavity walls complying with the exception to G 3 above.

(*c*)   A wall which needs to be fire resisting only because it is loadbearing (ie it is not a fire barrier).

(*f*)   Within the roof of a two-storey dwelling house.

or in any of the four cases illustrated in the diagram [3.40]. (The code letters used (a)(b) etc are those in the Approved Document itself).

G 5 [**3.40**] *Exceptions relating to cavities in certain floors and roofs.*
NOTE   This exemption does not apply to the sub-divisions of cavities required by para. G 6 for which only the conditions in G 7 below are applicable.

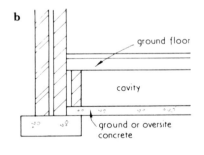

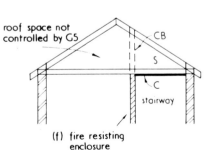

NOTE   In (f) the space S above a stairway must be separated from the roof space either by a ceiling C, complying with (e) above, or by cavity barriers above the walls, CB.

(i) extends throughout building or compartment
(ii) is not demountable
(iii) fire resistance not less than ½ hr
(iv) is imperforate (except as described in G 11
(v) its upper surface is Class O or I
(vi) its lower surface is Class O as defined in A8

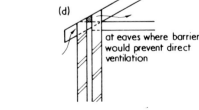

Subdivision of external cavities

G 6 There are limits on the extent of uninterrupted cavities even if none of the above circumstances occur. These are illustrated in diagram [3.41].

G 6 [**3.41**] *Limitation of cavity sizes.*

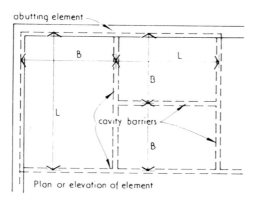

Plan or elevation of element

(a) Cavities between a roof and ceiling	
Dwelling house flats or maisonettes	No limit
Institutional Other residential	L or B not to exceed 15m L x B not over 100 m²
All other groups	L or B not to exceed 20m
(b) All other cavities	
Any purpose group Class O surface	L or B not to exceed 20m
Surface other than Class O	L or B not to exceed 8m

Note: the classes referred under (b) are for surface spread of flame and relate to the inner surfaces of cavities and any pipe, cable or conduit including its insulation There is no such requirement for (a)

G 7 These rules do not apply in an external cavity wall described in G 3 or below ground floors or between roof sheeting as shown in diagram [3.42].

G 7 [**3.42**] *Exceptions relating to subdivision of cavities.*

In each case:
1 *the sheeting should be of a material of limited combustibility and, dependent on type, as much of the sheeting as possible should remain in contact with the insulating layer, and*
2 *both surfaces of the insulating layer should have a surface spread of flame at least Class 1.*

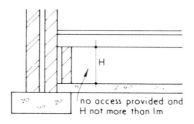

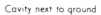

no access provided and H not more than 1m

Cavity next to ground

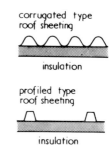

corrugated type roof sheeting

insulation

profiled type roof sheeting

insulation

Materials and fixings

G 8 The forms of construction to be used depend on the cross-section of the cavity. Clearly a large cavity above a ceiling requires a different approach to a 50 mm wall cavity. Over a certain size all cavity barriers must have a ½ hour fire resistance. This is illustrated in diagram [3.43], with a list of materials which are considered suitable for cavity barrier construction.

G 8 [**3.43**] *Construction of cavity barriers.*

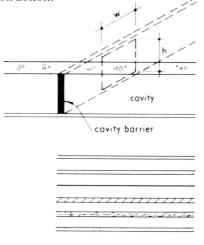

cavity

cavity barrier

if a cavity barrier can contain a square in which the sides h and w are not less than 1m it must have a fire resistance of at least ½ hr

cavity barriers not of such size may consist of :

	thickness to be not less than
Asbestos free board equivalent to asbestos building or insulation board	9 mm
Plasterboard	12·5 mm
Sheet steel	3 mm
Timber	38 mm
Wire reinforced mineral wool blanket	50 mm
Cement, mortar, plaster etc., polythene sleeved mineral wool or mineral wool slab, both under compression when installed, or any other construction to provide a ½ hr fire resistance period	25 mm

G 9 Cavity barriers must be tightly fitted to rigid construction or where not possible fire-stopped (eg at a junction with slates, tiles, corrugated sheeting etc).

G 10 They must also be fixed so that performance will not be made ineffective by:
(*a*) Movement due to subsidence, shrinkage or thermal changes.
(*b*) Collapse in fire of any services penetrating them.
(*c*) Failure in fire of fixings.
(*d*) Failure in fire of any abutting construction.
An example is quoted of a suspended ceiling continued over a fire resisting partition with a

fire barrier above the line of the partition, when premature failure of the cavity barrier could result from a collapse of the ceiling, but not if the ceiling also had a ½ hour fire resistance.

Openings   **G 11**   These should be restricted to those illustrated in diagram [3.44].

G 11 [**3.44**] *Penetration of cavity barriers.*

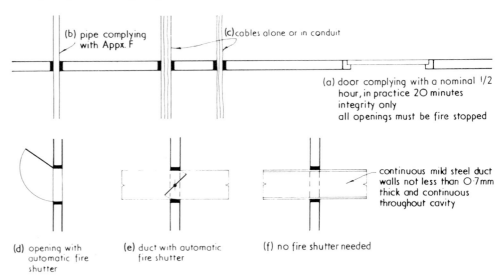

(d) opening with automatic fire shutter   (e) duct with automatic fire shutter   (f) no fire shutter needed

Appendix H Fire-stopping

H 1   In addition to any other provisions elsewhere, all openings for pipes, ducts, conduits or cables passing through fire barrier elements should be:
(*a*)   As few as possible.
(*b*)   As small as practicable.
(*c*)   Fire-stopped (in the case of a pipe or duct in a way which allows thermal movement).
H 2   To prevent displacement, materials used for fire-stopping should be reinforced or supported by MOLC wherever the unsupported span exceeds 100 mm and in any case where non-rigid materials are used, unless they have been shown by test to be satisfactory without.
NOTE   This does not say that the fire-stopping materials themselves should be of MOLC, but this would surely seem to be desirable, and the contents of H 3 suggest it.
H 3   Suitable fire-stopping materials are:
Cement mortar.
Gypsum based plaster.
Cement or gypsum based vermiculite/perlite mixes.
Glass, crushed rock, blast furnace slag or ceramic based products with or without resin binders.
Intumescent mastics.
Proprietary sealing systems (especially for services penetrations) shown by test to maintain the fire resistance of the element.
Similar provisions were included in E 14(10) but have been considerably expanded.

Appendix J   Space separation – External walls

Introduction   The superseded Model Bylaws did include regulations regarding the fire resistance of external walls, but exercised no control over window openings etc and were not therefore able to control the spread of fire from one building to another. The 1965 Regulations introduced rules that walls within 3 ft (now 1 m) of a boundary should be free of major openings, and that the extent of openings generally should be controlled by the distance from the boundary (amongst other things). Fire resistance from both inside and outside was required for walls within 3 ft of the boundary, but otherwise from inside only. These rules, with a few changes, are maintained today.

The proportion of the heat produced by a fire within a building, which can reach the boundary, (and hence another building, either existing or future) will depend upon the extent of the unprotected areas in the surrounding walls and on the distance of these from the boundary. The rules therefore define the extent of unprotected area which can be permitted by reference to:

(*a*)   The size of the wall facing the boundary.

(*b*)   The class of building and

(*c*)   The minimum distance of the wall from the boundary.

At a certain distance, depending on size, walls become completely free of control and can consist entirely of unprotected area. The maximum distance up to which control is exercised is 50 m.

J 1 to **J 8**   These are introductory clauses which cover briefly the same ground as the foregoing and also give a number of definitions as below:

J 3   Where the side of a building is on the boundary, that is the 'relevant boundary'. Otherwise it is the actual boundary of the land either parallel to, or making an angle of not more than 80° with the face of the building in question. Note that a boundary can be relevant to more than one face. Where land abuts a road or waterway the relevant boundary is taken as the centre of these. The points are illustrated in diagram [3.45].

J 3 [**3.45**] *Relevant boundaries.*

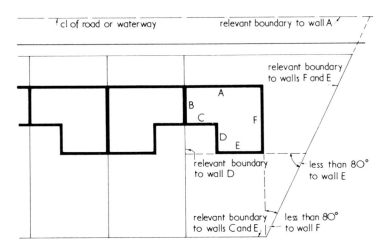

J 5   The term 'unprotected area' includes all those openings and certain cladding illustrated in the diagram from the Approved Document [3.46].

J 5 [**3.46**] *Definition of unprotected areas.*

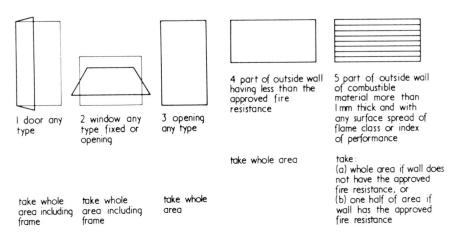

J 7 Buildings erected on land which they share in common (ie there is no actual boundary between them) and if one of them is in either one of the residential groups or the assembly group must be assumed to have a notional boundary between them placed as defined in the diagram. Although not mentioned in Appendix J a roof must be treated as a wall in certain circumstances which are illustrated [3.47, 3.48]. This information has for some strange reason been transferred into the list of definitions in Appendix L.

*J 7 [**3.47**] Buildings sharing common ground.*

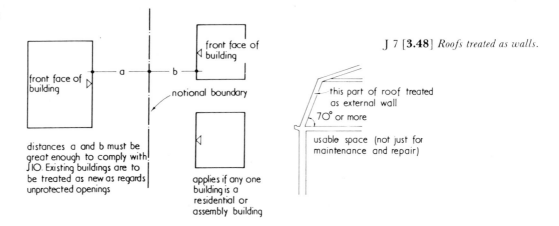

*J 7 [**3.48**] Roofs treated as walls.*

External walls within 1 m of the boundary

J 9 These must comply with Sections 1 to 6 and have no openings except those illustrated in diagram [3.49].

*J 9 [**3.49**] External walls within 1 m of boundary – permitted openings.*

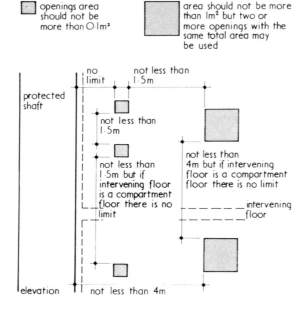

NOTE The countable unprotected area is not to include an area falling within the following rules:

1 *in the outside wall of a protected shaft – the whole area.*
2 *in the outside wall of a building not compartmented – any unprotected area which is 28 m or more above the mean ground level.*
3 *an area meeting the requirements in the diagram.*

NOTE This diagram is redrawn directly from the Approved Document, but that does not quite make clear all the circumstances covered by the wording of the old Schedule 10 (Regulation E 7). For instance, if such openings are separated by compartment wall there is no limiting distance between them (as for a compartment floor); also, if the openings are not in line vertically or horizontally the distance between them will have to be measured diagonally.

External walls 1 m or more from the relevant boundary

J 10 These must comply with Sections 1 to 6 and in addition to the openings in J 9 (which are always allowed) the extent of the unprotected areas must be determined by one of the three methods given below.

Method 1
This is the simplest but can only be used for small residential buildings, not including institu-

tional buildings. Because of its simplicity, the method may produce more restrictive results than the other two, in which case one of those may be used instead.

Method 2
The so-called 'enclosing rectangle' method in which distances are established from a set of tables related to the dimensions of a rectangle enclosing all the openings in the whole face, separated part or compartment. Two sets of figures are given, one for shop, industrial and other non-residential uses and one for all other groups. The former are the more onerous.

Method 3
Based on the use of 'aggregate notional areas', in which the areas of unprotected wall face are multiplied by various factors, depending on their distance from a vertical datum (the farther away, the lower the factor). It is more complicated but more precise and hence may be used in borderline cases or where either the building or boundary are irregular, or as a check on parts which cannot comply with Methods 1 or 2.

Method 1   Small residential

J 11   The method can only be used for a building to be used as a house, flats or other residential purposes (not institutional).
The building must not exceed three storeys (not counting basements) or 24 m in length (see note below). The rules determining the extent of unprotected areas are illustrated in diagram [3.50].

J 11 [**3.50**] *Calculation of permitted unprotected area in buildings of limited size in houses, flats and other residential buildings.*

Total extent of unprotected area permitted in side facing boundary:
boundary position A 5.6 m²; boundary position B 15 m²; boundary position C unlimited; boundary position D (in respect of buildings up to 12 m long) unlimited.

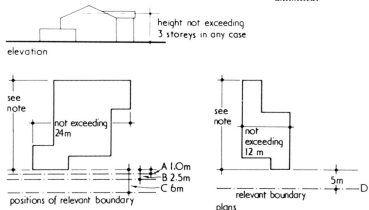

NOTE   The same rules apply to each side of the building.

Method 2   Enclosing rectangles

J 12   The method can be applied to any building and in the Approved Document it is set out in a series of steps from 1 to 12. These the reader can follow for himself, if he wishes, and there is no point in simply repeating them here. Instead a description of the principles is given, to assist in an overall understanding of how they work, illustrated rather more generously than in the Document.

Plane of reference
In the first place, a plane of reference has to be established for each side of the building which faces a boundary. This is a vertical plane which touches, but does not pass through the building (except for such projections as bay windows, balconies, cornices etc), nor does it cross the boundary (known as the 'relevant boundary'). It must not make an angle of more than 80° with the side of the building.
It will usually (but not always) be appropriate for it to be parallel to the boundary and in many cases it will coincide with the face of the building.
On to this all the unprotected areas facing the boundary are projected at right angles, but excluding any that are set at an angle of more than 80° to the plane. It is quite possible for a

plane of reference to take in more than one face of a building. All of this is illustrated in diagram 1 to J 12. See [3.51].

*Diagram 1 to J 12 [**3.51**] The interpretation of 'planes of reference' around a building.*
To find the nearest position that a boundary can be to a building, a series of planes of reference can be drawn around it. The projection of the unprotected areas upon each of these planes of reference and the calculation of the percentage of unprotected areas within the enclosing rectangles will give the minimum distances permitted between the relevant boundary and the planes of reference. If these minimum distances are superimposed upon one plan of the building a zone around the building is produced upon which a boundary cannot encroach.

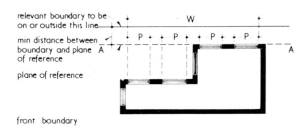

distance between plane of reference and relevant boundary related to dimensions of enclosing rectangle will determine the maximum percentage of unprotected area permitted. alternatively the total unprotected area in relation to the size of the enclosing rectangle will determine the minimum distance from the boundary

relevant boundary parallel to side or at an angle of not more than 80° to it

plane of reference in a position most favourable to the person erecting the building, but it must touch some part of the side under consideration and must not pass through the building

outer edges of unprotected areas projected perpendicularly to plane of reference

unprotected areas not included if at an angle of 80° or more to plane of reference

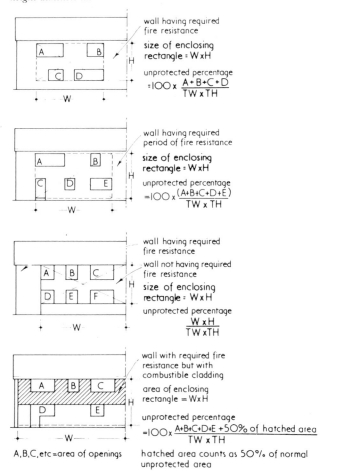

relevant boundary to be on or outside this line

min distance between boundary and plane A of reference

plane of reference

front boundary

*Diagram 2 to J 12 [**3.52**] Examples of 'enclosing rectangles' and 'unprotected percentage' (see p. 158).*
NOTE   TW and TH = the next greatest width and height dimensional in the tables to W and H.

wall having required fire resistance

size of enclosing rectangle = W x H

unprotected percentage

$$=100 \times \frac{A+B+C+D}{TW \times TH}$$

wall having required period of fire resistance

size of enclosing rectangle = W x H

unprotected percentage

$$=100 \times \frac{(A+B+C+D+E)}{TW \times TH}$$

wall having required fire resistance

wall not having required fire resistance

size of enclosing rectangle = W x H

unprotected percentage

$$\frac{W \times H}{TW \times TH}$$

wall with required fire resistance but with combustible cladding

area of enclosing rectangle = W x H

unprotected percentage

$$=100 \times \frac{A+B+C+D+E+50\% \text{ of hatched area}}{TW \times TH}$$

A,B,C,etc = area of openings

hatched area counts as 50% of normal unprotected area

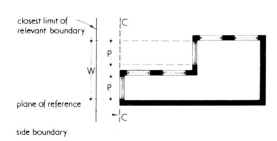

closest limit of relevant boundary

plane of reference

side boundary

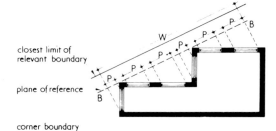

closest limit of relevant boundary

plane of reference

corner boundary

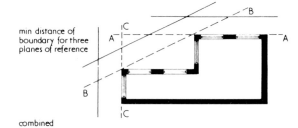

min distance of boundary for three planes of reference

combined

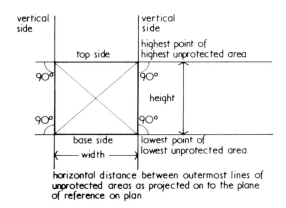

vertical side

vertical side

top side

highest point of highest unprotected area

90°   90°

height

90°   90°

base side

lowest point of lowest unprotected area

width

horizontal distance between outermost lines of **unprotected** areas as projected on to the plane of reference on plan

Enclosing rectangle

A rectangle is constructed on the plane of references so as to enclose the outer limits of all the unprotected areas on that side of the building or compartment. The *enclosing rectangle* is the one next above this size, in both height and width, in the tables provided. These give heights from 3 to 27 m in 3 metre steps and widths from 3 m up to no limit.

NOTE   This was not previously so, as Schedule 10 stated that the size of the enclosing rectangle was the actual size of the smallest rectangle which would enclose all the unprotected areas. This made quite a difference to the unprotected percentage and hence to the final result. However the looser interpretation, which is now confirmed, was frequently used. Diagram [3.52] illustrates how the rectangle is constructed and four examples of the result on a small elevation.

Unprotected percentage

This is established by taking the aggregate area of all the unprotected areas (see diagram [3.46]) as a percentage of the area of the enclosing rectangle.

The Tables

These give distances from the boundary for various combinations of height and width of enclosing rectangles and unprotected percentages from 20 per cent to 100 per cent by steps of 10 per cent. These distances represent the minimum distance between the plane of reference and the boundary, and will decide how near any particular side of the building can be to the relevant boundary. Alternatively, if the distance is fixed, they will decide how much unprotected area can be permitted.

There are two sets of figures, those in parentheses being for residential, office or assembly buildings and the others for the remainder (shop, industrial and other non-residential). They are the same as those in Schedule 10 where they were set out in two separate sets of tables.

Comment

It may be seen that even if the whole face of a building is an unprotected area the unprotected percentage will never be 100 per cent unless by coincidence the actual rectangle enclosing the outer limits of all unprotected areas is the exact height and width of one of the rectangles listed in the tables. According to how these dimensions work out the percentage may vary from just under 40 per cent to 100 per cent in the circumstances mentioned above. As an example take a building with a fully glazed face 30.1 m long × 3.1 m high

Unprotected area = 30.1 × 3.1	=	93.31
Next largest rectangle 40 × 6	=	240.00
Unprotected percentage	=	38.8%

Another example 60.1 × 9.1 m high all glazed comes out at 56.9 per cent. Also, what is not explained is how to calculate the area of an enclosing rectangle with a width of 'no limit' (the last item in each table). This is of course not possible (the mathematical answer is infinity m^2 which would make the unprotected percentage zero), so that the only recourse is presumably to take the *actual* length in conjunction with the appropriate height in the table. This problem did not arise if the exact wording in Schedule 10 was followed. To revert to the Approved Document, the distances given by the tables are in 0.5 m intervals and have obviously been rounded off from an exact figure produced by a mathematical formula. Furthermore they are visually just a large block of figures which can give no immediate impression of the relationships involved. It has therefore been thought worthwhile to present them graphically, one graph for each height of rectangle in each of the two categories of use. From the graphs, the relationship between the rectangle widths, unprotected percentage and distance from the boundary is immediately apparent.

The graphs are also a convenient tool for use during the design stages of a building, to determine the overall general situation where interrelated parameters are being considered. If the situation is critical it will be necessary to check with the tables themselves and if it is then still very close it may be advisable to check using Method 3 below. As the tables are in very close steps only the alternative width figures (3, 9, 15 etc) are shown to avoid congestion. However interpolation is quite in order [3.53].

J 12 [**3.53**] *Graphic representation of table for buildings or compartments in residential, office or assembly groups.*
(NL = no limit)

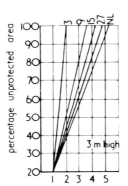

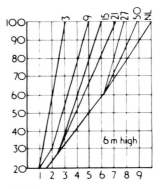

distance from relevant boundary in metres

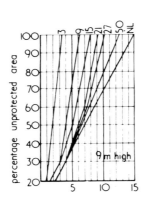

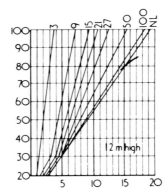

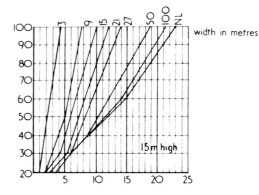

distances from relevant boundary in metres

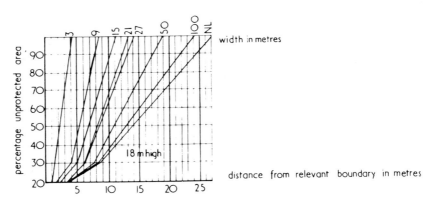

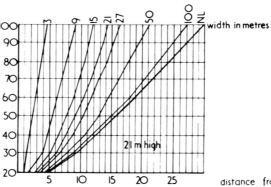

distance from relevant boundary in metres

J 12 [**3.53**] *(continued) Graphic presentation of table*
for buildings and compartments in residential, office or
assembly groups.

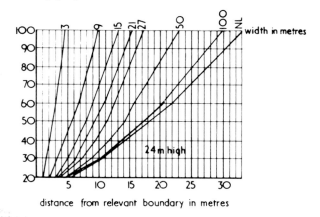

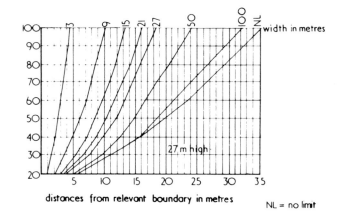

NL = no limit

J 12 [**3.53**] *(continued) Graphic presentation of table*
for buildings and compartments in shop, industrial
and other non-residential groups.

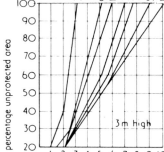

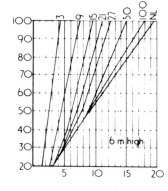

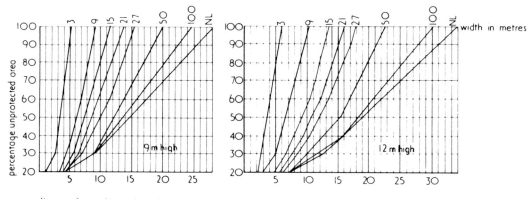

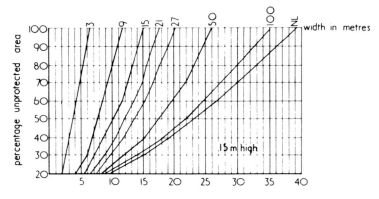

J 12 [**3.53**] *(continued) Graphic presentation of table*
for buildings and compartments in shop, industrial
and other non-residential groups.

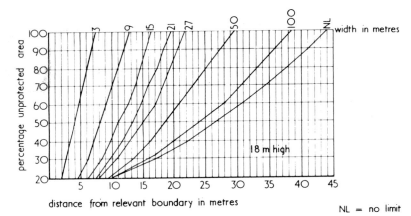

NL = no limit

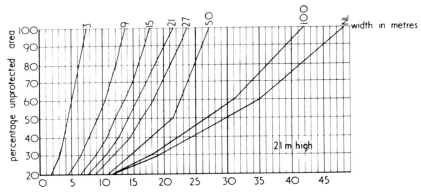

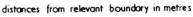

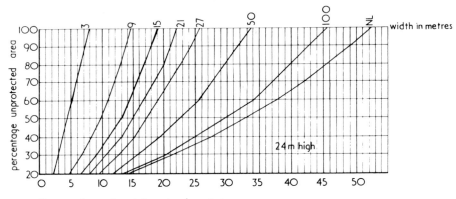

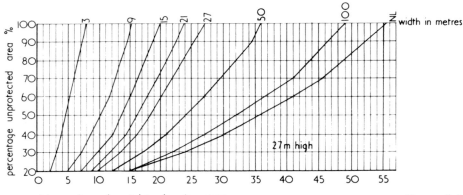

NL = no limit

If the above procedure produces an adverse answer the designer is left with three alternatives:

1   Reduce the total unprotected area.
2   Increase the distance from the boundary.
3   Reduce the size of the enclosing rectangle by compartmentation.

As 1 and 2 may not be acceptable, it may be necessary to resort to compartmentation (which may also have other advantages, such as a reduction in the minimum fire resistance period. The Approved Document contains a diagram illustrating how this can work; this is reproduced here as [3.54] (diagram 3 to J 12).

Diagram 3 to J 12 [3.54] Enclosing rectangles (effect of compartmentation on distance from boundary)
Compartmention of a building has a considerable

effect on the distance which its sides (or external walls) may be from the relevant boundary. This is shown and explained in the following diagrams which assume a residential, assembly or office use.

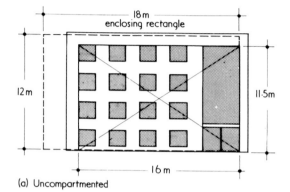

(a) Uncompartmented

1 *assume rectangle (enclosing unprotected areas) =*
 11.5 m × 16 m
2 *from Table J 2 enclosing rectangle =*
 12 m × 18 m = 216 m²
3 *assume unprotected areas (shaded) = 105 m²*
4 *unprotected percentage (unprotected areas as percentage of enclosing rectangle) = 105 m² as percentage of 216 m² = 48.6% use 50% column in Table J 2*
5 *from Table J 2 distance from boundary = 6 m (minimum)*

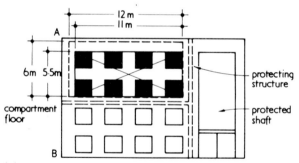

(b) Compartmented
(assume compartmentation as shown)

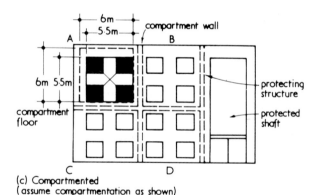

(c) Compartmented
(assume compartmentation as shown)

(a) as the entrance and stairways are now isolated the area becomes a protected shaft and the glazed area does not now count as part of the unprotected area
(b) the remainder of the building is divided by the compartment floor into compartments A and B. In this example the compartments have the same unprotected area. But where there are two (or more) compartments with different unprotected areas, take the compartment with the greatest unprotected area.
1 *assume rectangle = 5.5 m × 11 m*
2 *from Table J 2 enclosing rectangle = 6 m × 12 m = 72 m²*
3 *assume unprotected areas = 26 m²*
4 *unprotected percentage = 26 m² as percentage of 72 m² = 36% use 40% column in Table J 2*
5 *from Table J 2 distance from boundary = 3 m (minimum)*

With the inclusion of a compartment wall, the building is now divided into compartments A, B, C and D, each having the same unprotected area for the purpose of this example.

1 *assume rectangle = 5.5 m × 5.5 m*
2 *from Table J 2 enclosing rectangle = 6 m × 6 m = 36 m²*
3 *assume unprotected areas = 13 m²*
4 *unprotected percentage = 36% use 40% column in Table J 2*
5 *from Table J 2 distance from boundary = 2 m (minimum)*

NOTE   In the above diagrams the relevant boundary is assumed as parallel with the wall face, and the plane of reference to coincide with the wall face. But this will not always be so.

Method 3 Aggregate notional areas

J 13 This method may be used for any building or compartment more than 1 m from the boundary. It should produce a more precise result than Method 2, especially if the building or boundary is irregularly shaped, but it is more time consuming. Here again the Document gives a series of steps from 1 to 10. This Guide therefore gives a more general, perhaps more informative description of the procedure.

Aggregate notional area
The regulations are concerned with the possible effect of a fire at any point on a boundary. This grows less as the distance between increases. Thus for each point on the boundary an 'aggregate notional area' is calculated, by taking the sum of each unprotected area multiplied by a factor based on the distance from the boundary. The factors to be used are illustrated in diagram [3.55].
The total of these notional areas must fall within a fixed figure which is:
$210 \ m^2$ For residential, office and assembly buildings.
$90 \ m^2$ For shops, industrial and other non-residential groups.

*Diagram 1 to J 13 [**3.55**] Application of 'aggregate notional area' as set out in Method 3 of Appendix J.*
NOTE Measurements taken at any point on the boundary must not produce, for any side of a building or compartment, unprotected areas the aggregate of which, when multiplied by the relevant factors:
exceeds $210 \ m^2$ for purpose groups residential, office, assembly
or $90 \ m^2$ for purpose groups shop, industrial, other non-residential

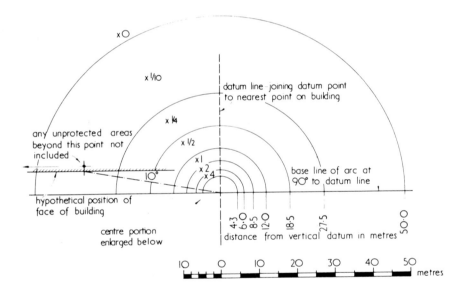

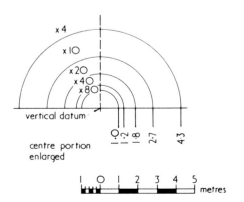

*Diagram 2 to J 13 [**3.56**] Multiplication factors at*
specified distances from vertical datum.

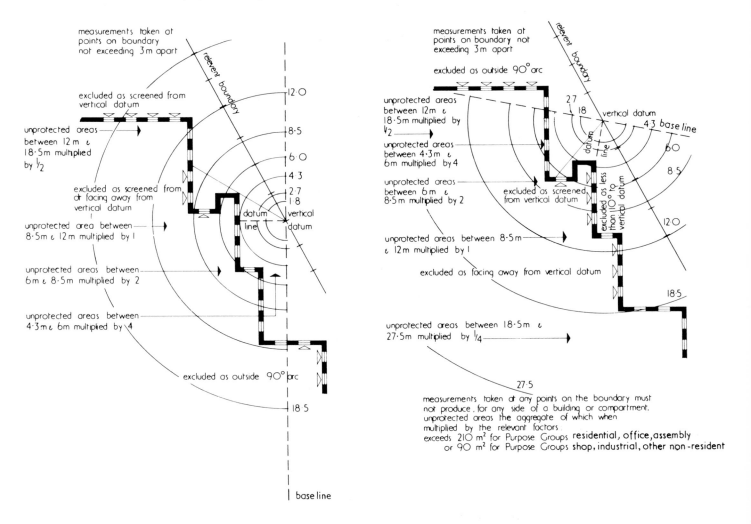

Vertical datum/Datum line/Base line

As it would be impossible to check an infinity of points on a boundary the method requires a series of points to be selected at not more than 3 m intervals on which an imaginary vertical line is set. Each of these is known as a 'vertical datum'. Considering one at a time a 'datum line' is drawn from the point to the nearest point on the building and a 'base line' is drawn through the vertical datum at right angles to the datum line. This becomes the base for a series of semicircles with radii corresponding to the distances at which the factors change: the largest of these is 50 m; diagram [3.56].

Excluded areas

Unprotected areas outside these limits have no effect on the calculation. Windows screened from direct view from the datum (except by other unprotected areas) are excluded as also are any areas which are beyond the limits of the baseline or semicircle or which face away from the datum or are at an angle of less than 10° to it. Diagram 2 to J 13 [3.56] illustrates the principles.

Procedure

To facilitate the checking of a full series of vertical data at 3 m intervals it will be useful to make a protractor of plastic film or tracing paper based on Diagram 1 and to the same scale as the drawing.
Where a building has an irregular outline it may well be necessary to check a series of points.

*Diagram 3 to J 13 [**3.57**] Effect of distance on continuously glazed building parallel to boundary in shop, industrial or other non-residential buildings. NOTE   The shaded bands represent continuous glazing. The total permitted depth is calculated by dividing the maximum aggregate of unprotected areas of 90 m² by the lengths of glazing multiplied by the appropriate factors (ie 8.99; 21.92 etc).*

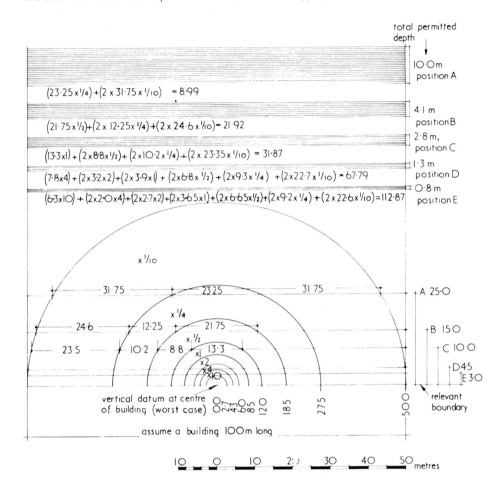

There will however also be cases where the critical datum is obvious, such as a plain facade standing on, or parallel to, the boundary and less than 100 m long, in which case the datum must be in line with the centre of the building (assuming evenly spaced glazing). The effect in such a case of varying distances from the boundary on the permitted unprotected area is illustrated in diagram [3.57].

There are many such buildings in urban areas placed on the site boundary where the relevant boundary is the centre of the road or street. If this is not very wide the regulation may well be restrictive, especially if shop windows are required. In such cases compartmention could be the only solution.

Appendix K Methods of measurement

K 1   Some form of measurement is an integral part of many of the provisions of this document. The rules as to how these are to be made is illustrated in the diagrams in [3.58], some of which are taken from the Approved Document itself and some from the guide to the 1976 Regulations.

K 1 [**3.58**] *Rules for measurement.*

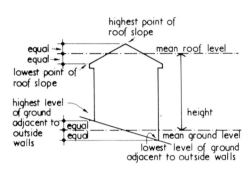

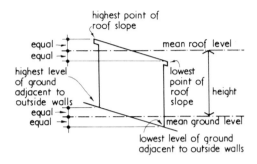

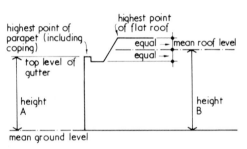

use height A or height B whichever is greatest

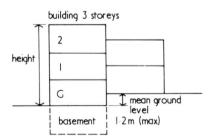

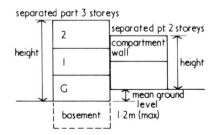

K 1 [**3.58**] *Rules for measurement (continued) Rules for measuring volume.*

To count the number of storeys in a building, or in a separated part of a building, count only at the position which gives the greatest number and exclude any basement storeys.

Number of storeys and height of building or separated part.

NOTE
In assembly buildings, a gallery is included as a storey, but not if it is a loading gallery, fly gallery, stage grid, lighting bridge, or any gallery provided for similar purposes, or for maintenance or repair.
In other purpose group buildings, galleries are not counted as storeys.

K 1 [**3.58**] *Rules for measurement.*

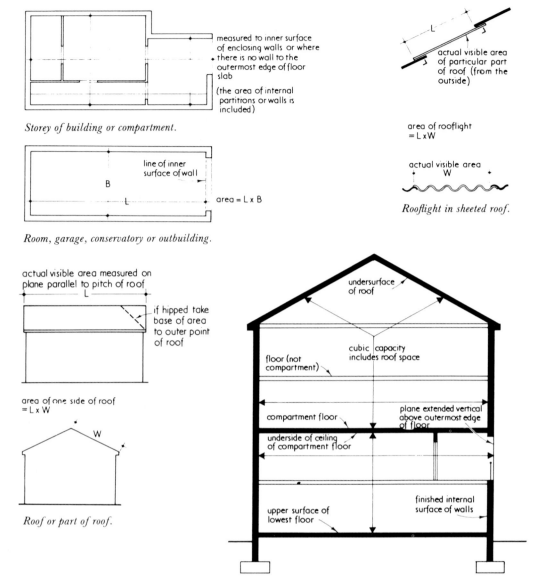

measured to inner surface of enclosing walls or where there is no wall to the outermost edge of floor slab

(the area of internal partitions or walls is included)

Storey of building or compartment.

line of inner surface of wall

B

L   area = L x B

Room, garage, conservatory or outbuilding.

actual visible area measured on plane parallel to pitch of roof

L

if hipped take base of area to outer point of roof

area of one side of roof = L x W

W

Roof or part of roof.

L

actual visible area of particular part of roof (from the outside)

area of rooflight = L x W

actual visible area
W

Rooflight in sheeted roof.

undersurface of roof

cubic capacity includes roof space

floor (not compartment)

compartment floor

plane extended vertical above outermost edge of floor

underside of ceiling of compartment floor

upper surface of lowest floor

finished internal surface of walls

Rules for measuring volume.

Appendix L

This contains a long list of definitions, some of which would have been better placed within the parts to which they are relevant.

In this guide they have been placed where they belong, where possible, and there is no point in repeating those. The following list therefore contains only those which are of general application.

Appliance ventilation duct   A duct provided to convey combustion air to a gas appliance.

Basement storey   A storey with a floor which at some point is more than 1.2 m below the highest level of ground adjacent to the outside walls. (However, *see Section 0* for concessions where the storey is considered to be a basement only because of a sloping site.)

Ceiling   A part of the building which encloses and is exposed overhead in a room, circulation space or protected shaft. (A soffit or rooflight is included as part of its surface, but not the frame of a rooflight.)

Circulation space   A space mainly used as a means of access between a room, or protected shaft, and an exit from the building or compartment.

Compartment   A part of a building separated from all other parts of the same building by compartment walls and/or compartment floors. (A roof space above the top storey of a compartment is included in that compartment – see diagram [3.58]). (A separated part is a special form of compartmentation.)

Compartment wall/floor   Construction provided to divide a building into compartments for the purposes of Sections 1 to 6, or Appendix J (Constructional requirements are given in Appendix D).

Concealed space (cavity)   A space enclosed by elements of a building (including a suspended ceiling) or contained within an element, but not a room, cupboard, circulation space, protected shaft or space within a flue, chute, duct, pipe or conduit.

Conservatory   A part of a building one storey in height where the roof and walls are substantially glazed with a transparent or translucent material.

Door   May have one or more leaves and includes a shutter, cover or other form of protection to an opening in a wall or floor, or in a structure surrounding a protected shaft.

External cladding   Material fixed to the outside face of an external wall for weather protection or decorative purposes.

[**3.59**] *Elements of structure; the structural elements of a building.*

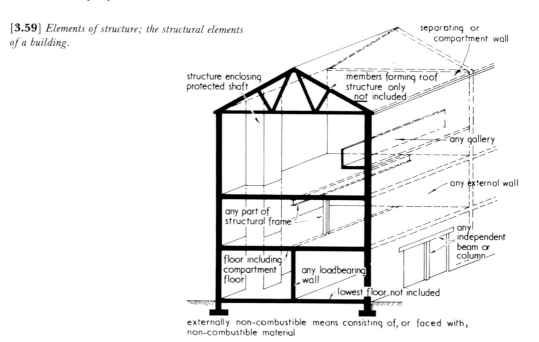

Fire stop   A seal provided to close an imperfection of fit between elements, components or construction in a building, or any joint, so as to restrict penetration of smoke and flame through that imperfection or joint.

Gallery   A floor, including a raised storage area, which is less than one-half of the area of the space into which it projects.

Pipe   (for the purposes of Appendix F) excludes – a flue pipe and a pipe used for ventilating purposes other than a ventilating pipe for an above ground drainage system: includes – pipe fittings and accessories.

Platform floor (access floor)   A floor supported by a structural floor above an intervening concealed space.

Rooflight   Includes any domelight, lantern light, skylight or other element intended to admit daylight.

Room   An enclosed space in a building that it not an enclosed circulation space or a protected shaft. (Thus the term would include not only conventional rooms, but also cupboards that were not fittings and large spaces such as auditoria.)

Separated part (of a building)   A form of compartmentation that is a part which is separated from another part of the same building by a compartment wall which runs full height of the part and is in one plane. (see diagram to D 2).

Separating wall   A wall separating adjoining buildings.

Single-storey building   A building consisting of a ground storey only. (A separated part which consists of a ground storey only, with a roof to which access is just for repair or maintenance, may be treated as a part of a single storey building.)

Wall surface   For the purposes of internal surfaces in Sections 1 to 6:

Includes
(i)   the surface of glazing, and
(ii)   any part of a ceiling which slopes at an angle of 70° or more to the horizontal.
Excludes
(i)   door frames and unglazed parts of doors, and
(ii)   window frames and frames in which glazing is fitted, and
(iii)   architraves, cover moulds, picture rails, skirtings and similar narrow members, and
(iv)   fireplace surrounds, mantleshelves and fitted furniture.
See also Appendix A – Internal Surfaces.

References

The following British Standards and other documents are referred to in the AD on the page(s) given at the end of the reference.

Parts B2/3/4

Association of Structural Fire Protection Contractors and Manufacturers. *Fire protection for structural steel in buildings* ASFPCM. 1983. £5. p. 39.
BS 476 *Fire tests on building materials and structures.* Part 3: 1958 *External fire exposure roof tests* p. 44. Part 4: 1970 *Non-combustibility test for materials* Amendment 1: AMD 2483. Amendment 2: AMD 4390, p. 47, 48. Part 6: 1968: *Fire propagation tests for materials. Part 6: 1981 Method of test for fire propagation for products* Amendment 1: AMD 4329. Part 7: 1971 *Surface spread of flame tests for materials.* Part 8: 1972 *Test methods and criteria for the fire resistance of elements of building construction* Amendment slip no. 1: AMD 1873. Amendment 2: AMD 3816, p. 39, 40, 41. Part 11: 1982 *Method for assessing the heat emission from building materials,* p. 47, 48. £10·20 (£5·10).
BS 747: 1977 *Specification for roofing felts* Amendment 1: AMD 3775. £10·20 (£5·10), p. 45.
BS 2782: 1970 *Methods of testing plastics* Amendment slip nos 1: AMD 936; 2; AMD 999. 3: AMD 1524. 4: AMD 2222. 5: AMD 3177. 6: AMD 3899. £41·00 (£20·50).
BS 2782 *Methods of testing plastics.* Part 1 *Thermal properties.* Method 102C: 1970 *Softening point of thermoplastic moulding material* (withdrawn). Methods 120A to 120E: 1976 *Determination of the Vicat softening temperature of thermoplastics* £5·20 (£2·60). Method 140D: 1980 *Flammability of a test piece 550 mm × 35 mm of thin polyvinyl chloride sheeting (laboratory method)* £7·00 (£3·50), p. 50. Method 140E: 1982 *Flammability of a small, inclined, test piece exposed to an ethanol flame (laboratory method).* £5·20 (£2·60), p. 50. Method 508C: 1970 *Degree of flammability of thin polyvinyl chloride sheeting* (withdrawn). Method 508D: 1970 *Flammability (alcohol cup test)* (withdrawn), p. 50.
BS 4514: 1983 *Specification for unplasticised PVC soil and ventilating pipes, fitting and accessories* Amendment 1: AMD 4517, £12·20 (£6·10), p. 58.
BS 5255: 1976: *Plastic waste pipes and fittings,* p. 58.
BS 5306 *Code of practice for fire extinguishing installations and equipment on premises* Part 2: 1979 *Sprinkler systems* Amendment 1: AMD 3586. Amendment slip no 2: AMD 4219. £16·20 (£8·10), p. 32, 34.
BS 6073 *Precast concrete masonry units* Part 1: 1981 *Specification for precast concrete masonry units* Amendment 1: AMD 3944. Amendment 2: AMD 4462. £12·20 (£6·10), p. 48.
CP144 *Roof coverings.* Part 3: 1970 *Built-up bitumen felt* Amendment 1: AMD 2527. £16·20 (£8·10), p. 45.
BRE Digest *Increasing the fire resistance of timber floors.* HMSO. 1984, p. 11. £1 from BRE
CONSTRADO *Fire and steel construction: the behaviour of steel panel frames in boundary conditions* 1980.. £2·50, p. 37.
Department of the Environment/Welsh Office *Mandatory rules for means of escape in case of fire* (Document B1). HMSO. 1985. £1·60.
Fire Offices' Committee *Rules for the construction and installation of firebreak doors and shutters.* FOC. 1985. £10, p. 39.
Fire Protection Association *Fire test and results on building products: fire resistance* FPA 1983. £8·00, p. 39.
Fire test results on building products: fire propagation FPA. 1980. £8.80, p. 46.
Fire test results on building products: surface spread of flame Revised edition 1981. £8·00, p. 46.
Fire Research Station *Heat radiation from fires and building separation* Fire Research Technical Paper No. 5. HMSO. 1963. Out of print, p. 4.
Fisher, R. W. and Smart, P. M. T. *Results of fire resistance tests on elements of building construction* BRE report two vols. HMSO 1975. £6·50. (£1·15), p. 39 from the BRE.
Fisher, R. W. and Rogowski, Barbara F. W. *Results of fire propagation tests on building products* BRE Report. HMSO. 1976. £1·50 from BRE, p. 46.

Results of surface spread of flame tests on building products BRE Report. HMSO. 1976. £6 from BRE, p. 46.

Home Office (and Scottish Home and Health Department) Fire Prevention Guide No 1 *Fire precautions in town centre development* HMSO. 1972 £3·30, p. 37.

Morgan, H. P. *Smoke control methods in enclosed shopping complexes of one or more storeys. A design summary* BRE Report. HMSO. 1979. £1·75 from BRE, p. 37.

Read, R. E. H., Adams, F. C. and Cooke, G. M. E. *Guidelines for the construction of fire resisting structural elements* BRE Report. HMSO. 1980. £2·75 from BRE, p. 5, 39, 43.

SI 1972 No 1178 *Gas safety regulations*. HMSO. 1972, p. 54.

Approved Document C
Site Preparation and Resistance to Moisture

Introduction

This deals with one of the most basic requirements of all buildings, the need to keep out moisture from both above and below ground. Originally, back in by-law times, only ground moisture was considered as a subject for control. This was when the introduction of a damp-proof course was first considered essential to avoid unhealthy conditions arising inside occupied buildings. By the time of the 1976 Regulations Part C had been expanded to cover the whole field, although the weather resistance of walls and roofs was very briefly dealt with as a simple requirement that they should not transmit moisture to the inside or to any part of the building that would be adversely affected. The new rules have expanded considerably on this, and might be described as an analysis of the principles involved in providing weatherproof enclosure above ground and moisture resisting structure below, and it is debatable whether they are not taking over the role of Mitchell or Jaggard and Drury, rather than being simply Regulations. Certainly they are far more than a simple presentation of the old Regulations in a few format, as was supposed to be the intention.

As in Part B the authors have again really 'made a meal of it' and what took 4 pages of the old smaller format now occupies 17 A4 size pages.

In one particular respect the rules break new ground; this is the introduction of ground contamination. Previously this was not part of the Regulations, but was dealt with under the so-called 'linked powers' in the Public Health Acts (and more recently in the Building Act 1984, Section 29), the operation of which was triggered by an application under the Building Regulations. These have now been brought within the Regulations themselves, something that was forecast in the 1982 Command Paper *The future of building control in England and Wales*. Part 1 of the Control of Pollution Act 1974 may also be relevant. As a matter of interest this is the only part of the new Regulations which carries the same code letter, C, as in the old.

The document is divided into two parts. The first, which deals with site preparation and contaminants (Requirements C 1/2 and 3) has 2 sections and the second which deals with resistance to weather and ground moisture (Requirement C 4) has 3 sections.

C 1/2/3   SITE PREPARATION AND CONTAMINANTS

The actual requirements are as follows:

	Requirement	Limits on application
	Preparation of site	
Site	C 1. The ground to be covered by the building shall be reasonably free from vegetable matter.	
	Dangerous and offensive substances	
Site	C2. Precautions shall be taken to avoid danger to health caused by substances found on or in the ground to be covered by the building.	
	Subsoil drainage	
	C3. Subsoil drainage shall be provided if it is needed to avoid –	

Requirement	Limits on application

(a) the passage of ground moisture to the interior of the building; or

(b) damage to the fabric of the building

0.1/0.2   This is followed by a description of an acceptable level of performance which says the same thing in other words and also gives a definition of 'contaminant' as 'any material in or on the ground to be covered by building (including faecal or animal matter) which is, or could become, toxic, corrosive, explosive, flammable or radioactive and so likely to be a danger to health or safety'.

Section 1   Site preparation and drainage (C 1/2/3)

1.1   Normal sites (not contaminated) need the following provisions.

Organic material
1.2   Turf and vegetable matter must be removed to sufficient depth to prevent future growth;
Note however that this does not apply if the building is to be used for:
(a)   Storage, where any persons employed are only engaged in taking care of, or the taking in or out of the goods, or
(b)   A purpose where such provision would not increase the protection to health and safety of persons employed in the building.
NOTE   These same exceptions apply to many of the provisions of this Part. The same was the case in Part C of the 1976 Regulations, where such cases were known as 'excepted buildings'. As this is a convenient term, which saves repetition, it is also used in this Guide where appropriate.
1.3   Where the ground to be covered contains tree roots or readily compressible material (even if not organic) which could affect stability (see also A 1/2).
The Approved Document stops here: it does not tell us what we must do. Presumably however, these undesirable items should be completely removed and the space back-filled with non-compressible material.
1.4   Building services below ground (including drainage) must be sufficiently robust or flexible to accommodate the presence of any roots, and joints are to be such that roots cannot penetrate.

Service entries
The following note is extracted from the explanatory notes to the *Manual* (p 41).
Where external walls or floors are penetrated by services the entry points should be sealed in accordance with the relevant Regulations which include:
Drainage: BSCP 8301: 1985.
Gas: The Gas Safety (Installation and Use) Regulations 1984, SI 1984 No. 1358 Regulation 18, and the Gas Safety Regulations 1972 (SI 1972 No 1178), Regulation 7.
Water: BS 6700: 1985.
Electricity: The Electricity Supply Regulations 1937, Regulation 22.
Telephone: British Telecom internal note.

Site drainage   **1.5**   The following provisions assume that the site is not subject to flooding, or if it is, it has been dealt with.
1.6   Where the extent of the groundwater could affect the stability of the building (see also A 1/2).
Here again there is a total blank; what we do is not stated. It seems likely however that a reference to the following provisions, 1.7 to 1.10, was intended.
1.7   If the water table can rise to within about 0.25 m of the lowest floor, or surface water could enter or adversely affect the building the ground should be drained by gravity, or other safeguards instituted (see 1.10).
1.8   A high water table is likely if the ground is damp in dry weather, the type of vegetation

indicates damp ground, or if the site is surrounded by higher ground.

1.9 If an active subsoil drain is cut, it should be dealt with as shown in diagram [4.1].

1.10 As an alternative to providing subsoil drainage, the building may be designed to prevent the passage of ground moisture to the inside, or to any materials which might be affected by it.

1.9 [**4.1**] *Subsoil drains cut during excavation.*

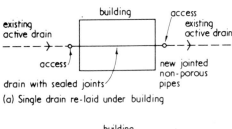

(a) Single drain re-laid under building

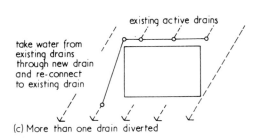

(c) More than one drain diverted

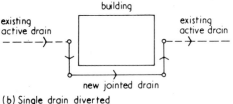

(b) Single drain diverted

Section 2   Contaminants

2.1 Sites which contain contaminants may be identified from planning records or local knowledge of previous uses. Table 1 of the Approved Document gives examples which include chemical works, gasworks, dumps, mines, sewage works and a number of others: see Table 1 for full list.

Where such identification has not been made, there are signs which can reveal the presence of contaminants, such as unusual colours or odours, unnatural vegetation, old drums or containers. Table 2 of the Document lists these and indicates the possible contaminant and appropriate action required. This generally involves removal, filling or sealing: see Table 2 for more detail.

2.2 If such signs are present the Environmental Health Officer must be told, and he will confirm or otherwise, the presence of contaminants. The recommended action in the Table assumes that the ground will have at least 100 mm of in-situ concrete laid on it after the removal.

2.3 In Table 2 the following definitions apply:

Removal The contaminant and any contaminated ground which is to be covered by the building (including its foundations) is to be removed to a depth of 1 m below the lowest floor level (or less if the Local Authority agrees). In some cases the Local Authority may require the work to be done by specialists.

Filling The ground to be covered to a depth of 1 m (less if the LA agrees) with suitable material which will not react adversely with any remaining contaminant. The type of filling and the design of the ground floor are to be considered together.

Inert filling Wholly non-combustible and not easily changed by chemical reaction.

Sealing A suitable imperforate barrier between contaminant and building sealed at joints, around edges and service entries. Polythene may not be suitable with liquid contaminants containing solvents.

2.4/5 Where the removal of large quantities of material is involved remedial measures should be the subject of expert advice. In the most hazardous conditions total removal may be the only answer, but in some cases remedial measures may reduce the risk to acceptable levels. The Appendix is an introduction to the work of the expert adviser, but is not part of the guidance given in Section 2 (whatever this means – perhaps that it would not affect any argument on interpretation). Since this is outside the field of the normal Building Regulation user, only a very brief summary is given here (refer to the Approved Document p. 6 for more detail).

Appendix   Introduction to the work of the specialist

Materials which are not themselves contaminants may react with others to become contaminants.

Some contaminants pose a direct threat to persons, eg those producing noxious fumes, fire or radioactivity.

Others pose an indirect threat by attacking the building fabric. There are usually four stages in preparing proposals:

(*a*)   Sampling to determine the extent and distribution.

(*b*)   Analysis to determine the types of contaminant present.

(*c*)   Assessment of the hazards in relation to the nature of the building and its occupants.

(*d*)   Proposals for remedial measures according to the type of contaminant. These may be:

    (i)   Gases, principally methane or carbon dioxide.

    (ii)   Solids or liquids such as hydrocarbons, solvents or inert refuse which may react in the presence of other chemicals to produce fumes.

    (iii)   Combustible materials which may be already burning or break out when disturbed.

    (iv)   Radioactive material in which case advice must be sought from the Radiochemical Inspectorate.

    (v)   Materials attacking the building fabric (such as sulphates). Remedial actions required in the various cases are mentioned, principally removal, filling or sealing and protection of the fabric with suitable membranes.

There is no mention of neutralisation of contaminants, using appropriate chemical reaction methods, although this is what one might expect from specialists.

C 4   Resistance to moisture

The Requirement itself is as follows:

	Requirement	Limits on application
	Resistance to weather and ground moisture	
Walls; roofs; floors.	C 4. The walls, floors and roof of the building shall adequately resist the passage of moisture to the inside of the building.	

0.1   The acceptable levels of performance are defined below.

0.2   A floor next to the ground must prevent ground moisture from reaching the upper surface.

0.3   A wall must prevent ground moisture from reaching the inside of the building, and if external resist the penetration of rain and snow to the inside.

0.4   A roof must resist the penetration of moisture from rain or snow to the inside.

0.5   All the above must not be damaged by moisture from the ground, rain or snow, nor carry such moisture to any part which would be damaged by it.

0.6   Floors include finishes which are part of the permanent construction.

0.7   Walls include piers, columns, parapets and integral chimneys.

0.8   Moisture includes vapour as well as liquid water.

NOTE   Under Section 74 of the Building Act 1984 the consent of the Local Authority is required for the construction of a room or cellar below subsoil water level in a house, shop, inn, hotel or office (except where subject to a justices' licence).

Provisions meeting the performance

In this document reference to 'moisture damage' means damage serious enough to a material or structure that it would present an imminent danger to health or safety, or reduce the performance of insulation. This can be avoided either by preventing the moisture getting at the material, or by using materials which would not be damaged.

Section 1 Floors next to the ground

1.1　Three types are described:
- ◯　　　Ground supported floors.
- ◯　　　Suspended timber floors.
- ◯　　　Suspended concrete floors.

1.2　They should all:

(*a*)　　　Prevent ground moisture from reaching the upper surface. This does not apply to 'excepted buildings' (see Site preparation 1.2).

(*b*)　　　Not be damaged by moisture from the ground.

Ground supported floors

1.3　Unless subject to water pressure (see 1.8) these will be adequate if constructed as below:

1.4 (*a*)　Concrete 100 mm thick minimum, mix at least 50 kg cement to 0.11 m^3 fine aggregate, 0.16 m^3 coarse aggregate or mix C10P* (if reinforced 50 kg/0.08 m^3/0.13 m^3 or mix C20P*).

* Mixes as described in BS 5328: 1981

(*b*)　　　Hardcore bed of clean broken brick or similar inert material free from substances which can damage concrete (including sulphates).

(*c*)　　　Damp-proof membrane above, below or through the concrete and continuous with, or sealed to damp-proof courses in walls, piers, etc.

1.5　Membranes below concrete to be at least 1000 gauge polythene with sealed joints on a bed of material which will not damage it (this usually means that the hardcore should be blinded with sand or topped with a weak mix to provide a flat surface).

1.6　A membrane above concrete may be as above or 3-coat cold applied bitumen or similar moisture and vapour-resisting material protected by screed or finish unless it is pitchmastic or similar material suitable itself as a floor finish.

1.7　A timber floor finish may be bedded on material which also serves as a damp-proof membrane. Timber fillets below the membrane to be treated with preservative (see BS 1282: 1975 *Guide to wood preservatives*), and diagram [4.2].

NOTE　C 5 of the 1976 Regulations required that the damp-proof membrane in a floor finished with timber be not lower than the highest level of the adjoining ground or paving. This seems to have been dropped.

1.8　Alternatively the relevant recommendations of Clause 11 of CP 102: 1973 *Protection of buildings against water from the ground*, may be used. This includes recommendations for floors subject to water pressure (eg in basements).

1.3 [**4.2**] *Ground supported floors.*　　　　　1.7 *Timber finishes on ground supported floors.*

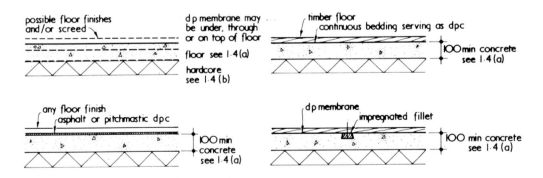

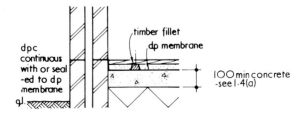

Suspended timber floors

1.9   These will be adequate if:

(a)   The ground is covered to resist moisture and prevent plant growth.

(b)   There is a ventilated space between this cover and the timber.

(c)   There are dpcs between the timber and any material which can carry ground moisture.

1.10   Unless the floor has a finish which is highly vapour-resistant (in which case see 1.11) it may be as follows:

(a)   A ground covering of either:

(i)   100 mm concrete mix 50 kg/0.13m³/0.18m³ cement, fine, coarse aggregate or mix C7.5P*, if not reinforced, on hardcore bed as in 1.4(b) or

(ii)   50 mm concrete as above on 1000 gauge minimum polythene with sealed joints on material which will not damage it.

The top of the covering should either be all above the highest adjoining ground level or laid to fall to an outlet at a point above the lowest adjoining level (see diagram [4.3]).

(b)   A ventilated air space as shown in diagram [4.4]. If pipes are used to convey ventilation air they must be at least 100 mm diameter. Each external wall should have ventilation openings to give at least the equivalent of 3000 mm² free openings for each metre run of wall and there should be a free path between walls (this is roughly the equivalent of one normal air brick every 3 m).

(c)   Damp-proof courses of impervious sheet material, engineerng brick, slates in cement or other moisture resisting material (see diagram [4.4]).

1.11   Alternatively, the relevant recommendations of Clause 11 of CP 102: 1973 may be followed.

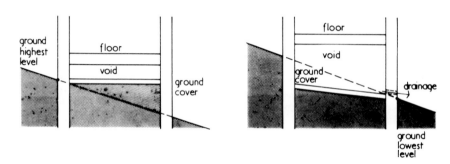

1.10 (a) [**4.3**] *Positioning of ground covering.*

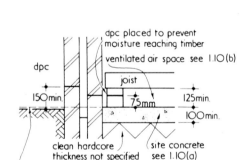

1.10 [**4.4**] *Suspended timber floor – Construction.*

Suspended concrete floors

1.12   In-situ or precast concrete floors will be adequate if they prevent moisture from reaching the upper surface and the reinforcement is protected against moisture

1.13   Diagram [4.5] illustrates the principles to be followed.

1.13 [**4.5**] *Suspended concrete ground floors.*

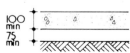

Insitu concrete, at least 300 kg cement/m³ or precast concrete with or without infill slabs

ventilated air space

ground not below lowest level of surrounding ground or effectively drained

Reinforcing steel to have at least 40mm cover in insitu slab, and cover required for moderate exposure if precast

If the air space is less than 75mm or not ventilated, or if the ground is too low and not drained, a damp-proof membrane must be provided (see 1.4–1.6 and 1.10(b)).

Section 2   Walls

The layout of this section is so sickeningly pedantic and repetitive that an explanatory summary is given instead of rigidly following the coding system. Nevertheless, all *relevant* information is included.

2.1/2.4   All walls must meet the performance standards in 0.3 with the usual limitation for 'excepted buildings'.

All walls must have a dpc of bituminous material, engineering bricks, slates in cement or other moisture-resistant material. They should be continuous with any damp-proof membrane in floors. In external walls they should be positioned as shown in diagram [4.6].

2.4 [**4.6**] *Positioning damp-proof courses.*
NOTE   The 150 mm minimum is not essential if a part of the building protects the wall.

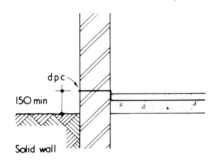

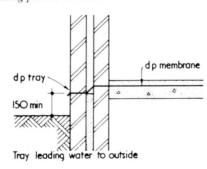

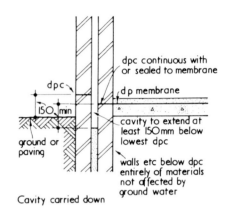

2.5   Alternatively the performance can be met by following the recommendations of Clause 10 of CP 102: 1973. This code also includes recommendations for walls subject to groundwater pressure (eg in basements).

External walls

2.6   These may be either solid or cavity.

Solid walls

2.7/2.8   The effectiveness of solid walls depends on their ability to absorb and hold moisture long enough for it to be dispersed during a dry period before reaching the inner face. This will depend on the type of brick or block and the severity of exposure. A method of classifying exposure conditions has been developed (see note on exposure in BS 5628: Part 3: 1985, or DD 1983: 1984. For 'very severe' exposure they should be protected by cladding. They may also be rendered as suggested in the AD for 'severe' (but not 'very severe') conditions if built as below

Brickwork at least 328 mm thick or dense aggregate concrete blockwork 250 mm or lightweight aggregate or aerated autoclaved concrete blockwork 215 mm thick. Mortar strength to be compatible with the brick or block used and joints raked back 10 mm.

20 mm rendering in two coats with textured finish, mix 1:1:6 cement, lime, sharp sand, except for dense concrete blocks which should be 1:½:4 proportion.

BS 5262: 1976 has recommendations for a wider range of mixes according to the type of masonry and severity of exposure.

Copings must be provided to exposed tops, and unless the coping is itself impervious (including joints) should be laid on a dpc.

Damp-proof courses should be provided to direct water towards the outer face:

○   Wherever the downward flow will be interrupted, such as by lintels and
○   Under openings, unless sills are impervious (including joints) and
○   Where an internal wall is carried up as an external wall.

NOTE   We are talking here of solid (not cavity) walls.

2.9   Alternatively the recommendations of the following BSS may be followed:

BS 5628: Part 3: 1985 *Structural masonry, materials, design and workmanship.*
BS 5390: 1976 *Stone masonry.*

Cavity walls

2.10/2.11   These rely on having two leaves separated by a drained air space or any other means of preventing water being carried to the inner leaf (such as impervious insulation). A suitable specification is:

(*a*)   An outer leaf of masonry (brick, block, stone etc).

(*b*)   A cavity 50 mm minimum width, bridged only by wall ties or dp trays provided to prevent moisture being carried to the inner leaf.

NOTE   Regulation C 9 (1976 Regulations) mentions the specific example of jambs to openings and an exception below the eaves of roofs which are not now included.

(*c*)   An inner leaf of masonry or frame and lining.

2.12   Alternatively the recommendations of BS 5628: Part 3: 1985 may be followed.

Cavity insulation

2.13/2.14   Insulation may be placed in a cavity under the following conditions:

(*a*)   Rigid material, the subject of, and installed in accordance with, an Agrément certificate.

(*b*)   Urea formaldehyde (UF) foam in accordance with BS 5617: 1985 suitable for walls with masonry or concrete inner and outer leaves, installed in accordance with BS 5618: 1985. The suitability of the wall is to be assessed before starting in accordance with BS 8208: Part 1: 1985, and the installer must hold a certificate of Registration of Assessed Capability from the BSI.

(*c*)   Other insulating materials to be installed in accordance with BS 6232: Part 1 and Part 2: 1982 (blown man-made mineral fibre in cavity walls with masonry or concrete leaves). Suitability and installation to be as in (*b*) above.

Alternatively, the insulation should be the subject of, and installed in accordance with the terms of a current Agrément Certificate.

NOTE   2.13/14 refers to insulation which fills the cavity and must therefore itself be water resistant. 2.11 recommends a minimum clear cavity width of 50 mm but makes no reference to the inclusion of rigid sheet insulation within the cavity. However, BS 5628: Part 3 considers this in some detail (see 21.3 of the BS). In general it is better to maintain a 50 mm clear cavity and allow extra space if insulation is to be installed, but less (e.g. 25 mm) may be acceptable in non-severe exposure conditions.

Section 3   Cladding for external walls and roofs

3.1/3.7   This can protect a building by either holding off the rain or snow at the face (totally impervious) or by stopping it penetrating beyond the back of the cladding (weather resisting).

Cladding will be adequate if it:

(*a*)   Is impervious and jointless or has sealed joints (in which case allowance must be made for structural and thermal movement) or,

(*b*)   Has overlapping dry joints and is backed by a material which will divert any water which penetrates back towards the outer face. The latter is the principle behind most framed or lapped cladding systems. Their suitability depends on the severity of exposure, especially to wind-driven rain and snow on the surfaces (such as tile hanging or sheeting). Very special consideration is required on large elevations where the direction of the wind-driven water may frequently be upwards (for example when the United Nations' building in New York was first occupied, water was seen to come spouting into the building through the outlets designed for drainage of the cavity behind the cladding grid).

The weather-resisting part of the wall must not rely on paint or include any coating or surfacing which does not, in itself, provide all the weather resistance. The meaning of this is not entirely clear, but seems to suggest that the wall should not rely on the combined effect of several partially resistant layers.

Claddings can be classified as follows [diagram 4.7].

(*a*)   Impervious: metal, plastic, glass and bituminous products.

(*b*)   Weather-resisting: stone, slate, cement products, fired clay and wood products.

(*c*)   Moisture-resisting: bitumen and plastic products (lapped at the joints if used as sheet material). These materials should be vapour-permeable unless there is an air space immediately behind them [4.7].

*Section 3 [**4.7**] Types of cladding to external walls.*

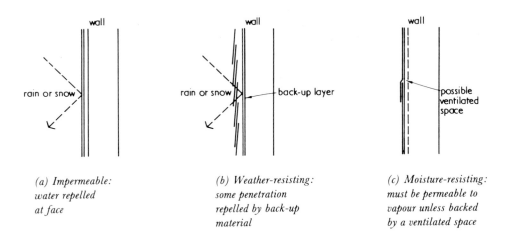

(a) *Impermeable:*
water repelled
at face

(b) *Weather-resisting:*
some penetration
repelled by back-up
material

(c) *Moisture-resisting:*
must be permeable to
vapour unless backed
by a ventilated space

Each sheet, tile and section of cladding should be securely fixed.

NOTE   This is contrary to traditional practice for tiled roofs.

3.8 Alternatively, the recommendations of the following British Standards may be followed:

(*a*)   Walls and roofs: CP 143 *Sheet roof and wall coverings of troughed and corrugated aluminium* Part 1: 1958.

Zinc: Part 5: 1964.

Galvanised corrugated sheet: Part 10: 1973.

Lead: Part 11: 1970.

Copper: Part 12: 1970.

Aluminium: Part 15: 1973.

Semi-rigid asbestos/bitumen sheet: Part 16: 1974.

(*b*)   Walls and roofs: BS 5247: Part 14: 1975 *Corrugated asbestos cement.*

(*c*)   Walls and steep roofs: BS 8200 *Non-loadbearing external vertical enclosures.*

(*d*)   Walls only: CP 297: 1972 *Precast concrete cladding.*

(*e*)   Walls only: CP 298: 1972 *Natural stone cladding.*

For the assistance of readers a brief summary of the more important BS publications referred to in this AD are given below.

CP 102: 1973 Protection of buildings against water from the ground

Section Two of this CP is concerned with structures below ground level which are subject to hydrostatic pressure. Two types are described:

Type A   Where a continuous membrane impervious to water and vapour is used, and

Type B   Which uses only high grade reinforced concrete to exclude water but not necessarily all vapour.

It recommends the provision of land drains around such structures wherever possible to reduce water pressure. Under Type A it deals with mastic asphalt and bitumen sheet tanking both internally and externally applied.

It should be consulted whenever the structure will be subjected to hydrostatic pressure.

Section Three deals with the problem of the capillary rise of moisture in walls and floors in contact with the ground (rising damp). It cover much the same ground as the Approved Document itself but in more detail. Clause 10 concerns the damp-proofing of walls, principally with the materials and workmanship involved in laying dpcs. It stresses the need for continuity between wall dpcs and floor membranes.

Clause 11 concerns the damp-proofing of floors. The degree of protection required depends on the nature of the floor finish (pervious or impervious and whether adversely affected by moisture). What is often critical is the adhesive used to fix the flooring.

There are two useful tables showing the properties and limitations of waterproof flooring and membranes, and of the various kinds of floor finish. It is interesting to note that although the Approved Document gives 1000 gauge polythene sheet as standard for membranes, the CP states that polythene film (minimum thickness 0.20 mm) may not be satisfactory for Group D finishes. These include pvc, lino, cork, rubber and wood.

Recommendations are given for mastic asphalt as flooring or membrane and for bitumen sheet, hot pitch or bitumen, cold bitumen and cold tar/pitch/rubber emulsions.

There is a section on suspended timber floors which expands on the material in the Approved Document with diagrams.

BS 5628: Part 3: 1985 CP for the use of masonry	This new code of practice supersedes CP 121: Part 1: 1973. It is a veritable encyclopedia of information (100 pages) on all aspects of masonry wall design and construction and its highly detailed approach goes far beyond the consideration normally given by designers or builders to this important subject. It has three principal sections covering materials, design and workmanship. Among its principal design considerations are: ○ Design and detailing for stability (but not detailed calculations, for which see Part 1). ○ Movement. ○ Exclusion of moisture. ○ Durability. ○ Fire resistance. ○ Thermal properties. ○ Sound reduction. Virtually all of these are the concern of Building Regulations. Part C is concerned with the exclusion of moisture and in this respect the BS describes a method of assessing the exposure category based on the local spell index method in DD 93. These indices are based on the amount of driving rain which might be expected to fall on a vertical surface during the worst spell in a period of three years. These run from 98 L/m^2 (very severe) down to 24 L/m^2 (very sheltered): six categories in all. The designer must select which category applies to any particular situation (by reference to DD 93 or local knowledge). The BS then gives tables from which suitable wall types can be chosen; Table 11A for single leaf walls of brick or concrete, rendered or plain, 11B for cavity walls with various finishes and cavities either clear or filled with insulation. The point is made that cavity filling reduces the resistance to penetration (UF foam being worse than other types) and that total resistance to penetration can only be achieved by cladding with metal, plastics, slates, tiles or timber, whether on single leaf or cavity walls.
BS 5390: 1976 CP for stone masonry	This BS covers all aspects of the design and construction of stonework. The information relevant to Part C is contained in Clause 20, exclusion of rain. Water penetration may occur through the porosity of the stone or mortar or through cracks. The latter are usually the result of using too strong a mortar. Reference is made to the classification system in CP 121 which has only three categories of exposure, severe, moderate and sheltered. Only walls incorporating a cavity or internal lining are suitable for severe conditions. Solid stone walls without sheltered are only suitable for sheltered conditions. The thickness, and the detailing at floors, openings, projections and parapets are all very important and the BS gives a great deal of information on these.
BS 5262: 1976 CP for external rendered finishes	This code deals with external renderings on all common backgrounds, whether for protective or purely visual reasons. It contains sections on materials, backgrounds, design, application and repair. Various mixes are recommended for undercoats and finishing coats to suit differing backgrounds and exposure conditions. The latter are defined on the basis of BRS Digest 127 (later included in CP 121 and now overtaken by DD 93) and two maps are included showing exposure gradings and an annual driving rain index for the British Isles. Resistance to water penetration is best achieved by using several coats with each coat being slightly more porous than the coat below. Two or three coats are normal depending on exposure. The theory is that it is better to have a surface that will absorb some water and subsequently dry out than a completely impervious surface that will almost certainly crack and then prevent drying out of moisture which has penetrated the cracks. There is helpful advice on detailing with diagrams.
BS 8200: 1985 CP for design of non-loadbearing vertical enclosures of buildings	This BS covers a very wide field indeed. It is intended principally as a general design guide for all non-loadbearing cladding systems, including masonry etc, as well as grid and large panel systems, although it does not deal specifically with any of them. It does deal with all the normal design problems eg ○ Thermal, moisture and structural movement. ○ Jointing and sealing. ○ Control of heat, sound and water.

The last item is dealt with in clause 33 which is a very interesting dissertation on how and why water may penetrate construction. The forces which cause this are the kinetic energy of raindrops, capillary action, gravity and pressure differentials.

The principles of watertight construction are explained as requiring three elements:

(*a*)   The rainscreen to prevent direct penetration.

(*b*)   An air space ventilated to ensure that the air pressure is equal to that outside, hence rain is not drawn in.

(*c*)   An air barrier across which is the pressure differential between outside and the interior of the building.

A lot of advice is also given on weathering and run-off, to avoid unsightly appearance as well as moisture penetration.

It should have a place on every architect's bookshelf.

References

The following British Standards and other documents are referred to in the Approved Document with the page number on which the reference is made.

BS 1282: 1975 *Guide to the choice, use and application of wood preservatives.* £12·20 (£6·10), p. 11.

BS 5247 *Code of practice for sheet wall and roof coverings.* Part 14: 1975 *Corrugated asbestos cement.* £12·20,, p. 16.

BS 5262: 1976 *Code of practice for external rendered finishes* Amendment slip no 1: AMD 2103. £16·20 (£8·10), p. 14.

BS 5328: 1981 *Specifying concrete, including ready-mixed concrete.* £16·20, pp. 10, 11.

BS 5390: 1976 *Code of practice for stone masonry* Amendment slip no 1: AMD 4272. £22·80. (£11·40), p. 15.

BS 5617: 1985 *Specification for urea-formaldehyde (UF) foam systems suitable for thermal insulation of cavity walls.* £10·20 (5·10), p. 15.

BS 5618: 1985 *Code of practice for the thermal insulation of cavity walls by filling with UF foam systems.* £22·80, p. 15.

BS 5628 *Code of practice for the structural use of masonry* Part 3: 1985 *Materials and components, design and workmanship.* £20·20, p. 15.

BS 6232 *Thermal insulation of cavity walls by filling with blown man-made mineral fibre.* Part 1: 1982 *Specification for the performance of installation systems.* £10·20 (£5·10), p. 15. Part 2: 1982 *Code of practice for installation of blown man-made mineral fibre in cavity walls.* £8 (£4), p. 15.

BS 8200: 1985 *Code of practice for design of non-loadbearing external vertical enclosures of buildings.* £35·50, p. 16.

BS 8208: *Guide to assessment of suitability of external cavity walls for filling with thermal insulants.* Part 1: 1985 *Existing traditional cavity construction.* £31, p. 15.

CP 102: 1973 *Protection of buildings against water from the ground.* £16·20, p. 14.

CP 143 *Sheet roof and wall coverings.* Part 1: 1958 *Aluminium corrugated and troughed.* Amendment 1: PD 4346. £10·20. Part 5: 1964 *Zinc* £10·20 (£5·10). Part 10: 1973 *Galvanised corrugated steel* £16·20 (£8·10). Part 11: 1970 *Lead.* Part 12: 1970 *Copper* Amendment 1: AMD 863. £12·20 (£6·10). Part 15: 1973 *Aluminium* Amendment slip no 1: AMD 4473. £16·20. Part 16: 1974 *Semi-rigid asbestos bitumen.* £16·20, p. 16.

CP 297: 1972 *Precast concrete cladding (non-loadbearing).* £16·20 (£8·10), p. 16.

CP 298: 1972 *Natural stone cladding (non-loadbearing).* £16·20, p. 16.

DD 93: 1984 *Methods for assessing exposure to wind-driven rain.* £26·20, p. 14.

Approved Document D
Toxic Substances

D1   CAVITY INSULATION

This is the shortest of the Approved Documents, which takes over from a recently introduced amendment to the 1976 Regulations (Part S), designed to officially bring the use of UF foam for cavity insulation within the orbit of the Regulations.

The reasons for its inclusion as a separate Part are very difficult to perceive, since the provisions required are already wholly dealt with in the Approved Document to Part C (C 4, 2.13 and 14). There is therefore no point in repeating them here.

The requirement itself is as follows:

	Requirement	Limits on application
	Cavity insulation	
Walls	D1. If insulating material is inserted into a cavity in a cavity wall reasonable precautions shall be taken to prevent the subsequent permeation of any toxic fumes from that material into any part of the building occupied by people.	

The performance level required is that the fumes given off should not penetrate occupied parts of the building to an extent which would give rise to an irritant concentration, and the provisions required to meet this standard are that there should be a continuous barrier which will minimise, as far as practicable, the passage of fumes to occupied parts.

The technical details are exactly as stated in 2.13(*b*) and 2.14 of C 4.

These rules apply to both new and existing buildings because under Regulation 3(2)(b) filling an existing cavity wall is a 'material alteration.'

NOTE   Unlike Part S of the 1976 Regulations the Approved Document does not actually rule out filling cavity walls that do not have a masonry inner leaf, but requires only that there should be a 'continuous barrier' against the passage of fumes. However the technical solution offered is only concerned with walls having a masonry inner leaf. In Scotland foam cavity fill has been used on timber framed houses in the past, but since April 1985 has been specifically prohibited by the Scottish Building Standards Regulations.

References

The following British Standards and other documents are referred to in the Approved Document with the page number on which the reference is made.

BS 5617: 1985 *Specification for urea-formaldehyde (UF) foam systems suitable for thermal insulation of cavity walls with masonry or concrete inner and outer leaves.* £10·20 (£5·10), p. 2.

BS 5618: 1985 *Code of practice for thermal insulation of cavity walls (with masonry or concrete inner and outer leaves) by filling with urea-formaldehyde (UF) foam systems.* £22·80 (£11·40), p. 2.

BS 8208 *Guide to assessment of suitability of external cavity walls for filling with thermal insulants.* Part 1: 1985 *Existing traditional cavity construction.*

Approved Document E 1/2/3 Airborne and Impact Sound

Layout and changes

In spite of a question mark placed against this subject in the DOE discussion document *Content of the Building Regulations*, it has been retained as a matter considered appropriate for control. In essence the content is the same as that of Part G of the 1976 Regulations. As before, the control applies only to walls and floors separating dwellings, and the mandatory regulations are almost identical with the earlier G 1 and G 3. They are as follows:

	Requirement	Limits on application
	Airborne sound (walls)	
Walls	E 1 – (1) A wall which – *(a)* separates a dwelling from another building or from another dwelling, or *(b)* separates a habitable room within a dwelling from another part of the same building which is not used exclusively with the dwelling, shall have reasonable resistance to airborne sound.	This requirement does not apply to a wall falling within the description in paragraph *(b)* which separates a habitable room within a dwelling from another part of same building if that part is used only for the inspection, maintenance or repair of the building, its services or fixed plant or machinery.
	(2) In this paragraph 'habitable room' means a room used for dwelling purposes but not a kitchen or scullery.	
	Airborne sound (floors)	
Floors	E 2. A floor which separates a dwelling from another dwelling, or from another part of the same building which is not used exclusively with the dwelling, shall have reasonable resistance to airborne sound.	This requirement does not apply to a floor which separates a dwelling from another part of the same building if that part is used only for the inspection, maintenance or repair of the building, its services or fixed plant or machinery.
	Impact sound (floors)	This requirement does not apply to a floor which separates a dwelling from another part of the same building if that part is used only for the inspection, maintenance or repair of the building, its services or fixed plant or machinery.
Floors	E 3. A floor above a dwelling which separates it from another dwelling, or from another part of the same building which is not used exclusively with the dwelling, shall have reasonable resistance to impact sound.	

There is a introduction explaining the nature of the problem, after which there are three sections:

Section 1   Walls: widely used constructions.
Section 2   Floors: widely used constructions.
Section 3   Methods of similar construction.

The first two sections give details of suitable constructions which will meet the provisions and are the equivalent of the second method described in the old deemed-to-satisfy regulations G 2/4/5 by reference to Schedule 12. They are however a considerable expansion on Schedule 12 and maximum use has been made of diagrams.

Section 3 is the same as the first method described in G 2/4/5, namely the use of a construction similar to an actual example which has been tested and has satisfied the standards prescribed. This also has been somewhat expanded and changed as a result of further work at the BSI.

There are two Appendices A and B which give methods of determining the weights of masonry walls specified in Sections 1 and 2.

Introduction to the provisions

0.2/3/4   There are two types of sound source: (1) airborne, such as speech and musical instruments (2) impact, such as footsteps, moving furniture etc.

An airborne source sets up vibrations in the air, which in turn cause the surrounding elements to vibrate. An impact causes the element to vibrate directly. These vibrations are passed on to adjoining elements in contact with them. All these elements cause the air in adjoining spaces to vibrate and thus noise is transferred. To achieve insulation this flow of energy, either direct or indirect (flanking) must be restricted.

Direct transmission
0.5/0.9   The factors affecting airborne sound transmission are as follows:
○   Weight: heavy materials are less easily vibrated.
○   Stiffness or damping: this resists vibration and turns sound energy into heat. Thin walls made from materials of differing mechnical properties may need different weights to achieve the same result. Cavity walls may need at least as much weight as solid walls because of their lower stiffness.
○   Structural isolation by means of cavities or resilient layers; timber framed walls rely almost entirely on isolation and are much lighter than masonry.
○   The avoidance of airpaths: porous materials and gaps must be sealed.
○   Avoidance of resonance, the phenomenon which occurs when a membrane vibrates at the same frequency (pitch) as the sound source, which reinforces the source itself (what happens in an organ pipe).

Impact sound transmission is reduced by using a soft covering or an upper layer isolated by a porous spongy material (floating layer) in which case it is important to avoid rigid bridges. Such isolation also assists in reducing airborne sound transmission.

Flanking transmission
0.10/0.12   This happens when there is a path along which sound can travel between elements on opposite sides of a wall or floor. The path may be through solid structure or via an airspace (such as the cavity of an external wall). The structural paths are usually important with solid masonry elements and airspace paths with thin panels (such as studding or ceilings) in which the structural waves do not travel so freely.

Thus the weight of masonry flanking elements is also important unless it is divided into small areas by windows or other openings, in which case vibration will be reduced. Minimum weights may also be needed for thin panels connected by airspaces, such as ceilings below roof spaces. The weight required will be less if the air path is blocked.

Special factors
0.13/0.14   The presence of steps or staggers between adjacent dwellings improves the insulation and needs to be considered when using the method in Section 3.
Careless detailing or workmanship can easily reduce the insulation.

Section 1   Walls

The actual requirement is that 'the wall shall have reasonable resistance to airborne sound'. G 1 required it to have 'adequate resistance to the transmission of airborne sound'. Why what was previously 'adequate' now has to be 'reasonable' resistance is one of those mysteries we are unlikely ever to solve, but both words are freely used throughout the new Regulations (indeed almost the whole of the Regulations rely entirely on their use and we really ought to have a definition).
1.1   Diagram [6.1] shows which walls should be sound resisting.

E 1 [**6.1**] *Walls in dwellings which must be sound resisting.*
NOTE   'Habitable room' does not include a room used only as a kitchen or scullery.

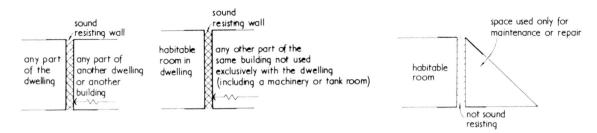

1.2   Four types of wall are described:
Type 1   Solid masonry: resistance depends mainly on weight.
Type 2   Cavity masonry: resistance depends on weight and isolation.
Type 3   Masonry core with freestanding panels: resistance depends partly on weight and partly on cavities and panels.
Type 4   Timber frame and absorbent curtain: resistance depends on isolation and absorbtion of sound in airspace.
1.3   For each type there is a selection of specifications. Attention must be paid to all details of the walls themselves and junctions with other elements. These are diagramatically illustrated separately for each type, which involves a lot of repetition. In this guide therefore new diagrams are used which illustrate the general principles, many of which are the same for all four types, with additional notes or sketches to define the differences where these occur. All the information is still there, but should the user wish to refer solely to a single type he may prefer to refer to the Approved Document itself. This however does contain some anomalies (see notes at the end of this section).

Refuse chutes
1.4   There are special rules for these illustrated in diagram [6.2].

1.4 [**6.2**] *Wall separating refuse chute from habitable room and other rooms.*

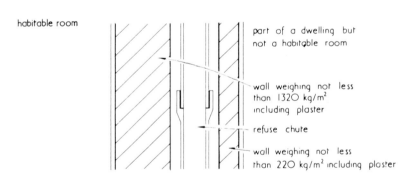

Weights of masonry walls

1.5/1.7   A means of determining these is given in Appendices A and B. The density of any particular material may be taken from a current Agrément certificate or from the manufacturer in which case the Local Authority may ask for confirmation.

Diagrams
In the diagrams which follow [6.3–6.12] measurements and weights are written simply in figures and so:
(*a*)   All references to dimensions are in millimetres.
(*b*)   All references to weights of walls and floors are in kg/m².
(*c*)   The abbreviation SR stands for sound resisting.

[6.3] *Walls: Type 1 Solid masonry.*

Core	A Brickwork	B Brickwork	C Concrete block	D Dense concrete*
Finish	Plaster 12.5	Plasterboard 12.5	Plaster 12.5	Plaster or none
Weight kg/m³ including plaster	375	375†	415	415

NOTES

1 Lay bricks frog up. Use blocks which extend full thickness.
2 Fill all joints completely with mortar (to achieve weight and avoid air paths).
* In-situ or large panel.
† Minimum weight for core only 355.

[6.4] *Walls: Type 2 Cavity masonry.*

Leaves	A Brickwork	B Concrete block	C Lightweight concrete block	D Brick
Finish	Plaster 12.5	Plaster 12.5	Plaster 12.5 or dry lining	Plaster 12.5
Weight kg/m³ including finish	415	415	250	355

NOTES

1 and 2 as above.
3 Use butterfly ties spaced 900 horizontally, 450 vertically.
4 In type C seal blockwork with cement paint throughout contact area with an intermediate floor.
5 Type D is only suitable for step and stagger situations.
6 Avoid cavity insulation from external wall entering cavity.

[6.5] *Walls: Types 3 Masonry and lightweight panels.*

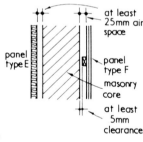

NOTES

1 and 2 as above.
3 Support panels only at floor and ceiling; do not tie to core.
4 Use only with concrete ground floor (to prevent air paths).

	Core type	Weight (min)
A	Brickwork	300
B	Concrete block, density at least 1500 kg/m³	300
C	Concrete block, density less than 1500 kg/m³	200
D	Autoclaved aerated concrete block	160

	Panel type
E	Cellular cored plasterboard partition. Weight including plaster (if any) 18 minimum. Tape joints.
F	2 sheets plasterboard with or without framework. Combined thickness 30 minimum. Stagger joints.

Specifications
Cladding
2 sheets plasterboard with or without plywood sheathing; combined thickness 30; staggered joints.

Absorbent curtains
Unfaced mineral fibre quilt (may be reinforced); density 12 kg/m³ minimum.
Thickness 25 if suspended in cavity
           50 if fixed to one frame

Firestops
Flexible, or if rigid, fixed to one frame only.

Wall specifications: types 1, 2, 3 and 4 **[6.3–6.6]**.

[6.6] *Walls: Type 4 Timber frame*

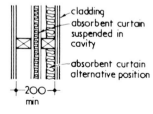

Construction 2
(no weight is specified for the brick or block wall)

Construction 1

NOTES

1 If frames need to be connected, use 14/16 g metal straps, below ceiling level, 1200 minimum apart, horizontally.
2 Avoid penetration by services. Power points may be set in if cladding is repeated behind recess. They should not be back to back.

[**6.7**] *Section: general principle for all types. See [6.8] for types 3 and 4 special details.*

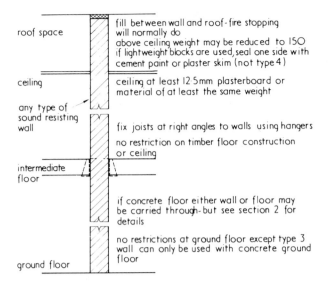

roof space — fill between wall and roof - fire stopping will normally do
above ceiling weight may be reduced to 150 if lightweight blocks are used, seal one side with cement paint or plaster skim (not type 4)

ceiling — ceiling at least 12·5mm plasterboard or material of at least the same weight

any type of sound resisting wall

fix joists at right angles to walls using hangers

no restriction on timber floor construction or ceiling

intermediate floor

if concrete floor either wall or floor may be carried through - but see section 2 for details

no restrictions at ground floor except type 3 wall can only be used with concrete ground floor

ground floor

[**6.8**] *Section: details special to types 3 and 4.*

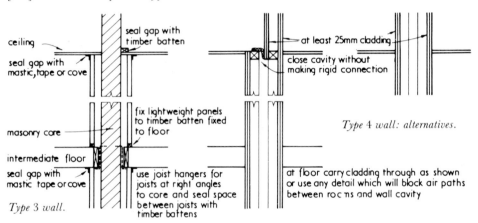

ceiling — seal gap with timber batten

seal gap with mastic, tape or cove

masonry core — fix lightweight panels to timber batten fixed to floor

intermediate floor

seal gap with mastic tape or cove — use joist hangers for joists at right angles to core and seal space between joists with timber battens

Type 3 wall.

at least 25mm cladding

close cavity without making rigid connection

Type 4 wall: alternatives.

at floor carry cladding through as shown or use any detail which will block air paths between rooms and wall cavity

[**6.9**] *Plan: general principles for Types 1, 2 and 3 (see also further notes over page).*

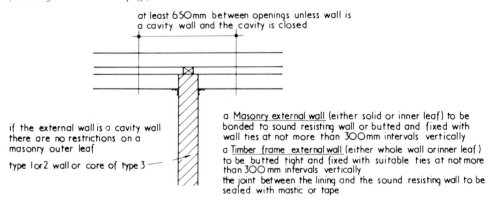

at least 650mm between openings unless wall is a cavity wall and the cavity is closed

if the external wall is a cavity wall there are no restrictions on a masonry outer leaf

type 1 or 2 wall or core of type 3

a Masonry external wall (either solid or inner leaf) to be bonded to sound resisting wall or butted and fixed with wall ties at not more than 300mm intervals vertically

a Timber frame external wall (either whole wall or inner leaf) to be butted tight and fixed with suitable ties at not more than 300 mm intervals vertically

the joint between the lining and the sound resisting wall to be sealed with mastic or tape

NOTE   There are significant changes here from the rules which applied in Part G of the 1976 regulations. The same also applies to the construction adjacent to sound resisting floors.

[6.10] *Plan: additional details for Type 3.*

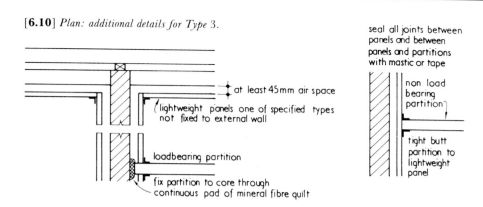

seal all joints between panels and between panels and partitions with mastic or tape

‣ at least 45mm air space

lightweight panels one of specified types not fixed to external wall

non load bearing partition

loadbearing partition

tight butt partition to lightweight panel

fix partition to core through continuous pad of mineral fibre quilt

[6.11] *Plan: Type 4 wall.*

Block air path in cavity of any external wall.

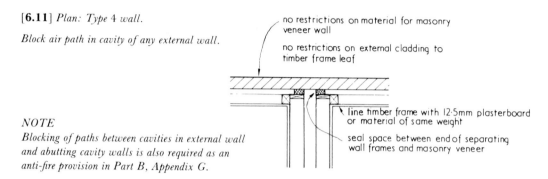

no restrictions on material for masonry veneer wall

no restrictions on external cladding to timber frame leaf

line timber frame with 12·5mm plasterboard or material of same weight

seal space between end of separating wall frames and masonry veneer

NOTE

Blocking of paths between cavities in external wall and abutting cavity walls is also required as an anti-fire provision in Part B, Appendix G.

[6.12] *Stepped and staggered construction: plan and elevation.*

Limiting pathways between elements on opposite sides of SR wall.

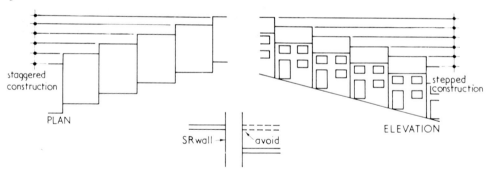

staggered construction

PLAN

SR wall ‣

avoid

stepped construction

ELEVATION

NOTES   The rules regarding the weight and nature of the external wall (solid or inner leaf) appear somewhat confused. Generally it would seem desirable that they should weigh at least 120 kg/m², but the following exceptions are mentioned.

○   In Type 1 walls, if the external wall (or inner leaf) weighs less than 120, openings should be at least 1 m high and no more than 700 mm from the face of the SR wall.

○   In Type 2 walls (except for specification B) the weight of the inner leaf should be at least 120.

○   If the area of the openings is 20 per cent or less of the area of the external wall the weight of the wall or inner leaf should be at least 120. This does not apply if the area exceeds 20 per cent.

In Type 1 the notes state 'limit the pathways between walls and opposite sides of the SR wall (to reduce flanking transmission)'. What this means is not entirely clear, but it may suggest that where possible walls or partitions abutting the SR wall on each side should be staggered. (see diagram [6.12]).

○   In Type 2 walls there is mention of 'step and stagger' situations. These are not explained but no doubt refer to the type of arrangement shown in diagram [6.12].

Section 2   Floors

The requirements are that they should have 'reasonable' resistance to airborne sound (E 2) and if the floor is above the dwelling to impact sound also (E 3).

2.1   There are the same limitations as for walls and diagram [6.13] illustrates exactly which floors must be sound-resistant.

*E 2, E 3 [**6.13**] Floors in dwellings which must be sound resisting.*

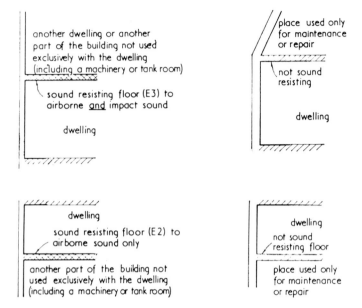

2.2   Three types of floor are illustrated:

Type 1   Concrete base with soft covering: resistance to airborne sound depends on the weight of the base and the soft covering reduces impact noise at source. This type, and this type only, may be used without the soft covering if only resistance to airborne sound is required. The other two types cannot be changed.

Type 2   Concrete base with floating layer: resistance to airborne sound depends on the weight of both the base and the floating layer, which also reduces the transmission of impact sound to the base and to adjacent construction.

Type 3   Timber base and floating layer: resistance to airborne sound depends on the weight of the base (especially type C with pugging) and of the floating layer, which also reduces the transmission of impact sound. This type needs less weight because the materials are softer and radiate sound less efficiently.

2.3   The following diagrams show several specifications for each type, identifying features requiring special attention and illustrate suitable details for junctions with walls and pipe penetrations. As with walls the diagrams in the guide have been redrawn to illustrate the general principles, together with details of individual circumstances.

Weight of concrete floors

2.4/2.5   These are expressed in kg/m². The density of the materials used on which these depend is in kg/m³. These may be taken from a current Agrément certificate or the manufacturers (in which case the Local Authority may require confirmation).

Note on Schedule 12 of the 1976 Regulations

The foregoing details of walls and floors replace Schedule 12 of the earlier Regulations. They are however in a great deal more detail. In general the same principles are followed.

Walls

Schedule 12 gave three types of solid masonry wall and two of cavity construction using bricks, blocks or dense concrete. These were roughly equivalent to types 1 and 2 in the new document. There were no equivalents to either type 3 or 4 walls.

The requirements for adjoining structure details were quite different. One alternative was for the SR wall to extend 460 mm beyond the external wall. The minimum distance between openings on each side of the wall was then 690 mm, but under certain conditions this was not necessary. These exceptions have gone. Where external walls were of timber construction the separating wall had to extend beyond the outer face unless this was tile hanging. There are now no conditions regarding the outer leaf.

There were also very rigid conditions attached to the use of timber framed external walls which were only allowed in conjunction with a solid concrete ground floor and a suspended concrete intermediate floor and roof. None of this now applies.

Floors

Similar specifications were given to the two concrete floor types 1 and 2 but the new document defines these more carefully. In the type 3 (timber) floor only the variant with heavy pugging was given. The requirements for adjoining structure required concrete floors to extend to the outer face of the inner leaf and be tied or bonded to all other separating or loadbearing walls. There was no mention of weights or glazing areas in external walls.

There were also very inhibiting rules for timber floors which had to be bounded on three sides by walls weighing at least 415 kg/m² and external flanking walls had to have no openings less than 600 mm above the underside of the floor (except over a balcony). These requirements no longer apply.

Diagrams

In the following diagrams [6.14–6.19] the same conventions apply as for walls:

[6.14] *Floors: Type 1: Concrete base; soft covering.*

In each case the weight of the base floor including any floor screed or ceiling finish bonded to the floor to be at least 365. All joints to be filled.

Soft covering: use resilient material or material with a resilient base; thickness including any backing to be at least 4.5.
(Resilient material is one which returns to former thickness after compression).

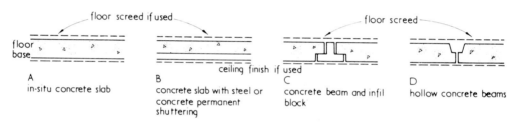

A in-situ concrete slab

B concrete slab with steel or concrete permanent shuttering

C concrete beam and infil block

D hollow concrete beams

[6.15] *Type 2: Concrete base; floating layer.*

Floor base: the same 4 types (A, B, C, D) illustrated in Type 1 may be used, but in each case the weight including any screed or the ceiling finish should be at least 220.

Floating layer: two types may be used: see below.

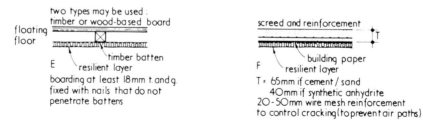

E boarding at least 18mm t. and g. fixed with nails that do not penetrate battens

F T = 65mm if cement / sand
40mm if synthetic anhydrite
20–50mm wire mesh reinforcement to control cracking (to prevent air paths)

Resilient layer:
G flexible material. 13 minimum mineral fibre, density at least 36 kg/m³ laid tightly butted.

H Board material (to be used only with screed type F) – pre-compressed expanded polystyrene (impact sound duty grade) laid tightly butted.

NOTE   The AD gives no minimum thickness for this layer, but presumably the thicker the better. An amendment may be expected.

Combination: any of the four bases can be combined with either of the floating layers.

[6.16] *Type 3: Timber base; floating layer.*

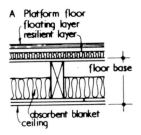

A Platform floor
floating layer
resilient layer
floor base
absorbent blanket
ceiling

All sizes and weights are minima.

Floating layer: 18 thick t and g timber or wood-based board on 19 thick plasterboard or material of the same weight.
Resilient layer: 25 thick mineral fibre of density 60–100 kg/m³.
Floor base: 12 thick timber or wood-based board nailed to joists, ceiling 30 plasterboard in two layers, joints staggered.

Absorbent blanket 100 thick mineral fibre-density 12 kg/m³ laid on ceiling.

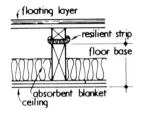

B Ribbed floor with absorbent blanket

floating layer
resilient strip
floor base
absorbent blanket
ceiling

Floating layer: 18 thick timber or wood-based board on 19 thick plasterboard or material of the same weight nailed to 50 (nom.) wide battens.

Resilient strip: 25 thick mineral fibre of density 80–140 kg/m³ (see note to Type C below).

Floor base: 50 (nom) wide joists, ceiling 30 plasterboard in two layers; joints staggered. Absorbent blanket as for Type A.

Take care nails do not penetrate through battens into resilient strip (also applies to C).

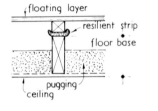

C Ribbed floor with heavy pugging

floating layer
resilient strip
floor base
pugging
ceiling

Floating layer: 18 thick t and g or wood-based board (joints glued) nailed to 50 (nom) wide battens.

Resilient strip: as for B but density stated as 80–140 kg/m³ (a fine distinction which seems a little pointless).

Floor base: 50 (nom) wide joists; ceiling 19 thick dense plaster on expanded metal.

Pugging: of dry sand or fine gravel; weight at least 80 kg/m²

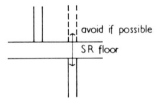

avoid if possible
SR floor

NOTE
In all three types limit the pathways between elements on opposite sides of the floor (to avoid flanking transmission).

[**6.17**] *Wall and floor junctions.*

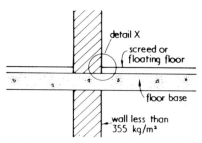

if wall exceeds 355 kg/m² either wall or floor base may pass through
if wall passes through tie floor base to wall and grout joint

Concrete floor with separating or solid internal wall.

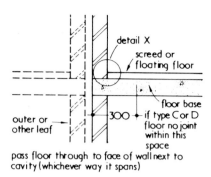

pass floor through to face of wall next to cavity (whichever way it spans)

Concrete floor with external or cavity separating wall.

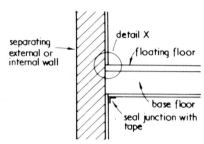

use any method of connecting floor to wall

Timber floor with heavy masonry wall (360 kg/m² or more).

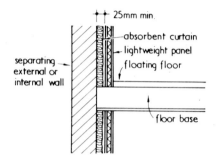

Light solid masonry less than 360 kg/m³

Lightweight panels: 18 kg/m² minimum of 2 layers plasterboard, either cellular-cored or framed; fixed top and bottom only.
Absorbent curtain: 25 thick mineral fibre of density 12 kg/m³.

Timber floor with light masonry and lightweight panel wall.
NOTE
This appears almost identical with a Type 3 wall, but there are detail differences and the absorbent curtain is additional. Presumably these are only necessary when this type of wall is used in conjunction with a timber SR floor.

There is no detail showing this type of wall used with a concrete SR floor.

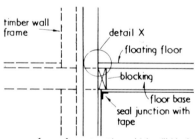

use any form of construction which will block air paths between wall and floor cavities

Timber floor with timber frame external or separating wall.

[**6.18**] *Pipe penetrating floor.*

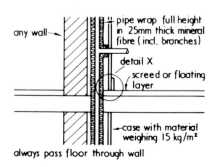

always pass floor through wall

[**6.19**] *Detail X.*

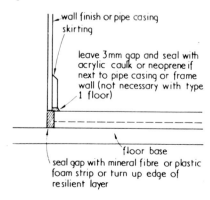

Section 3   Similar construction

3.1/3.2   This method depends on repeating as closely as possible an existing construction which has been tested and proved to have an acceptable standard. The existing and proposed design must have sufficiently similar features (described later).

Performance of existing construction

3.3/3.4   This is acceptable if the values in the table are achieved after testing as follows:
(a)   Tests to be carried out between at least 4 pairs of rooms, at least one of which is a habitable room.
(b)   One set of measurements to be taken between each pair.
(c)   If both rooms are habitable and not equal, place the sound source in the larger room.
(d)   If one room is non-habitable, place the sound source in that room.
(e)   Carry out the tests in accordance with:
BS 2750: Part 4: 1980 *Field measurements of airborne sound insulation.*
and   Part 7: 1980 *Field measurements of impact sound insulation.*
to determine the:
Standardised Level Difference D_{nT} for airborne sound and
Standardised Impact Sound Pressure Levels L^1_{nT} for impact sound.
(f)   Using the methods defined in:
BS 5821: Part 1: 1984 *Method for rating airborne sound insulation.*
and   Part 2: 1984 *Method for rating impact sound insulation.*
calculate the:
Weighted Standardised Level Difference D_{nTw} for airborne sound and
Weighted Standardised Sound Pressure Level L^1_{nTw} for impact sound.
These values must be not less than (airborne) or not more than (impact) those in the table.

Table to E 3   Sound transmission values

Type of performance	Individual values	Mean values	
		Test in at least 4 pairs of rooms	Test in at least 8 pairs of rooms
Airborne sound (minimum values)*	49 (walls) 48 (floors)	53 (walls) 52 (floors)	52 (walls) 51 (floors)
Impact sound (maximum values)**	65	61	62

NOTES
*   Airborne sound – Weighted Standardised Level Difference (D_{nTw})
**   Impact sound – Weighted Standardised Sound Pressure Level (L^1_{nTw})

As may be seen the standard required for floors (airborne) is slightly lower than that for walls and a slight reduction is also allowed if 8 pairs are tested instead of only 4.

Note on BS 2750 and BS 5821

Parts 4 and 7 of BS 2750 deal with field tests, as opposed to laboratory tests. The latter are useful for defining a sound reduction index for individual elements after blanking out all other routes for sound to pass. Field tests which take into account actual conditions, including flanking transmission, are necessary to define realistic standards.
In the tests for airborne sound the results are given as the difference in the level of sound between the room containing the sound source and the receiving room. Thus the figures to be achieved are minima. With impact sound tests only one measurement is taken in the receiving room and the standards to be achieved are therefore maxima (not to be exceeded).
The measured results have to be adjusted to take account of the acoustic absorption of the receiving room which will also affect the final sound level in addition to the various transmission factors. The method used is to measure the actual absorption of the room and relate this to an assumed standard (taken in m^2 as 0.32 times the volume in m^3), thereby producing a factor by which the actual measured value can be adjusted. This adjusted figure is then

known as the 'standardised' level difference or impact sound pressure level referred to in the Approved Document (in the 1956 edition of the BS the term 'normalised' was used).

The BS gives details of how the sounds should be created and at what frequencies measurements should be taken. There are 16 of these from 100 to 3150 (not 3200 as one might expect) covering five octaves in $\frac{1}{3}$ octave steps and recommended minimum (airborne) or maximum (impact) values for each frequency are given. These are the figures quoted in Part G of the 1976 Regulations. In these the standard required was that the aggregate of all the actual decibel reductions (or sound levels for impact) should not fall short of (or exceed) the aggregate of the stated figures by more than 23 dB, which is an average of about $1\frac{1}{2}$ dB per individual figure.

BS 5821 was not available to the authors of the 1976 Regulations. It was intended to 'simplify the formulation of acoustical requirements in building codes'. It does this by defining a reference curve (graph) of values over the frequency band. This is placed next to the actual curve formed by the test results and its position is adjusted in relation to the actual curve in accordance with specified rules. It is then possible to quote the figure at the frequency of 500 Hz (which being a logarithmic scale is the mean frequency) as a single figure standard. These are the figures which are now quoted in the Table, instead of the 16 figures which had to be used in the 1976 Regulations, and which are known as the 'weighted' standardised level difference and sound pressure levels.

Similar features

3.5   The insulation between rooms depends not only on the wall and floor specifications but on other factors mentioned below:

The following features should be similar (but not necessarily identical).

3.6   *Walls and floors*
(*a*)   The specification of the SR walls and floors.
(*b*)   The construction of adjacent walls and floors.
(*c*)   The general arrangement of windows and doors in adjacent external walls (or inner leaves).
(*d*)   The general shape and size of the rooms.

3.7   *Walls only*
The extent of any step or stagger (see Walls Type 2). If there were none, one may be provided.

Allowable differences

3.8   *Walls and floors*
(*a*)   The construction of a masonry cavity wall outer leaf.
(*b*)   The inner leaf of a masonry cavity wall if of the same general type and the weight is not reduced.

3.9   *Walls only*
(*a*)   The material and thickness of the flooring of a Type 2 or 3 floor.
(*b*)   A small reduction in a step or stagger – an increase is counted as beneficial.
(*c*)   The type of timber floor if not an SR floor.

Limits on the use of test evidence

This test procedure is only intended to enable evidence to be provided that a comparable *existing structure* has attained the values specified before new construction is undertaken. A failure of the new construction to achieve the same values is not in itself evidence of failure to comply with the regulations.

This means that a dispute cannot be settled by simply applying the test to the structure in question.

Appendices A and B

These give details of the weights of bricks, blocks and other materials (concrete, mortar, plaster) which together will make up walls of the minimum weights required by the specifications in Sections 1 and 2. Appendix A deals with the SR walls in Section 1, whilst Appendix B deals with walls associated with SR floors in Section 2, which have different weight requirements. There are 7 different specified weights in Appendix A ranging from 160 to 415 and two in Appendix B, 120 and 355. In certain cases the weights of components are adjusted to take account of a specified minimum density (as well as a minimum weight per m²). In-situ concrete and concrete block weights are taken at 3 per cent moisture content.

The weights are such that there will clearly be no difficulty in achieving them using normal materials and there seems little point in reproducing the tables here. Specifiers should refer to the Appendices themselves.

The nature of sound and its effects

Sound is one of those earthly phenomena to which animals (including *homo sapiens*) are receptive. In physics it is usually grouped with heat and light. All three are transmitted by creating vibration at the source, which sets up a wave motion. Since the speed of the wave remains constant, the faster the vibration the shorter the wave length. Sound and heat have comparatively slow speeds which can easily be comprehended by the human brain. Sound at around 700 mph is slow enough for the ear to detect echoes when the difference between the direct and reflected routes is only about 30 m. Light on the other hand (together with electricity and radio waves) travels at 186,000 miles per second, a velocity which only means anything in terms of inter-stellar space (eg light could circle the earth eight times in one second). The speed of sound is also affected by the medium through which it is passing, thus the aircraft sound barrier is less at high altitudes. The expert manipulation of sound (music) has brought enormous pleasure to the human ear which is an instrument of extraordinary refinement and accuracy. It can, however, be equally repellent and at high intensities can produce actual physical pain and deafness. This is where it becomes a matter of concern to the Building Regulations.

There are two main divisions in the need for the control of sound in buildings. The first concerns the acoustics of internal spaces; mainly the period of reverberation, controlled by introducing sound absorptive material. The second concerns the transmission of sound between internal spaces and two kinds of sound are considered, *airborne* and *impact* sound.

The transmission of sound is related not only to its strength or intensity, measured in decibels (dB), but also to its frequency expressed in Hertz (Hz) ie cycles per second.

The disturbance or nuisance value of sound generated in another room increases as the frequency rises, hence the table in the 76 Regulations required higher decibel reduction values for sound in the upper frequency ranges. This, however, is not so with impact sound. In this case the highest permitted levels are in the 200 to 500 Hz frequency band. This implies that such sound can best be tolerated at these frequencies and nuisance value is more at both the lower and upper frequency levels. The question of acoustic absorption in the rooms does not affect the resistance value of the separating wall or floor, but a high level of absorption will reduce the overall sound level in the room.

Although of no technical value it is interesting to consider the octave band structure. There are seven distinct notes in the musical scale (eight if one includes *doh* twice) which are clearly discernible to the human ear and which the human voice can not only reproduce exactly, but can also move from one note to another, jumping a whole octave or more if necessary. Although one might consider the musical scale as an arbitrary selection of progressively increasing frequencies, it clearly is not, as the frequency at the top is exactly double (from *doh* to *doh*) that at the bottom. To achieve this the frequency of each note (*ray*, *me*, *fah* etc) is 1.104× its predecessor. That the human ear and voice can tune in exactly to these very fine limits with the greatest of ease (at least for some) is really quite remarkable. The frequencies in the tables to Part G cover five octaves at intervals of one third of an octave.

The subject of sound and its suppression is a highly complex and technical affair. Part G offers a particularly good example of how the statutory rules concerning the design of buildings now require a detailed knowledge of highly complex technology which must be beyond the scope of the average (or even above average) architect, calling for increasing resort to the specialist consultant.

References

The following BSs are referred to in the AD on the page given at the end of each reference.

BS 2750 *Methods of measurement of sound insulation in buildings and of building elements.* **Part 4**: 1980 *Field measurements of airborne sound insulation between rooms.* £7 (£3·50), p. 22. **Part 7**: 1980 *Field measurements of impact sound insulation of floors.* £7 (£3·50), p. 22.

BS 5821 *British Standard method for rating the sound insulation in buildings and building elements.* **Part 1**: 1984 *Method for rating the airborne sound insulation in building and of internal building elements.* £8 (£4), p. 22. **Part 2**: 1984 *Method for rating the impact sound insulation.* £12·20 (£6·10), p. 22.

Approved Document F Ventilation

This document is divided into two parts:
F 1   Means of Ventilation.
F 2   Condensation.

This is a hybrid made up of the remains of the old Part K and extracts from the old Part F and Part P.

Part K dealt with open space outside windows (K 1, 2, 3) and height of habitable rooms (K 8) as well as ventilation (K 4, 5, 6, 7). As a matter of policy it was decided that the question of zones of open space outside windows were a matter for designers, not legislation. There was in any case no compulsion to provide windows except for ventilation, and even this could be dealt with mechanically if necessary. Also K 6, which dealt with the ventilation of larders, has been transferred to Part G Hygiene.

The content of K 4, 5 and 7 has been retained and is, in essence, the same as before.

The content of the new F 2 on condensation is drawn from the old F 5, where it formed part of the revised Part F on thermal insulation of dwellings. It has been somewhat modified.

Part P dealt with sanitary conveniences and it has been thought appropriate to extract the material which dealt with the ventilation of these, and place it here. The logic of this new grouping is not easily discernible.

F 1   MEANS OF VENTILATION

The actual requirement is as follows:

	Requirement	Limits on application
	Means of ventilation	
Walls roofs	F 1. There shall be means of ventilation so that an adequate supply of air may be provided for people in the building.	This requirement applies only to – (a) dwellings; (b) buildings containing dwellings; (c) rooms containing sanitary conveniences; and (d) bathrooms.

This is amplified by saying that the requirement will be met if the ventilation, under normal conditions, is capable of preventing the accumulation of moisture and pollutants originating inside the building reaching a level at which they would become a hazard to the health of the occupants.

From the limits on application it can be seen that the general requirements apply only to dwellings and buildings containing dwellings and it would seem that the requirements regarding sanitary conveniences and bathrooms apply to all buildings. This is not, however, confirmed by the table which refers to bathrooms in dwellings only. This has since been clarified in a list of corrections issued by the DOE, to the effect that the Regulation does apply to bathrooms in any type of building.

Section 1 Natural ventilation

1.1/1.2 A ventilation opening includes any opening whether permanent or closable which opens directly to the external air, such as doors, opening windows, louvres, airbricks or progressively opening ventilators. If a door is the only means there must also be a permanent opening equal to a 100 mm square. All such openings must have a minimum dimension of 10 mm.

The basic requirements for habitable rooms, kitchens and bathrooms in dwellings are illustrated in diagram [7.1].

F 1 [7.1] Ventilation of habitable rooms and kitchens left, by windows or other ventilation openings only; centre, by ventilation in external door;

right, by external door and other ventilation openings
NOTE   A 100 mm square = 10,000 mm²

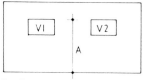
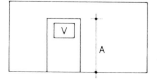
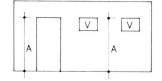

In all cases A to be not less than 1·75m

total area of one or more vents (V1+V2) etc must exceed ¹/₂₀ th floor area

V= ventilation opening

external door area must exceed ¹/₂₀ th floor area of room; total area of one or more vents must not be less than 10,000mm² doors must open directly to open air (both cases)

Common spaces in buildings containing dwellings

These must have one or more ventilation openings with a total area of at least ¹/₅₀ of the floor area. In the old regulations K 4 required any storey of a building containing dwellings to have 'effective means of ventilation' and K 7 required common stairways to have 'adequate means of ventilation'. Common spaces would appear to cover both these situations and a definite requirement replaces the previous generality.

Sanitary accommodation (including bathrooms) in any building

This means a space containing a closet or urinal, whether or not it contains any other equipment. These like habitable rooms require one or more openings totalling at least ¹/₂₀ of the floor area. Cubicles which do not form a complete seal count as part of the general space (see sketch [7.2]).

F 1.1 [7.2] Definition of sanitary accommodation.

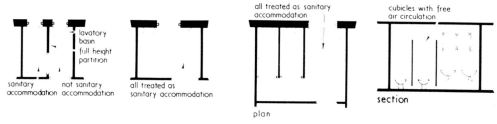

1.3 Two rooms can be treated as one space if there is a permanent opening equal to ¹/₂₀ of the combined area between them.

Ventilation through other spaces

1.4 If a habitable room adjoins a conservatory or similar space it may be ventilated through that space in the circumstances illustrated in sketch [7.3].

F 1.4 [7.3] Ventilation through a conservatory.

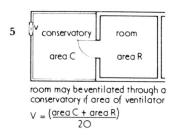
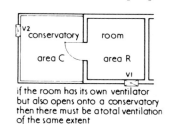

room may be ventilated through a conservatory if area of ventilator

$$V = \frac{(\text{area C} + \text{area R})}{20}$$

if the room has its own ventilator but also opens onto a conservatory then there must be a total ventilation of the same extent

area of vents v1 and v2 : $= \frac{(\text{area C} + \text{area R})}{20}$

some part of a ventilation opening must be more than 1·75m above floor level

Ventilation openings into courts

1.5   If a ventilation opening serving a habitable room opens into a court (either fully enclosed or open one side) and is within 15 m of the opposite wall the rules illustrated in diagram [7.4] apply.

F 1.5 [**7.4**] *Ventilation on to courts: left, fully enclosed; right, open-sided.*

British Standard approach	**1.6** Alternatively the recommendations of BS 5925: 1980, *CP for design of buildings; Ventilation principles and natural ventilation*, Clauses 11 to 15 may be followed. A note on this is appended. NOTE See also J 1 for supply of air to heat producing appliances.
BS 5925: 1980 CP for the design of buildings — ventilation principles and designing for natural ventilation.	The Approved Document concerns itself only with dwellings (including common spaces in buildings containing dwellings) sanitary accommodation and bathrooms, and gives simple rules of thumb. The BS, on the other hand, is concerned with all types and sizes of buildings and is a highly technical document whose use must be restricted to those having expert knowledge. It deals with the general principles of ventilation in Section Two and with natural ventilation in particular in Section Three. The AD refers only to clauses 11 to 15, which are the major part of Section Three. However, by far the most useful part of the BS for the ordinary designer is Section Two (clauses 6 to 9). This covers the various factors which create a need for a supply of outside air in all buildings. They are:

(*a*)   Human respiration.

(*b*)   Dilution and removal of odours, tobacco smoke, toxic or inflammable gases and other contaminants.

(*c*)   Control of humidity.

(*d*)   Provision of air for fuel burning appliances.

(*e*)   Control of thermal comfort.

(*f*)   Clearance of smoke in the event of fire.

Tables and graphs are provided for arriving at the quantity of air required for these diverse reasons. These are usually expressed in L/s (litres per second) per person or per m^2 of floor area, which by simple mathematics can be converted into the more easily comprehensible air changes per hour, when the size of the space is known.

As an example 8 L/s which is a normal sort of rate per person is equal to approximately one air change per hour in a room $4 \times 3 \times 2.5$ m in size.

Examples are given of how to calculate the ventilation rates required for the dilution of contaminants and body odours and for reducing the risk of condensation.

Clause 8 deals with the general considerations of the provision of ventilation and Clause 9 with the choice between natural and mechnical means.

Section three on natural ventilation is technically complex. Paradoxically the calculations required for natural ventilation are more complicated than those for mechanical systems. Basically, the volume of air movement in a building is controlled by the difference between the air pressure outside and inside or between two faces and this is a function of either wind speed and direction or temperature difference. The calculations to arrive at the volume flow of air in even the simplest of single cell buildings are complex and depend entirely on making arbitrary assumptions about wind speed and direction for any location, pressure coefficients, condition of openings etc, still further complicated by temperature conditions. Furthermore it cannot be done by using the BS alone but requires reference to a large number of other sources (which are listed). The BS admits that for more complex buildings a digital computer is essential and to date no suitable programs exist. They may be developed in the future, but in view of the unpredictability of wind and temperature conditions it hardly seems worth it. If ever there was a case of taking a sledge hammer to crack a nut this is it. The provision of natural ventilation to clear smoke in case of fire is an entirely different matter.

Section 2   Mechanical ventilation

2.1   Natural ventilation may not always be possible, in which case mechanical means may be used if the rate of air change is at least that shown in the table.
The sketch [7.5] with the table illustrates the ventilation requirements of sanitary accommodation by either natural or mechanical means.

Table to 2.1   Mechanical ventilation

Room or space	Ventilation to be provided (air changes per hour)
1 In dwellings:	
(a) habitable rooms	1
(b) kitchens	3
2 In buildings containing dwellings:	
(a) common spaces	1
3 In any building:	
(a) sanitary accommodation	3*
(b) bathrooms	3*

NOTE
* The ventilation may be intermittent but
  should run for at least 15 minutes after the use
  of the room or space stops.

[7.5] *Ventilation of sanitary accommodation.*

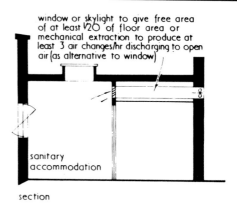

window or skylight to give free area of at least 1/20 of floor area or mechanical extraction to produce at least 3 air changes/hr discharging to open air (as alternative to window)

sanitary accommodation

section

British Standard approach

2.2   Alternatively the recommendations of BS CP 5720: 1979 *Code of Practice for mechanical ventilation in buildings*, may be used. The relevant clauses are 2.3.2.1, 2.5.2.10–11 and 3.1.1.1.

BS 5720: 1979   CP for mechanical ventilation and air-conditioning

This replaces CP 352: 1958 and reflects the enormous developments in the field of building services engineering since that date. It deals with the work involved in the design, installation, commissioning, operation and maintenance of mechanical ventilation and air-conditioning systems, which automatically brings in heating and cooling, which is a vast field. It is not however written simply for experts, and it is hoped that it will be used by all concerned with client satisfaction, who wish to understand the 'interrelation of the multitude of actions necessary to achieve that end'. It therefore includes brief descriptions of some systems and equipment to assist those without specialist training. This clearly points (*inter alia*) towards the architect. It is nevertheless, a pretty indigestible chunk of material (73pp). The Approved Document refers only to four specific clauses in Section Two (fundamental requirements) and Three (design considerations). These are:

Fresh air supply.

2.3.2.1   This is required to dilute odours, tobacco smoke and carbon dioxide exhaled by people. A table gives recommended quantities for various spaces. In deciding quantities account should be taken of natural infiltration. The amount of air introduced may be increased to provide a cooling effect, or reduced to limit the heating load (or the cooling load in warm conditions).

Fire and smoke detection

2.5.2.10   When recirculation of air is involved, consideration must be given to the install-ation of detection devices to either shut off the plant and close dampers or discharge the smoke laden air outside. This should not be near to any escape stairs etc. Smoke detectors can be used to operate alarms and/or dampers.
The Fire Research Station publish a number of notes on various building types. The local Fire Authority should be consulted.

Smoke control

2.5.2.11   Smoke can spread for a number of reasons (eg the stack effect in tall buildings). Centralised ducted ventilation systems have a potential for spreading smoke far beyond the source, so that many regulations and authorities require fan systems to be shut down auto-matically when smoke or a temperature rise is sensed. Even then smoke dampers may be needed to prevent migration of smoke through the ductwork. Systems should be designed with smoke in mind, including if possible arrangements to permit their operation in a positive way for controlling smoke.
One method of using ventilation for smoke control is the positive pressuration of escape routes, mainly stairways and lobbies. These may operate at slow speeds, switching to high speed if smoke is detected, or switch on only in emergency.

Mechanical extract/natural supply

3.1.1.1   This is the simplest form of ventilation system, comprising either one or more fans in the walls or roof, or ductwork connected to a central fan with suitable extract points and dampers. Provision for replacement air must be made.
It should be regarded as a palliative system to meet the need for ventilation in crowded rooms, offices or restricted areas with local conditions which might otherwise be objection-able such as lavatories, kitchens, plant rooms or parts of workshops and laboratories, or to meet a statutory requirement. These may be found in:

- The Building Regulations (and Building Standards in Scotland)
- The Clean Air Act 1968
- The Control of Pollution Act 1974
- The Factories Act 1961
- The Fire Precautions Act 1971
- The Health and Safety at Work Act 1974
- The London Building Acts 1939
- The Offices, Shops and Railway Premises Act 1963
- The Water Act 1973.

F 2   CONDENSATION

The requirement is as follows:

Requirement	Limits on application
Condensation	This requirement applies only to dwellings.
F 2. Reasonable provision shall be made to prevent excessive condensation in a roof void above an insulated ceiling.	

Roof voids

The standard of performance required is stated as being to limit condensation in spaces above insulated ceilings to such an extent that under normal conditions
(*a*)   The thermal performance of the insulation, and
(*b*)   The structural performance of the roof construction will not be permanently reduced.
This requirement takes the place of Regulation F 5 which was introduced in 1980 as part of the second amendment to the 1976 Regulations. It is a simplification to the extent that F 5 contained separate rules for flat roofs. These are now just counted as part of the class of roofs below 15° pitch.
1.1   The document deals only with roofs having the insulation below the void (cold roofs). Those with insulation above the void (warm roofs), which do not have the same problem, are not considered.
Although part of a roof with a pitch of over 70° is treated as a wall for other purposes, the rules in this document apply to roofs of any pitch.
1.2   Ventilation openings may be continuous or distributed along the length providing the equivalent area is maintained. Care must be taken to see that insulation does not block the ventilation gap at eaves. (Purpose-made components are available).

Roofs at 15° pitch or more
1.3   Where ceilings follow the roof pitch the rules for roofs below 15° pitch apply.
1.4/1.5   The requirements are illustrated in diagram [**7.6**].

Roofs with less than 15° pitch
1.7   These rules also apply to roofs over 15° if the ceiling follows the roof pitch.
1.8/1.9   The requirements are also illustrated in the diagram [**7.6**].
NOTE   In F 5 there were separate rules for flat roofs which took into account both the length and the span. The formula was that the ventilation area required amounted to 0.3 per cent of the roof area distributed along two sides and maintained throughout the cross section. This in effect meant 0.3 per cent of the span for each 1 m of width. As an example this would have meant a continuous gap of say 12 mm for a roof with a 4 m span. It has clearly been thought that this was not enough and the new rule which applies to all roofs below 15° is much more onerous.

[**7.6**] *Ventilation of roof (see also next page).*

Pitched roof

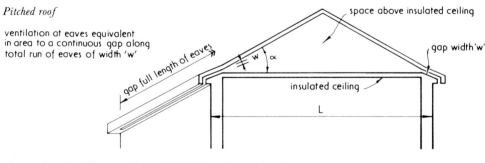

when angle ∝ > 15°   w ⩾ 10 mm (10,000 mm² per m length)
when angle ∝ ⩽ 15°   w ⩾ 25 mm (25,000 mm² per m length)

[**7.6**] *continued*.

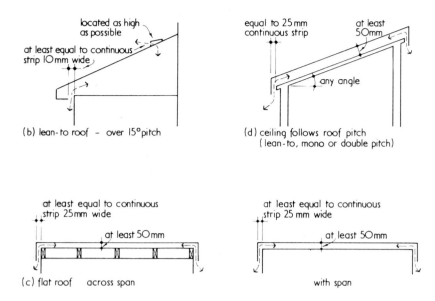

(b) lean-to roof – over 15°pitch

(d) ceiling follows roof pitch
(lean-to, mono or double pitch)

(c) flat roof across span

with span

1.10 When the edges of a roof abut a wall or other obstruction in a way that prevents free cross-ventilation, or restricts the movement of air outside ventilation openings, a different form of roof construction should be used.

1.11 Vapour checks can reduce the amount of vapour reaching the void but cannot be relied upon as an alternative to ventilation. A complete moisture barrier is needed for this (see also B 2/3/4 paragraph G 5 re-cavity barriers in roof spaces).

British Standard approach

1.6 and **1.12** Alternatively the recommendations of BS 5250: 1975 *Code of basic data for the design of buildings – control of condensation in dwellings* may be used. The relevant clauses are 22.8 to 22.16. BS 6229: 1982 *Code of practice for flat roofs* clause 18 contains further information; a note on BS 5250 follows.

BS 5250: 1975 Code of basic data for the design of buildings – the control of condensation in dwellings

Although the Approved Document refers only to some parts of clause 22 (see below) the whole of this BS is very useful. In Section One there is a clear explanation of the terms used in heat loss and condensation calculations, which are frequently confusing to the less technically minded. There are sections on the occurrence of mould growth, the basis of design for the control of condensation and recommended design assumptions (these are necessary because the conditions causing condensation – temperature, humidity etc – are wildly variable). Section Five considers design details including planning and heating and ventilation as well as clause 22 which deals with the elements of construction. The specified parts concern roofs but there are equally useful parts on walls and it seems somewhat strange that the Approved Document should ignore those.

There are two types of condensation, surface and interstitial. The first is the more obvious, but the second may be more damaging to the structure. Both occur when the temperature of the surface or the point within the structure fall below the dewpoint temperature at that position.

22.8 Serious interstitial condensation can occur unless precautions are taken. Most flat and some pitched roofs are covered with a waterproof barrier which prevents the outward escape of water vapour. Complete prevention of water vapour escaping through the ceiling into the roof void is difficult. If this reaches the cold underside of the waterproof layer condensation occurs. Prevention depends on dispersal by adequate ventilation of the roof space or providing a vapour barrier under the thermal insulation.

Timber joist roofs

22.9 There are two types – 'warm' or 'cold'. The first depends on dry insulation placed between a vapour barrier and the waterproof finish. Some vapour may penetrate ceilings so treatment of the timber is advisable. These roofs are not the concern of Approved Document

F which is concerned with 'cold' roofs. These depend on ventilation of the void to disperse vapour. Recommendations are given which conform with the Approved Document. A good vapour check above ceilings and pressure treatment of the timber are also recommended (belt and braces!).

In-situ concrete roofs

22.10 The treatment of these is dictated by the inevitable presence of construction water which must be allowed to dry out downwards. The usual solution is to sandwich dry insulation between a vapour barrier and the waterproof finish. A low thermal capacity ceiling lining is also a good idea.

Roofs of preformed units

22.11 Roofs of precast concrete units are similar to in-situ, but if the units can be kept dry a vapour barrier at ceiling level can be considered. Roofs of other materials (eg metal or asbestos) may be constructed on either the 'warm' or 'cold' system and the same principles apply.

Inverted roofs

22.12. These employ a suitable insulation above the waterproof finish, thus dispensing with the need for a vapour barrier.

Pitched roofs of tiles or slates

22.13 These come in for a lot of attention. The recommendations include those in the Approved Document and in addition:

○ Lean-to roofs should have high level ventilation equal to a 5 mm wide continuous opening.

○ Monopitch roofs should have similar provision.

○ Where there are rooms in the roof or the insulation is at rafter level, eaves ventilation and a free air space similar to flat roofs is required *plus* high level ventilation at the ridge equal to a 3 mm continuous opening.

○ These are minima and may be increased with advantage, particularly in double pitched roofs over 20° or spanning over 10 m. Ventilation at ridge level equal to a 3 mm gap is advisable in such cases.

○ It is important to prevent vent openings being blocked and to exclude water, small birds and flying insects.

○ If such ventilation cannot be provided, ventilating tiles and gable end openings may be used if correctly positioned.

○ High level ventilation is additional to the low level provisions and should never be used on its own.

○ The minimum free air space above insulation should preferably never be less than 50 mm.

Pitched roofs waterproofed with impermeable materials

22.14 These are similar to flat roofs.

Pitched roofs containing rooms

22.15 These are also similar to flat roofs. If there are problems in using the 'cold roof' approach a 'warm roof' method is advised.

Roof glazing

22.16 This is very vulnerable to condensation and provision should be made for the escape of condensate. Risk of dripping is greatest with long spans or low pitches.

References

British Standards and other documents referred to in the AD, with the page on which the reference appears.

BS 5720: 1979 *Code of practice for mechanical ventilation and air conditioning in buildings.* £26·20, p. 4.
BS 5925: 1980 *Code of practice for design of buildings: ventilation principles and designing for natural ventilation.* £16·20, p. 3.
Part F2
BS 5250: 1975: *Code of basic data for the design of buildings: the control of condensation in dwellings* Amendment slip no 1: AMD 3025. Amendment slip no 2: AMD 4210. £16·20, p. 6–7.
BS 6229: 1982 *Code of practice for flat roofs with continuously supported coverings.* £22·80, p. 7.

Approved Document G   Hygiene

Part G contains four Requirements:

G 1   Food storage.

G 2   Bathrooms.

G 3   Hot water storage.

G 4   Sanitary conveniences.

Three of these are matters not previously in the Regulations, but dealt with under the 'linked powers'. Originating in the Public Health Act 1936 they were recently incorporated in the Building Act 1984 as Sections 26, 27 and 28 and are now finally brought into the Regulations (as forecast in the Command Paper of 1982).

The fourth (G 3) concerns water supply and would previously have been a matter for Water Board control (the LA's only duty being to see that a supply of pure water was installed). The reason for now bringing this into the Regulations no doubt has to do with the fact that public safety is involved (the risk of explosion in unvented hot water systems).

NOTE   In three of these regulations there is reference to 'a house in multi-occupation'. This means a house in which the occupants are not part of a single household, and in such cases the same provision is required as for a dwelling and must be accessible to all the occupants.

G 1   FOOD STORAGE

The Requirement is as follows:

Requirement	Limits on application
Food storage	This requirement applies only to dwellings.
G 1. There shall be adequate accommodation for the storage of food or adequate space for the provision of such accommodation by the occupier.	

This is amplified by saying that any food store or space for a food store should be:

(*a*)   Of sufficient capacity.

(*b*)   Capable of being ventilated or refrigerated.

(*c*)   Easily accessible for preparing food.

The Requirement replaces Section 28 of the Building Act 1984.

Capacity

1.1   The food store, space or both together should be at least:

0.75m^3 in a dwelling with one bedroom.

1.75m^3 in a dwelling with more than one bedroom.

1.2.   Multi-occupation: see note above.

Ventilation and refrigeration

1.3   Some part of the store or space must be capable of ventilation by natural or mechanical means or of being refrigerated.

1.4/1.5   The rules for natural ventilation are illustrated in the diagram [8.1].

1.6   A space for a refrigerator must have a 13 amp electric or a gas point.

section
opening portion
of window at
least equal to a
300mm square
and fitted with
durable flyscreen
window direct to
external air

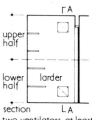

section
two ventilators, at least
one in upper half and
one in lower half, each
capable of being closed,
fitted with durable
flyproof screen and having
an unobstructed area of
at least equal to
a 70mm square

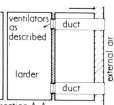

section A·A
if not direct to the external
air each ventilator must be
connected by a duct at
least equal to a 125mm square
in area with smooth internal
surface

G 1 [**8.1**] *Larder ventilation: left, by windows; centre,
by ventilators; right, ducted ventilators.*

G 2   BATHROOMS

The Requirement is as follows:

	Requirement	Limits on application
	Bathrooms	This requirement applies only to dwellings.
Bathrooms.	G 2. A bathroom shall be provided containing either a fixed bath or a shower bath, and there shall be a suitable installation for the provision of hot and cold water to the bath or shower bath.	

The usual acceptable level of performance statement says the same thing as the Regulation
plus a requirement that the bath be connected to a foul drainage system.
This requirement replaces Section 27 of the Building Act 1984.

1.1   All dwellings must have at least one room with a fixed bath or shower (see also Part F
for ventilation).

Multi-occupation: see note above on G 1.

1.2   There must be a piped supply of cold water and of hot water from a central source or
unit heater.

1.3   The bath or shower should discharge via a trap and branch pipe into a gulley or discharge stack or directly to a foul drain (see Approved Document H 1 for details).

1.4   Alternatively they may be connected to a macerator and pump small bore drainage
system which is the subject of a current Agrément certificate if the conditions of use are in
accordance with the terms of the certificate.

G 3   HOT WATER STORAGE

The Requirement is as follows:

	Requirement	Limits on application
	Hot water storage	
Hot water supply systems	G 3. If hot water is stored and the storage system does not incorporate a vent pipe to the atmosphere, there shall be adequate precautions to –	This requirement does not apply to –
		(a) a system having a storage capacity of 15 litres or less;
	(a) prevent the temperature of the stored water at any time exceeding 100°C; and	(b) a space heating system;
	(b) ensure that the hot water discharged from safety devices is safely conveyed to where it is visible but will cause no danger to persons in or about the building.	(c) a system which heats or stores water for the purposes of an industrial process.

NOTE   that unlike G 1 and G 2 the application of G 3 is NOT restricted to dwellings.

The use of this type of system has been common on the Continent for some time, but has only recently been accepted here. Previously all systems had to have an open vent (or expansion pipe) which virtually ruled out the possibility of an explosion. Such systems do, however, have the disadvantage of requiring a storage tank of adequate capacity, in which the purity of the water cannot be guaranteed. Clearly, however, unvented systems must have very foolproof anti-explosion devices and it is with this aspect that the Regulation is concerned.

1.1   Hot water storage systems can be heated either directly (immersion heater) or indirectly (calorifier).

1.2   Such systems may be either a proprietary unit or package which is the subject of a current Agrément certificate and used in accordance with the terms of the certificate.

A unit is a system which incorporates the safety devices described below and also the operating devices designed to prevent backflow, control working pressure, relieve excess pressure and accommodate expansion.

A package is a system which incorporates the safety devices and includes a kit containing all the other operating devices to be fitted by the installer.

1.3   To meet the requirements of the Agrément certificate will require a minimum of two temperature activated devices operating in sequence.

1   A non-resetting thermal cutout to BS 3955: Part 3: 1979.

2   A temperature relief valve to BS 6283: Part 2: 1982 (temperature relief valves for pressures up to 10 bar) or Part 3: 1982 (combined temperature and pressure relief valves for pressures up to 10 bar).

These two devices are additional to any thermostatic control fitted to maintain the stored water temperature.

1.4(*a*)   If the system is directly heated the thermal cutout should be on the storage unit.

(*b*)   If the system is indirectly heated it should only be connected to an energy source (eg boiler etc) fitted with a temperature operated energy cutout.

1.5   In both types the second device (temperature relief valve) should be directly on the storage vessel, preferably within 150 mm of the top, but always within the top 20 per cent of the volume of water.

1.6   Other devices providing an equivalent safeguard can be considered by the British Board of Agrément (BBA).

Installation   **1.7**   The system must be installed by an Approved Installer as defined in the BBA Certificate and include the installation of the discharge pipe from any safety device.

1.8   The discharge pipe should:

(*a*)   Be of suitable metal (what this is, is not stated, but presumably any pipe normally used for hot water would do).

(*b*)   Be the same size as the outlet on the device.

(*c*)   Discharge via an airbreak over a tundish.

(*d*)   Be no longer than 9 m unless the bore is increased.

(*e*)   Discharge in a visible but safe place such as a gully, where it will not constitute a danger to people.

1.9   The non-resetting thermal cut-out should be connected in accordance with the Regulations for Electrical Installations (fifteenth edition 1981) of the Institute of Electrical Engineers.

1.10   If all the above devices were to fail a storage vessel with a low bursting pressure would be subject to a less severe explosion than one with a high bursting pressure. This statement is not followed up by any advice, but seems to suggest that high pressure vessels are not the best answer.

In addition to the above the system must also comply with the bylaws of the relevant water authority.

G 4   SANITARY CONVENIENCES

The Requirement is as follows:

	Requirement	Limits on application
	Sanitary conveniences	
Sanitary accommodation.	G 4. Sufficient sanitary conveniences shall be provided which shall be –	
	(*a*) in rooms separated from places where food is stored or prepared; and	
	(*b*) designed and installed so as to allow effective cleaning.	

This is amplified by saying that closets should be provided:

(*a*)   In sufficient number and of appropriate type for the sex and age of the persons using the building.

(*b*)   Sited, designed and installed so as not to be prejudicial to health.

1.1   Closets and urinals using chemical or other means of treatment may be used where there is no suitable water supply or foul drain.

Number and type

1.2   A dwelling, including a house in multi-occupation (see note before G 1) should have at least one closet.

1.3   Regulations made under other legislation lay down rules as to the number and type of closets and urinals to be provided in certain types of buildings. For example in schools the sizes of the appliances must suit the age of the children and in workplaces employing more than six persons separate accommodation for each sex is required.

NOTE   This provision replaces Section 26 of the Building Act 1984 (previously in the Public Health Acts). This simply required one or more wcs to be provided and also referred to accommodation for both sexes in workplaces.

The Manual (p. 45) gives further information on other legislation under which Local Authorities or the Health and Safety Executive have a duty to see that sanitary conveniences are provided in certain premises which include:

The Building Act 1984, Section 65 Factories and Workplaces.

The Public Health Act 1936, Section 51 Water supply for wcs.

The Offices, Shops and Railway Premises Act 1963.

Food Hygiene (General) Regulations 1970 (SI 1172) Premises for the purposes of food business.

British Standards approach

1.4   Alternatively the recommendations of Clauses 2, 3, 6, 7, 8 of BS 6465: Part 1: 1984, *CP for scale of provision, selection and installation of sanitary appliances*, may be followed. A note on this follows.

BS 6465: Part 1: 1984. CP for the scale of provision, selection and installation of sanitary appliances.

This replaces CP 305: Part 1 which is withdrawn.

Sufficient space should be provided around all sanitary conveniences. Detailed information on this will be provided in a future Part 2. In the meantime information is available in Design Bulletin No. 6 *Space in the home* and No. 24 *Spaces in the home – bathrooms and WCs*, issued by the DoE.

The Approved Document refers only to Clauses 2 and 3, definitions and information and clauses 6, 7, 8 which cover design, scale of provision and workmanship.

Clause 6 suggests that sanitary accommodation should not be entered from:

(*a*)   A habitable room.

(*b*)   A room used for preparing food.

(*c*)   An office or other working area.

Of these only (*b*) now remains in the Regulations, which is not to say that it will be considered good practice to ignore the other two. There are recommendations on siting in public buildings, layout of appliances, grouping for economy of service installations, noise, doors and locks, ventilation, ease of cleaning, partitions and cubicles, finishes, selection of appliances and their support. Clause 7 contains a series of tables showing the recommended scale of provision for 12 types of building or accommodation which pretty well covers the whole range of purpose groups in the Regulations. Clause 8 deals with work on site and inspection. The remaining clauses not mentioned in the Approved Document are still useful and comprise mainly the detailed consideration of the factors affecting selection of the whole range of available sanitary fittings and accessories.

Siting

1.5   Sanitary accommodation must not open directly into a space used for preparing food (including a kitchen or scullery).

Thus the previous condition that it should not open into a habitable room (except bedrooms) or a room in which persons are employed has been dropped.

Design and installation

1.6   A closet or urinal should have a smooth, non-absorbent, easily cleaned surface.

1.7   Flushing apparatus must be capable of efficiently cleansing the receptacle.

1.8   A closet must discharge through a trap and branch into a discharge stack or drain (the term 'discharge stack' seems to have been adopted in preference to the old soil and vent pipe or stack).

1.9   A urinal should discharge through a grating, trap and branch pipe into a discharge stack or drain (see Approved Document H 1).

1.10   A closet with a macerator and pump may be connected to a small bore drainage system discharging into a stack if:

(*a*)   There is also access to a closet on a normal gravity system

(*b*)   The macerator and pump are the subject of, and the conditions of use are in accordance with, a current Agrément certificate.

References

The following British Standards and other documents are referred to in the Approved Document with the page on which the reference appears.

BS 3955 *Electrical controls for domestic appliances.* Part 3: 1979 *General and specific requirements* Amendment slip no 1: AMD 3306. Amendment slip no 2: AMD 4068. £26·20 (£13·10), p. 6.

BS 6283 *Safety devices for use in hot water systems.* Part 2: 1983 *Specification for temperature relief valves for use at pressures up to and including 10 bar.* £10·20 (£5.10), p. 6. Part 3: 1983 *Specification for combined temperature and pressure relief valves for pressures up to and including 10 bar.* £10·20 (£5·10), p. 6.

Part 3: 1983 *Specification for combined temperature and pressure relief valves for pressures up to and including 10 bar.* £10·20 (£5·10), p. 6.

BS 6465 *Sanitary appliances.* Part 1: 1984 *Code of practice for scale of provision, selection and installation of sanitary appliances.* £16·20 (£8·10), p. 8.

Institution of Electrical Engineers *Regulations for electrical installations.* 15th edition. 1981. £12, p. 6.

Approved Document H
Drainage and Waste Disposal

The Local Authorities' powers to require satisfactory drainage are contained in Section 21 of the Building Act 1984. The Water Authority also has powers, contained in the Control of Pollution Act 1974, regarding the discharge of trade effluent and further treatment of effluent from septic or settlement tanks.

This document deals with four requirements:

H 1   Sanitary pipework and drainage.
H 2   Cesspools and tanks.
H 3   Rainwater drainage.
H 4   Solid waste storage.

The first three replace Part N of the 1976 Regulations and all concern the safe disposal of sewage and rainwater. They constitute another case where the Approved Document goes far beyond the ground covered by the old Regulations. These covered the subject in general terms, requiring the various elements to be of 'adequate size, suitable materials, watertight, laid to proper falls etc' but apart from a few minima gave no detailed requirements on sizes, dimensions, gradients etc. The Approved Document on the other hand is virtually a design guide and gives a great deal of detailed information. This seems somehow to go against the general principles of limiting the Regulations to the basic requirements and leaving the rest to the expert knowledge of the designer (which was the general impression given, intended or not, of at least one main purpose of the revision). It should be useful to the designer whose knowledge of the principles of drainage is limited, but probably constitutes one of those cases where, to deliberately misquote, a little information may well be a dangerous thing (see later comments), and designers might be well advised to study the BSS in any case. To help in assessing this situation brief summaries of the most important BSS are included.

H 4 is partly another of those matters not previously contained in the Regulations which has been brought in for administrative convenience. It replaces Section 23 of the Building Act 1984 (originally 55(1) of the 1936 Public Health Act). It is however partly concerned with refuse chambers and chutes, which were covered by Part J of the 1976 Regulations.

H 1   SANITARY PIPEWORK AND DRAINAGE

The requirement itself is as follows:

	Requirement	Limits on application
	Sanitary pipework and drainage	
Discharge pipes; drains; private sewers.	H 1. – (1) Any system which carries foul water from appliances within the building to a foul water outfall shall be adequate.	
	(2) "Foul water" in sub-paragraph (1) means waste from a sanitary convenience or other soil appliance, and water which has been used for cooking or washing, but does not include waste containing any trade effluent.	

As this gives virtually no information, the amplification given under the heading 'acceptable level of performance' is in this case useful. It states that the foul water drainage system should:

(*a*)   Convey the flow of foul water to a foul outfall (meaning a sewer, cesspool, septic or settlement tank).

(*b*)   Minimise the risk of blockage or leakage.

(*c*)   Prevent foul air from the system entering the building.

(*d*)   Be ventilated.

(*e*)   Be accessible for clearing blockages;

which is an admirably concise summary of the requirements.

There are two sections:

Section 1   Sanitary pipework (within the building).

Section 2   Foul drainage (external).

There is also an Appendix dealing with larger buildings.

General

0.1/0.3   The capacity of the whole system, which depends on the size and gradient of the pipes, must be large enough to carry the flow at any point. The flow depends on the type and number of appliances and the table shows the flow rate which can be assumed for most types.

Table to 0.2   Flow rates from appliances

Appliance	Flow rate [litres/sec]
wc (9 litre washdown)	2.3
washbasin	0.6
sink	0.9
bath	1.1
shower	0.1
automatic washing machine	0.7
urinal (per person unit)	0.15

Section 1   Sanitary pipework

Traps

1.1/1.4   All points discharging into the system must be trapped to prevent foul air entering the building. The minimum sizes and seal depth are given in the table below. Ventilation of branch discharge pipes to prevent seals being broken by negative pressure in the system may be needed, (but see later). Either the trap, or the appliance if it has an integral trap, must be removable for clearing blockages.

Table to 1.2   Minimum trap sizes and seal depths

Appliance	Diameter of trap [mm]	Depth of seal [mm]
washbasin bidet	32	75
sink* bath* shower* food waste disposal unit urinal bowl	40	75
wc pan	(min. dimension) 75	50

* Where these appliances are installed on a ground floor and discharge to a gulley the depth of seal may be reduced to not less than 40 mm.

NOTE   In this Section new designations namely 'branch discharge pipe' and 'discharge stack' have been adopted to replace the old waste and soil pipe references. They are not strictly interchangeable since a branch discharge pipe can include a branch from one or more wcs (this reflects the nomenclature used in the BS).

Branch discharge pipes

1.5/1.6   These should always discharge into a discharge stack unless from appliances on the ground floor in which case they may discharge directly into a drain or, for waste water only, into a gulley.

1.7/1.11   These rules are illustrated in diagram [9.1, 9.2, 9.3, 9.8].

1.12   Sizes: pipes serving one appliance only should have at least the diameter of the trap. Sizes and other details for *unvented* branches are shown in the table below.

Table to 1.12   Common branch discharge pipes (unvented)

Appliance	Max number to be connected	OR	Max length of branch [m]	Min size of pipe [mm]	Gradient limits (fall per metre) min [mm]		max [mm]
wcs	8		15	100	9	to	90
urinals: bowls	5		*	50	18	to	90
stalls	6		*	65	18	to	90
washbasins	4		4 (no bends)	50	18	to	45

NOTE
* No limitation as regards venting but should be as short as possible.
  A fall of 18mm equals 1°.

1.13/1.19   These rules are also illustrated in the following diagrams: [9.1, 9.4–9.7].

[**9.1**] *Single stack system: discharge pipe and stack details.*

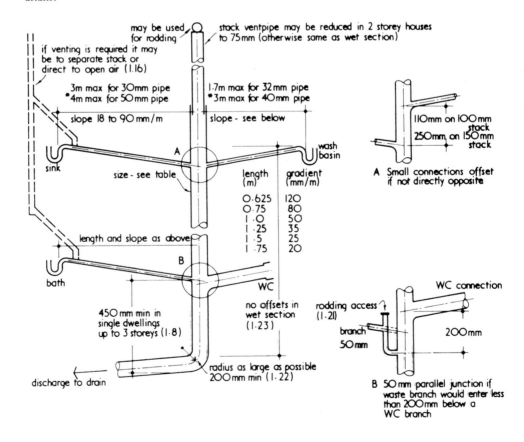

length (m)	gradient (mm/m)
0.625	120
0.75	80
1.0	50
1.25	35
1.5	25
1.75	20

NOTE   Separate ventilation is not required for the branch pipes illustrated above (1.15).

* NOTE   When larger pipe sizes are used the trap diameter is not increased but the tail of the trap is lengthened by 50 mm.

Above: details to avoid cross-flow.

1.9 [**9.2**] *Ground floor closet direct to drain.*

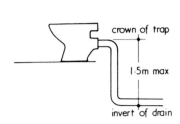

1.11 [**9.3**] *Branch pipe discharge to gulley.*

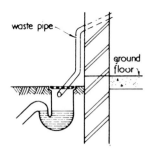

1.18 [**9.4**] *Branch ventilation pipes (but see text).*

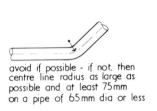

1.13 [**9.5**] *Bends in branch pipes.*

1.14 [**9.6**] *Alternative junctions.*

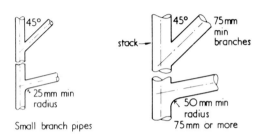

Authors' note

The rule on ventilation (1.16) is misleading. In the BS the connection of a branch ventilation pipe to a discharge stack is only permitted above the spillover level of the *highest* connected appliance (not just the highest appliance on each storey) and this then becomes a modified single stack system, not a ventilated system as stated; this would require ventilation of the stack itself (see notes on BS 5572 at end of section).

1.20   Branch ventilation pipes serving one appliance should be 25 mm diameter unless the branch exceeds 15 m long or has over 5 bends, when it should be increased to 32 mm.

1.21   Rodding points should be provided for access to any length of pipe which cannot be reached by removing traps.

Discharge stacks

1.22/1.23   Discharge and offsets: see diagram [9.1]. Stacks should be run inside buildings over 3 storeys high.

1.24   Sizes: stacks should have at least the diameter given in the table 1.24 and should not reduce in the direction of flow.

NOTE   The reader might think that this table, taken together with the table to 0.1/0.3 should be used to establish the size of discharge stacks. If this were so a 100 mm stack would be limited to a maximum of 3 wcs, since no mention is made of the probability of simultaneous use. BS 5572 however explains this and gives a table for sizing both discharge stacks and ventilating stacks which shows up to 30 domestic appliance groups connected to a 100 mm discharge stack (a domestic appliance group is one each of wc, bath, sink and washbasin). There is also a system of sizing by using discharge units which shows that up to 53 appliance groups may be connected to a 100 mm stack.

1.25/1.28   Stub stacks, ventilation pipe outlets (see diagram [9.8]).

Table to 1.24   Maximum capacities for discharge stacks

Stack size [mm]	Max capacity [litres/sec]
50 (min for urinals)	1.2*
65	2.1*
75	3.4†
90	5.3
100	7.2

* No wcs.
† No more than 1 siphonic wc with 75 mm outlet.

1.19/1.27 [**9.7**] *Termination of ventilating stacks or ventilation part of stack.*

1.10/1.25 [**9.8**] *Stub stacks and ventilation pipe outlets.*

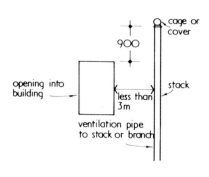

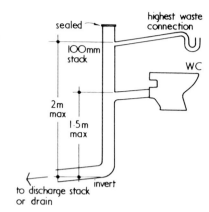

1.29 Discharge stacks may terminate inside a building if fitted with air admittance valves the subject of, and the conditions of use in accordance with, a current BBA Certificate. The valve must not impede the ventilation of the underground drainage usually provided by the open stacks.

1.30 Rodding points should be provided for access to any lengths of pipe which cannot be reached from any other part of the system (eg through the removal trap or appliance).

Materials and fixing

1.31 Any of the materials in the table may be used. Different metals should be separated by non-metallic material to avoid electrolytic corrosion.
Pipes should be firmly supported without resisting thermal movement.

Table to 1.31   Materials for sanitary pipework

Material	British Standard
Pipes:	
cast iron	BS 416
copper	BS 864 BS 2871
galvanised steel	BS 3868
Plastics, ABS, mupvc, polythene	BS 5255
upvc	BS 4514
polypropylene	BS 5254
Plastic	BS 5255
Traps:	
copper	BS 1184
plastics	BS 3943

Watertightness

1.32 The system should withstand an air or smoke test to a pressure of 38 mm water gauge for 3 minutes, during which every trap should maintain a water seal of 25 mm min.

Note
On the face of it this should be quite feasible for traps requiring a 75 mm minimum seal but not possible with traps to wcs which need only a 50 mm minimum.

British Standard approach
1.33 Alternatively the recommendations of BS 5572: 1978 *Code of Practice for sanitary pipework*, Clauses 3, 4 and 7–12, can be followed. A note on this follows.

Note on BS 5572: 1978

This deals with sanitary pipework above ground.
It supersedes CP 304: 1968 on which it considerably enlarges. It covers the requirements of domestic, commercial and public buildings but it does not deal with the special requirements of hospitals, laboratory buildings, trade effluents and the like.

It outlines the general principles involved and gives performance data. There are detailed recommendations for the design of traps, discharge pipes and stacks, ventilating pipes and stacks and access. Four types of discharge system are described and since the Approved Document is somewhat confused over the basic differences between these, they are illustrated below by single line diagrams [9.9 A–D]. These show the arrangement for one storey but can be applied to any number of storeys.

All are designed to protect the seal in the traps.

Type A, fully ventilated, protects the seals by ventilating both the stack and the individual branch pipes.

Type B may be used where the disposition of branch pipes (length and gradient) make individual venting (to prevent self-syphonage) unnecessary and the only danger lies in the effect of the flow in the stack on branch connections (ie only the discharge stack itself is ventilated by cross connection to a separate vent stack).

Type C can be used where the discharge stack is large enough to limit pressure fluctuations without requiring a separate ventilating stack (the single stack system).

Type D is a modified version of this to provide ventilation only to those branches whose disposition might cause loss of seal. In this case only the branch, and not the stack, is connected to the ventilating stack, which means this can be smaller and need not extend below the lowest connected branch.

The rules in the Approved Document are based on the single stack, or modified single stack systems, which suit the most commonly found conditions, but many of the requirements are the same for all systems.

Clause 9 illustrates commonly used arrangements including sizes for both discharge and ventilating branch pipes and stacks including connections for both single and ranges of appliances.

Clause 10 gives another method of sizing by using the discharge unit method which is based on the same assumptions as to flow rates and frequency of use as that used for drains (see note on BS 8301: 1985 later). Since the maximum capacity of the system is seldom the deciding factor in selecting sizes for above ground pipework, it is only likely to be used for very large installations.

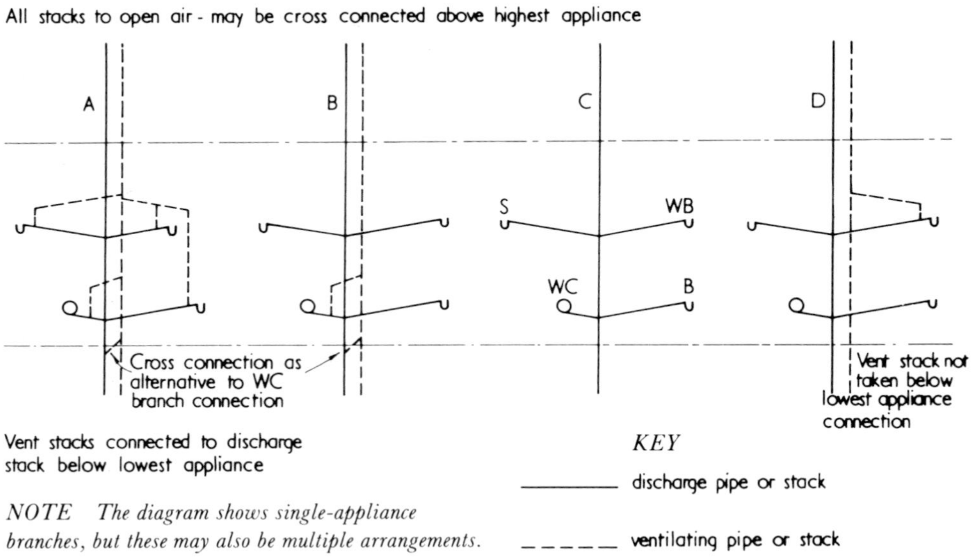

[9.9] *Types of discharge systems*
A Ventilated
B Ventilated stack
C Single stack
D Modified single stack

All stacks to open air - may be cross connected above highest appliance

Vent stacks connected to discharge stack below lowest appliance

NOTE The diagram shows single-appliance branches, but these may also be multiple arrangements.

KEY

———— discharge pipe or stack

– – – – ventilating pipe or stack

Section 2   **Foul drainage**

2.1/2.2 Public sewers sometimes carry both foul and rainwater. If the drainage system is also designed to carry both (a dual system) pipe sizes may need to be increased above those required for foul water only.

This document does not deal with pumped sewerage systems (although the BS does).

Layout and cover

2.3   Keep the system simple. Changes of direction and gradient are to be as few and as gentle as possible. Provide access points only where blockages cannot be cleared without them.

2.4   The system should be ventilated at the head of each main drain and any branch over 10 m long.

2.5   Lay pipes to even gradients; any changes to be at access points.

2.6   Lay in straight lines where practicable, but slight curves are permissible if blockages can be cleared. Bends should be in or close to inspection chambers and have as large a radius as possible.

2.7   Allow for settlement where drains run under or close to a building (see Appendix A 9 to A 11).

2.8/2.9   The depth of drains will mainly depend on the required gradients and ground levels, however protection from damage must also be considered, and if the primary factors result in too little cover for pipe protection (or too much, when the weight of the backfill becomes a problem) different combinations of cover, pipe strength and bedding may need to be considered, or special protection provided (see Appendix A 12/A 14).

Gradients and sizes

2.10/2.13   The size and gradients of drains should be such as to accommodate the flow (see table to 0.1/0.3).

NOTE   These flow rates are what might be expected from each individual appliance and this requirement seems to suggest that drains be sized on the assumption that all appliances would be discharged simultaneously; an unlikely event even in a small installation. Here again, as in the last section, no mention is made of reduction factors such as are applied in most situations of this type. However reference to BS 8301 (from where these figures are taken) shows that the use of reductions based on probability theory is intended (see note on BS 8301 later).

The chart [9.10] shows the capacity of foul drains of three diameters at various gradients (these are for drains running ¾ full which is as much as is practicable without causing pressure problems; a drain running full bore draws air behind it).

2.10 [**9.10**] *Discharge capacities of foul drains running 0.75 proportional depth.*

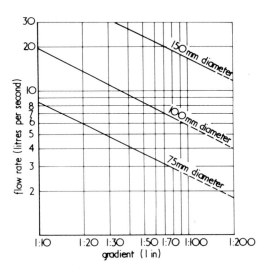

NOTES

1   No waste water drain to be less than 75 mm. No soil water drain to be less than 100 mm.

2   Drains carrying a peak flow of less than 1 litre/sec should not be laid at less than 1:40. (NOTE   These would be limited to drains not connected to a wc).

3   For drains carrying more than 1 litre/sec gradient to be not less than 1:80 for 75 mm or 100 mm if at least 1 wc is connected; not less than 1:150 for 150 mm with at least 5 wcs connected.

4   Gradients may be reduced with high standards of design and construction (see dotted lines on chart).

2.14   Combined systems which carry both foul and rainwater must be designed to accommodate the total peak flow of both (see Requirement H 3).

Materials

2.15   Acceptable materials and the appropriate British Standards are shown in the table and:

1   All joints must remain watertight under working conditions.

2   Nothing must project into the pipe or cause obstruction.

3   Different metals to be separated by non-metallic materials to avoid electrolytic corrosion.

4   Rigid pipes should have flexible joints.

The last item means that cement or lead caulked joints are no longer acceptable (although the BS gives some isolated situations in which they can be used).

Table to 2.15   Materials for below ground gravity drainage

Material	British Standard
Rigid pipes	
asbestos	BS 3656
vitrified clay	BS 65
concrete	BS 5911
grey iron	BS 437
Flexible pipes	
upvc	BS 4660
	BS 5481

Note   Some of these materials may not be suitable for conveying trade effluent.

Bedding and backfilling

These rules are entirely new so far as the Regulations are concerned and were not covered at all in the old Part N.

The notes and diagrams are a good deal less than satisfactory and leave a lot of doubt as to the intentions. For example the difference between Class N and Class F bedding is not apparent. Because of this the table and diagrams [9.11, 9.12] are reproduced exactly as in the Approved Document, since any attempt to clarify or annotate them would have to be based on guesswork. Reference to BS 8301, from which they are drawn, does help, but even this is not explicit on some points (see note on BS which follows the end of this section).

The table is a cut-down version of Table 6 of the BS, the figures chosen being those given for pipes of the lowest crushing strength.

2.16   The choice of bedding and backfilling will depend on the depth, size and strength of the pipes and in some cases the width of the trench (there is no further explanation of this last proviso).

2.17   Rigid pipes of standard strength may be laid as shown in the diagram, in which case the minimum and maximum depths of cover are as shown in the table. It is not stated whether this depth should be measured from the top of the selected fill or the crown of the pipe. No explanation is given of what is meant by 'bedding factor', or by the note '45° min.' on the class F diagram (but see note on BS 8301).

2.17 [**9.11**] *Bedding for rigid pipes.*

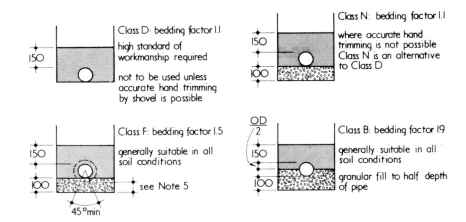

2.18   Flexible pipes will deform under load and require support to limit this to 5 per cent of the diameter. The diagram shows the recommended systems which will presumably achieve this (although this is not stated it is confirmed by the BS). A question arises here as to whether Local Authorities will have to devise some method of measuring the deformation under load.

Minimum depth should be 0.9 m under any road and 0.6 m under fields and gardens; maximum 10 m in all cases (see also A 13/A 14).

2.18 [**9.12**] *Bedding for flexible pipes.*

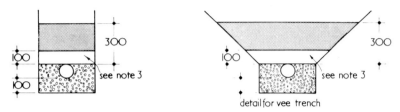

detail for vee trench

KEY (to [**9.11**] *and* [**9.12**]*)*

1 *Selected fill: free from stones larger than 40 mm, lumps of clay over 100 mm, timber, frozen material, vegetable matter.*

2 *Granular material: should conform to BS 882: 1983 Table 4 or BS 8301: 1985 Appendix D.*

3 *Selected fill or granular fill free from stones larger than 40 mm.*

4 *Provision may be required to prevent ground water flow in trenches with Class N, F or B type bedding.*

5 *Where there are sockets these should be not less than 50 mm above the floor of the trench.*

Table to 2.17   **Limits of cover for standard strength rigid pipes in any width of trench**

Pipe bore	Bedding class	Fields and gardens		Light traffic roads		Heavy traffic roads	
		Min	*Max*	*Min*	*Max*	*Min*	*Max*
100	D or N	0.4	4.2	0.7	4.1	0.7	3.7
	F	0.3	5.8	0.5	5.8	0.5	5.5
	B	0.3	7.4	0.4	7.4	0.4	7.2
150	D or N	0.6	2.7	1.1	2.5	—	—
	F	0.6	3.9	0.7	3.8	0.7	3.3
	B	0.6	5.0	0.6	5.0	0.6	4.6

Comment

Note 4 below the diagrams (which is not taken from the BS) presumably means that the granular bed might act as an undesirable subsoil water drain and some means of dealing with this might be needed.

Clearance of blockages

Siting and provision of access points

2.19/2.23   Sufficient and suitable access for clearing blockages must be provided. The provisions described are for normal rodding and not where mechanical means are available.

Access points are of four types:

(*a*)   Rodding eyes – capped extensions of the pipe.

(*b*)   Access fittings – small chambers on the pipes (or on an extension of the pipes).

(*c*)   Inspection chambers – large chambers with open channels, but not working space (of limited depth).

(*d*)   Manholes – large chambers with an open channel and working space (any depth).

They should be provided:

(*a*)   At or near the head of each drain.

(*b*)   At a bend or change of gradient.

(*c*)   At a change of pipe size (but see (*d*) if at a junction).

(*d*)   At a junction unless each run can be cleared from another access point (some junctions can only be rodded through from one direction).

(e)   At maximum intervals on straight runs.
The table and diagram [9.13] show greatest depths and least dimensions for access points and maximum distances between them according to type.

Table to 2.21   Minimum dimensions for access fittings and chambers

| Type | Depth to invert (m) | Internal sizes | |
		Length × width (mm × mm)	Circular (mm)
Rodding eye	–	As drain but min 100	
Access fitting			
small	0.6 or less	150 × 100	150
large		225 × 100	–
Inspection chamber	0.6 or less	–	190*
	1.0 or less	450 × 450	450
Manhole	1.5 or less	1200 × 750	1050
	over 1.5	1200 × 750	1200
Shaft	over 2.7	900 × 840	900

NOTES
* Drains up to 150 mm
Covers to be same size as fittings or chambers, except manhole covers to be 600 square or diameter

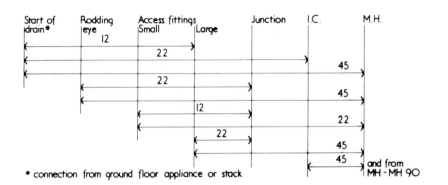

2.23 [**9.13**] *Maximum spacing (in metres) of access points for drains up to 300 mm.*

Construction
2.24   Access points must contain the foul water under working conditions and resist the entry of ground and rainwater. The materials which may be used include the traditional bricks, blocks and in-situ concrete and also vitrified clay, precast concrete and plastic, in which a range of factory-made units are available.

Table to 2.24   Materials for access points

Material	British Standard
1 Inspection chambers and manholes	
Clay	
bricks and blocks	BS 3921
vitrified	BS 65
Concrete	
precast	BS 5911
in situ	CP 110
Plastics	BBA Certificates
2 Rodding eyes and access fittings (excluding frames and covers)	as pipes see Table to 2.15 BBS Certificates

2.25/2.26   Detailed requirements for manholes and inspection chambers are shown in diagram [9.14].

2.25/2.26 [**9.14**] *Inspection chambers and manholes.*

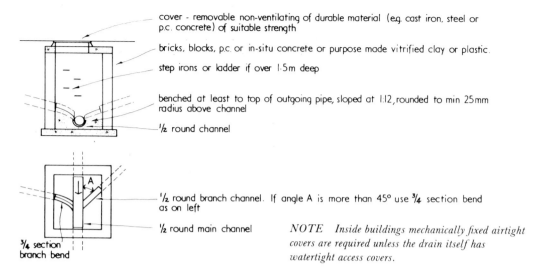

cover - removable non-ventilating of durable material (e.g. cast iron, steel or p.c. concrete) of suitable strength

bricks, blocks, p.c. or in-situ concrete or purpose made vitrified clay or plastic.

step irons or ladder if over 1·5m deep

benched at least to top of outgoing pipe, sloped at 1:12, rounded to min 25mm radius above channel

½ round channel

½ round branch channel. If angle A is more than 45° use ¾ section bend as on left

½ round main channel

¾ section branch bend

NOTE   Inside buildings mechanically fixed airtight covers are required unless the drain itself has watertight access covers.

Watertightness

2.27/2.29   Drains up to 300 mm should be either:

(*a*)   Air tested to give a maximum loss of head on a manometer of 25 mm in 5 minutes for 100 mm gauge or 12 minutes for a 50 mm gauge.

(*b*)   Water tested to 1.5 m head measured above the invert at the head of the drain. The section being tested should be filled, left to stand for 2 hours and topped up. The leakage over the next 30 minutes should not exceed 0.05 litres for each metre run of 100 mm drain (a drop of 6.4 mm/m) or 0.08 litres for a 150 mm drain (a drop of 4.5 mm/m). The head of water should never exceed 4 m, so it may be necessary to test in sections.

British Standard approach

2.30   Alternatively the relevant recommendations of BS 8301: 1985 *Code of practice for building drainage* may be followed. The relevant sections are One, Two, Three (except Clauses 10 and 15) Four (except Clause 23) five (Clause 25 only) and Appendices. A note on this follows.

Note on BS 8301: 1985 Building drainage

This is a complete revision of CP 301: 1971, which it supersedes. It is mainly concerned with pipes of DN 100 and DN 150 but covers sizes up to DN 300 (DN = nominal diameter in mm). For larger sizes CP 2005 is appropriate.

It emphasises the need for pipeline flexibility to avoid failure from ground movement (hence rigid joints are out).

It covers pretty well the whole field, including foul drainage, surface water drainage and combined systems, but not septic tanks etc.

The excluded clauses mentioned in 2.30 relate to ground water and pumped systems.

Section Three contains the bulk of the information for the designer. In particular it gives details of how to calculate the flow in a system based on discharge units. These take account not only of the characteristics of the individual appliances, but also the duration of discharge and likely intervals of use.

If the flow rates given in the Approved Document were simply multiplied by the number of appliances, a vastly excessive figure would result. For example, the four basic appliances in a single house (wc, sink, bath and washbasin) give a total of 4.9 litres/sec whereas the BS chart shows only 2.5. For 10 houses the reduction is much greater, giving only 4.1 litres instead of 49, and for larger numbers still the reduction is even more dramatic. The use of straight totals would result in serious oversizing; which can result in solids being deposited and causing blockages, as well as being unnecessarily expensive.

The section on bedding and backfilling gives more information than the Approved Document, but even this is not fully explicit. The term 'cover' is not defined but must surely refer to the depth from the crown of the pipe to the surface. As in the Document, no definition of 'bedding factor, is given, and the difference between Class N and Class F is still not very apparent, except that the diagram for Class F [9.15] indicates the pipe is slightly sunk into the granular fill. This might suggest that it should be laid that way but since the note on the diagram states it is 'illustrated after settlement' and the text says that 'settlement should in no case exceed that illustrated for Class F bedding', it is to be inferred that the depression in the granular fill is due purely to subsequent settlement. If this were the case one would expect the note '45° min.' to read '45° max.' (ie a limitation on the amount of settlement). On the other hand the table shows Class F as superior to Class N, which suggests there is some significant difference between them. The only other difference is that the CF is not greater than 0.2 for Class F and B, and 0.3 for Class N. (CF = Compaction Fraction: a measurement of the compaction of the granular material under load, for which a test method is given).

The contents of the Approved Document are clearly simply a selection of the information contained in the BS.

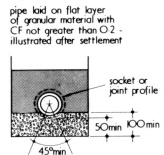

pipe laid on flat layer of granular material with CF not greater than 0·2 - illustrated after settlement

socket or joint profile

50min 100min

45°min

[**9.15**] *Bedding Class F as illustrated in BS* 8301.

Appendix Additional guidance for large buildings

Quite why this small amount of information has been separated into an appendix is not clear, but since it has, the same arrangement is adopted here to make direct reference possible.

Flow rates and traps

A 1   One additional flow rate is given: ie 0.06 litres/sec for a spray tap basin. No mention is made of industrial kitchen units, wash troughs etc, although they are mentioned in the BS.

A 2   Some additional minimum trap sizes are given as shown in the table below.

Table to A 2   Minimum trap sizes and seal depth additional to Table 2

Appliance	Diam of trap (mm)	Depth of seal (mm)
sanitary towel macerator	40	75
food waste disposal unit (industrial type)	50	75
urinal (stall, 1 to 6 person positions)	65	50

Discharge and ventilating pipes and stacks

These are some additional criteria generally applicable to multi-storey buildings both residential and commercial.

A 3/A 4   In buildings up to 5 storeys the lowest branch connections should be at least 750 mm above the invert of the bend at the base of the stack (apart from single dwellings up to 3 storeys: see Section 1).

In buildings from 6–20 storeys there should be no ground floor branch connections at all. In buildings over 20 storeys both ground and first floor branch connections should be excluded.

These should be taken either into a separate stack, or if ground floor, into a drain or gulley.

A 5   Where ventilation of branch pipes is necessary the ventilation pipes may be taken to the outside air or to a separate dry stack. (A 5 also states 'or to a ventilated discharge stack' but this must be treated with caution as such connections must not be below the overspill level of the highest connected appliance – such connections cannot be made at each storey of a multi-storey building and the Approved Document reveals some misinterpretation of the BS in respect of ventilation generally: see note on BS 5572).

A 6   Ventilation stacks in 10-storey flats may be 32 mm or more.

A 7   This states that 'the lower end of a stack may be connected to a *bend*' but the meaning of this is unclear. The original reference to paragraph 3.15 has been corrected to 1.22 which refers to a bend of at least 200 mm radius at the bottom of all stacks. Alternatively, it may be connected to the discharge stack below the lowest branch connection, which is also recommended in the BS.

A 8   The upper end may be carried to the outside air (when the same rules apply as for the upper end of open discharge stacks) or cross connected to the discharge stack above the spill-over level of the highest connected appliance.

Special protection

This concerns underground drains.

A 9   Under a building a pipe should be surrounded by at least 100 mm of granular material or other flexible fill.

A 10   A drain passing through a wall or foundation should be treated as shown in diagram [9.16].

A 11   The trench for a drain near a building should be filled with concrete if the circumstances are as illustrated in [9.17].

A 10 [**9.16**] *Pipe penetrating wall.*

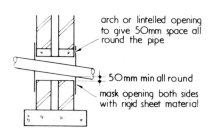

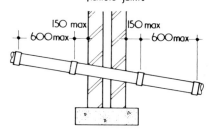

A 11 [**9.17**] *Drain trench near building.*

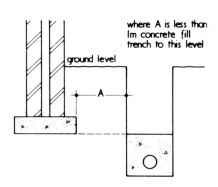

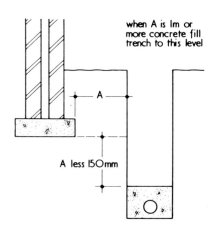

Ground loads

A 12/A 14   Where ground cover is limited, special precautions are needed, as illustrated in diagrams [9.18, 9.19].

A 12 *to* A 14 [**9.18**] *Special protection: ground loads.*

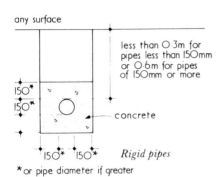

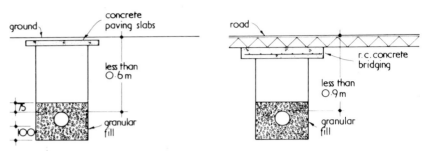

Rigid pipes

* or pipe diameter if greater

Flexible pipes not below road (or as for rigid pipes)

Flexible pipes below road

[**9.19**] *Movement joint in concrete surround.*

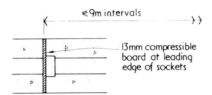

Note on BS 65: 1981

This supersedes BS 65 and BS 540 Parts 1 and 2, also BS 539 and BS 1143. It covers the requirements for vitrified clay pipes and fittings, with or without sockets and includes normal, surface water, perforated and extra-chemically-resistant pipes. It applies to both glazed and unglazed products.

The requirements specified cover some dimensions and tolerances, also physical and performance characteristics and testing procedures. A range of preferred and other diameters is given, but the BS no longer includes any details of recommended lengths, socket dimensions, radius and curvature of bends etc, but merely specifies allowable tolerances on the manufacturers' stated values, plus a test for straightness. The diameters range from 75 mm to 1000 mm.

Performance standards specified include crushing strengths, bending moment resistance, impermeability, internal pressure test, chemical and acid resistance and water absorption. Flexible mechanical joint assemblies are tested for deflection, straight draw and shear resistance, including both socketed and sleeve type joints for use with plain ended pipes.

Many of the tests require internal pressure to be applied and the unit of measurement used is the kPa (kilo Pascal). (1 kPa = 10 mbar = 1kN/m^2).

H 2   CESSPOOLS AND TANKS

Unfortunately there are still locations where connection to a public sewer is not possible and the need for other solutions will still recur. The requirement is as follows:

	Requirement	Limits on application
	Cesspools, septic tanks and settlement tanks	
Cesspools; septic tanks; settlement tanks.	H 2. Cesspools, septic tanks and settlement tanks shall be sited and constructed so as to – *(a)* permit access for emptying; and *(b)* avoid contamination of water supplies by leakage or spilling over of the contents.	

This very brief statement is amplified by an acceptable performance level as follows:

(*a*)   Cesspools to have enough capacity to store the foul water until they are emptied.

(*b*)   Cesspools, septic and settlement tanks to be accessible and designed so as not to contaminate water supplies or be prejudicial to health.

(*c*)   Septic and settlement tanks to have sufficient capacity to break down and/or settle solid matter in the flow of foul water.

Introduction

It may be helpful for those not very familiar with this branch of engineering (and many of us are not) to explain the basic differences between the three types of unit.

1   Cesspools are simply storage tanks which hold the whole of the piped foul waste (solids and liquids) with no (planned) biological action. They have to be emptied frequently (probably monthly).

2   Settlement tanks are chambers in which the solids are separated out as sludge and removed at frequent intervals (probably weekly). This may be done hydraulically. Liquid waste is filtered.

3   Septic tanks are a form of settlement tank in which the sludge is retained for sufficient time for organic matter to undergo anaerobic decomposition. Filtration of liquid waste may be necessary. They are the best solution to the small installation providing ground conditions permit, as desludging is normally required only once every 12 months.

The provisions of the Approved Document itself are very brief, as follows:

Capacity

1.1   Cesspools: at least 18m³ below the inlet level.

1.2   Septic and settlement tanks: at least 2.7 m³ below the inlet level.

Siting

1.3   Cesspools requiring to be emptied by tanker should be within 30 m of a vehicle access, and arranged so that they can be emptied and cleaned without the contents being taken through a dwelling or a place of work. Access may however be through an open covered space.

Design and construction

1.4/1.9   The principal points are illustrated in diagram [9.20]: Materials may include brickwork, concrete, GRC, GRP or steel (corrosion protected). Brickwork should be at least 220 mm engineering brick in cement mortar and in-situ concrete at least 150 mm thick.

The entry velocity into the tank should be limited by laying the last 12 m of incoming drain at a gradient not steeper than 1:50 (for drains up to DN 150) or by providing a dip pipe.

NOTE   BS 6297 suggests the use of ventilating covers for septic tanks but for cesspools recommends ventilation via the building drainage system with a fresh air inlet valve on the cesspool itself.

1.4 to 1.9 **[9.20]** *Requirements for cesspools and septic tanks.*

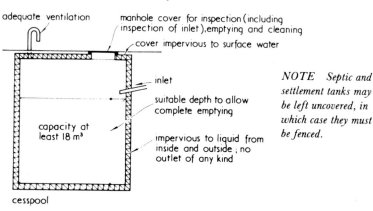

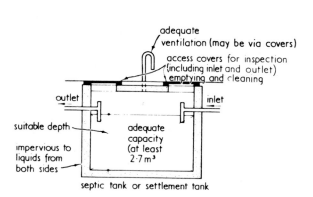

septic tank or settlement tank

**British Standard
approach**

Alternatively the relevant recommendations of BS 6297: 1983: *Code of Practice for the design and installation of small sewage treatment works*, may be followed. The relevant clauses are in Sections one, two, three (clauses 6 to 11), four and Appendices. A note on this follows.

Note on BS 6297: 1983

This replaces CP 302: 1972. Its scope includes small sewage treatment plants for domestic type discharge ranging from single households to about 1000 population equivalent, and also sewage storage in cesspools. It does not deal with trade effluents.

It is strongly recommended that the information should be supplemented by skilled engineering advice.

There is a note on materials which as well as the traditional brick and concrete include GRC, GRP and steel which should be corrosion protected both inside and out.

Sewage treatment works operate by the settlement and retention of solids and usually include biological treatment by the use of biological filters or by biological treatment of the raw sewage followed by the separation of solids.

Cesspools receive and retain raw sewage and form no part of sewage treatment.

Surface water should always be excluded or if not possible, specialist advice sought. Collective treatment is better than a number of individual units. Small treatment works (two or more premises) should be sited at least 25 m from any dwelling and this distance increased for larger works. Good access is needed to enable the tanker to operate its suction lift facility.

All tanks must be impervious to both contents and ground water. Cesspools should always be covered to exclude rain. Other tanks may be covered or protected by fencing but all must have access for cleaning and inspection including inspection of inlets and outlets. Access openings should have at least 600 mm clear opening. They should also be vented and have rodding access.

Cesspools

An average household of three persons may produce 7 m^3 (the capacity of an average tanker) every three weeks. Cesspools should be sited at least 15 m from any dwelling and away from any source of drinking water. There should be vehicle access to within 30 m.

The capacity should be based on 1 m^3 per head per week, which allows for some infiltration of ground water via the drains. The best shape is as shown in diagram [9.21]:

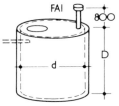

FAI

800

d

D

d = D
D (depth from cover to floor)
to be not more than 4m

May be rectangular

[9.21] *Septic tanks venting via the house drainage system. FAI with non-return valve 800 mm above ground.*

Septic tanks

The capacity where desludging is once per year should be:

C (litres = 180 P + 2000.

where P is the design population with a minimum of 4. Thus the minimum size becomes 2720 L (approximately, as required by the Approved Document). This formula is adjusted for other types of building by deciding the degree of partial occupancy as compared to dwellings. Multi-compartment tanks may be needed in which case the settlement (first) zone takes up ⅔ of the total capacity.

For rectangular tanks two in series or two compartments is a good arrangement. A typical two-compartment arrangement is shown in the diagram [9.22] (redrawn from the BS).

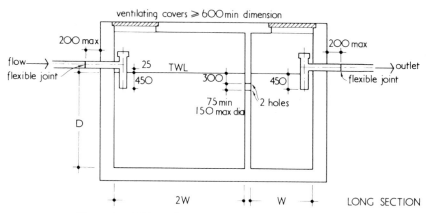

[9.22] *Typical septic tank, two in series, for up to 30 persons. (For larger installations base of first tank to be sloped at 1:4 and baffles used instead of dip pipes).*

W = width ≤ 1200mm - (if more than 1200 two inlets required at the same level)
Single inlets to be placed on longitudinal centre of tank
D = 1200 mm for up to 10 persons 1500 for over 10
TWL = top water level (ie invert of outfall)

Sometimes a small integral inspection chamber is included on the inlet side which also facilitates rodding.

For populations over 60, duplicate tanks should be provided in parallel, allowing one to be in use whilst the other is desludged.

If further treatment of the effluent is required a biological filter is usually provided. This is simply a bed of inert material such as clinker or slag to promote natural aerobic degradation of the sewage (ie by contact with air, as opposed to the anerobic action in the tank itself).

Settlement tanks
These usually form part of larger installations and the BS whilst giving recommendations stresses that specialist advice is essential.

Other stages
The BS also gives recommendations for biological filters, activated sludge units, tertiary treatment (where a better standard of effluent is required), final effluent disposal, pumping and automatic alarm systems. These are not the concern of Building Regulations.

H 3   RAINWATER DRAINAGE

The requirement itself is as follows:

	Requirement	Limits on application
	Rainwater drainage	
Roofs	H 3. Any system which carries rainwater from the roof of the building to a rainwater outfall shall be adequate.	

This must be the ultimate example of reducing regulations to the bare minimum. It tells us absolutely nothing but is amplified by a statement of acceptable performance which states that the system should:

(*a*)   Carry the rainwater to an outfall (being a surface water or combined sewer, soakaway or watercourse).
(*b*)   Minimise the risks of blockage or leakage.
(*c*)   Be accessible for clearing blockages.
As in H 1 there are two sections:
Section 1   Gutters and rainwater pipes: this replaces N 8 and N 9 of the old Regulations.
Section 2   Rainwater drainage: Part N had no specific requirements for rainwater drains as distinct from foul drains and this section really adds nothing to what is contained in H 1.

Capacity

0.1   Areas less than 6 m² can be ignored unless they receive a flow from other sources.

0.2/0.4   The flow to be accommodated should be based on a rainfall of 75 mm per hour. The capacity must be enough to accommodate this at any point in the system and this depends on the size and gradient of the gutters and pipes. Figures are given later.

NOTE   BS 6367 explains that the time a particular intensity of rainfall has to be sustained to create a maximum run-off is assumed to be 2 minutes, as being typical for most roofs. It gives a number of alternatives to the 75 mm figure which are based on differing return periods (T): see note on BS 6367 later.

Section 1   Gutters and rainwater pipes

1.1   The flow from a roof depends on the area and pitch. For flat roofs the actual area is taken and the table shows the allowance to be made for various pitches. Roofs over 70° are treated as walls.

NOTE   The BS gives a method of calculating these factors for any pitch of roof (plan area + half area on elevation) which gives the same results for the pitches shown in the table. It is clear therefore that interpolation is in order.

Table to 1.1   Calculation of area drained

Type of surface	Design area (m²)
1 flat roof	plan area of relevant portion
2 pitched roof at 30°	plan area of portion × 1.15
pitched roof at 45°	plan area of portion × 1.40
pitched roof at 60°	plan area of portion × 2.00
3 pitched roof over 70° or any wall	elevational area × 0.5

Table to 1.2   Gutter sizes and outlet sizes

Max roof area (m²)	Gutter size (mm dia)	Outlet size (mm dia)	Flow capacity (litres/sec)
6.0	–	–	–
18.0	75	50	0.38
37.0	100	63	0.78
53.0	115	63	1.11
65.0	125	75	1.37
103.0	150	89	2.16

NOTE
Refers to half round eaves gutters laid level with outlet at one end sharp edged. Round edged outlets allow smaller downpipe sizes.

1.2   The maximum areas which can be drained by half-round gutters a maximum of 8 m long, laid level with a sharp-edged outlet at one end, are shown in the Table, which also shows minimum outlet sizes. It also includes flow capacities, but the provision of figures for areas of roof relieves the designer of having to do this calculation. The Approved Document does not say whether it is referring to true or nominal half-round sections (the latter has less capacity) but the flow figures given are those quoted for true half round in the BS and the table should not therefore be used if nominal half-round sections are being used (see also note on BS 6367 below).

1.3   Where there is more than one outlet a gutter should be sized to suit the largest area draining into it. This would allow the Table to be used for RWPs up to 16 m apart.

NOTE   Placing RWPs at the end is clearly the least economical arrangement so far as gutter size is concerned.

1.4   If there is any fall it should be towards the nearest outlet. (The BS recommends a minimum fall of 1:350, really just to guard against a backfall occuring). Other types of gutter section and outlets with rounded edges can increase the capacity (see BS 6367).

Rainwater pipes

1.5   These should discharge into a drain or gulley and any entry into a combined system must be trapped. They may however discharge onto another surface if it is drained. NOTE   The BS describes the practice of connecting roof outlets into a discharge stack at roof level, but this would be ruled out by the above.

1.6   RWPs should be at least the size of the gutter outlet and if serving more than one gutter, should have an area at least equal to the combined area of the outlets. NOTE   This is not quite the same thing as saying 'large enough to serve the combined areas of roof', and would often result in a larger size than this.

Materials

1.7   The table shows the materials which may be used and the British Standard numbers appropriate to them. In addition:

(a)   All gutter joints should remain watertight under working conditions. Pipes within buildings must be able to withstand the water test for sanitary pipework (see H 1. 1.32).

(b)   Gutters and RWPs should be firmly supported but allow for thermal movement.

(c)   Different metals should be separated by non-metallic material to avoid electrolytic corrosion.

Table to 1.7   Materials for gutters and rainwater pipes

Material	British Standard
aluminium	BS 2997
cast iron	BS 416, BS 460
copper	BS 1431
galvanised steel	BS 5493
lead	BS 1178
low carbon steel	BS 5493
pressed steel	BS 1091
unplasticised pvc	BS 4514, BS 4576
zinc	BS 1431

British Standard method

1.8   Alternatively the relevant recommendations of BS 6367: 1983 can be followed. The relevant clauses are in Sections one, two, three (except clause 9) four, five (except clause 18) and appendices. In fact the Approved Document itself contains so little information that in all but the simplest of buildings the designer will find a need to look to the BS for advice. A note on this follows.

Note on BS 6367: 1983 CP for drainage of roofs and paved areas

This fairly new standard supersedes CP 308: 1974 and is a very complete guide to surface water drainage, including paved areas which are not covered by the Approved Document or by the old Regulations.

It has a section on materials, but the main body of the work is devoted to the hydraulic design of roof drainage. A rainfall of 75 mm/hour is taken as generally satisfactory (but see later). A simple calculation turns this into a figure of 0.02083 L/s m^2 (litres per second per square metre).

A method of allowing for roof slopes is given, namely to take the plan area of the roof plus half the area on elevation. This works for any angle, the outer limits being the net area for flat roofs and half the vertical area for walls.

Methods of design for eaves, valley and boundary or parapet wall gutters are given. Assuming adequate outlet sizes, gutter sizing depends largely on the area to be drained and the spacing of the outlets. The design method assumes that the distance between a stop end and an outlet is never more than 50 y_u or between two outlets more than 100 y_u when y_u = the upstream water depth (which for eaves gutters can be taken as the depth of the gutter).

To take an example of a 100 mm half-round gutter (depth 50 mm) this would amount to a length limitation of 2.5 m and for longer lengths the BS states that a reduction factor should be applied. The 8 m length stated in the Approved Document would give a depth/length ratio of 1:160 which would require a reduction factor of 0.85, so that the figures in the Document really overstate the true capacity.

Tables and graphs are given for sizing half-round and trapezoidal gutters.

The subject of outlets is dealt with in detail and the design of these has a great effect on the capacity of the whole system. Round, as opposed to sharp edged junctions, improve the performance, as also do tapered outlets and box receivers. Tables and charts are provided to determine the capacity of outlets and hence of the RWPs into which they discharge. Outlets from flat roofs are also dealt with.

Appendix A gives details for designing for higher rainfalls or higher categories of risk. A series of meteorological maps gives the return periods (T) in years where the chosen rate of rainfall sustained for two minutes may occur once. These are given for four intensities of 75, 100, 150 and 225 mm/hour. Strangely enough, the records show that although more rain falls on the upland areas of the north it is the lowland areas of the south and east that have the most short high-intensity bursts. From these maps the designer can decide, by using the appropriate return period, what intensity to use. The return period may be a fraction or multiple of the life of the building, depending on the degree of security required. The maximum security category 5 assumes a return period of 35,000 years, but this is a purely statistical figure (there are lies, damned lies and statistics!).

Section 2   **Rainwater drainage**

2.1/2.3   The provisions apply to rainwater only systems. There is no guidance on pumped systems.

Rainwater drains should only be discharged into a combined sewer if it has sufficient capacity to take the extra flow.

Layout and depth   **2.4/2.5**   Paragraphs 2.3 to 2.9 of H 1 apply.

Gradient and size   **2.6/2.7**   Drains must have enough capacity to carry the flow (see 0.2/0.4). They should be at least 75 mm diameter. The diagram shows the capacity of drains of 3 diameters at various gradients.

0.2/0.4 [**9.23**] *Discharge capacities of rainwater drains running full.*

NOTES   (1) The capacity can be increased by increasing the gradient or by using larger pipes (see solid lines).
(2) the gradient can be reduced with high standards of design and construction (see dotted lines).

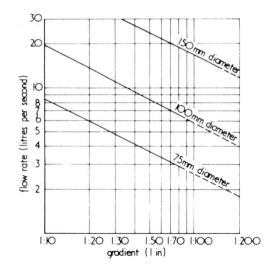

Comment
This is simply taken from the chart in BS 8301 for drains running full whereas the similar chart in H 1 is for drains running ¾ full. The capacity is only slightly increased (about 5 per cent). It should be noted that there are problems with drains running full, such as the creation of -ve pressure, and this basis should therefore never be used for combined systems.

Materials, bedding, backfilling, blockages, watertightness	**2.8/2.11** The provisions are the same as those in H 1, see 2.15–2.28 (this only shows how unnecessary subdivision of subject matter leads to repetition).

British Standard method	Alternatively the recommendations of BS 8301: 1985 *Code of Practice for building drainage*, may be adopted. The relevant clauses are in Sections One, Two, Three (except 7 and 10) Four (except 23) Five (25 only) and appendices. This is the same reference as for H 1.

Note on BS 8301: 1985 (regarding rainwater)	Clauses 8 and 9 of this BS deal with rainwater drainage. They make the same recommendations as the Approved Document but expand on these as follows.

Outlets
Soakaways may be suitably filled pits, lined roofed pits or seepage trenches, not closer than 5 m to a building. They work best in pervious soils. In soils of limited permeability they should have a storage capacity equal to at least 12 mm of rain below the inlet.
Entry into a watercourse should be at least 150 mm above normal water level and if back-flooding is likely, a non-return valve should be fitted.
Balancing ponds or tanks may sometimes be needed upstream of the soakaway to cope with peak flows.

Flow calculations
The whole of the rainfall on impervious areas (roofs and paved areas) should be assumed to reach the drain. A formula for calculating the run-off from very large areas is given but this is not applicable to normal building drainage.

Trapping
RWPs should only enter a foul or combined drain via a trapped gulley, but may sometimes be used as vents if constructed to the standard of foul discharge pipes and vented to the open at points where they would not be a nuisance (away from any openings). Note that this would not be permitted by the Approved Document (1.5) but it seems likely that Local Authorities would accept a method approved in a British Standard. A series of RWPs may be connected together without trapping if an interceptor is provided at the point of entry into the foul drain.

H 4   SOLID WASTE STORAGE

The requirement is a follows:

Requirement	Limits on application
Solid waste storage	
H 4. There shall be – *(a)* satisfactory means of storing solid waste; and *(b)* adequate means of access to a street from the building for the removal of solid waste.	

This is amplified by the following acceptable performance level. Solid waste storage should be:
(a)   Of sufficient capacity having regard to the quantity and frequency of removal.
(b)   Designed and sited so as not to be prejudicial to health.
(c)   Accessible for filling and emptying.

Capacity	**1.1** Any dwelling should have access to a movable container of at least 0.12 m³ per dwelling (this assumes weekly collection). **1.2** Dwellings up to the fourth storey may each have their own or share a container. Above four storeys refuse chutes should be provided.

1.3   For dwellings and other buildings the performance can be met by following the relevant clauses of BS 5906: 1980, *Code of Practice for storage and on-site treatment of solid waste from buildings*. The relevant clauses are:

 3   Definitions
 5   Materials and components
 6   General principles for design and facilities
 8   Choice of method of storage and collection of waste in various types of buildings
10   Waste storage chambers
12   Storage containers

Design

1.4   Containers should have close-fitting lids unless fed by chute.

1.5   Chutes should have a smooth non-absorbent surface, close fitting access doors and be ventilated at top and bottom.

1.6   Containers need not be enclosed, but if they are the enclosure should allow room for filling and emptying and be at least 600 × 600 × 1000 mm high in any case, with ventilation openings at top and bottom (this size presumably relates to a space for a single bin).

Siting

1.7/1.8   Containers should be within 25 m of the building they serve and of a vehicle access. In new buildings they should be capable of collection without passing through a building (except for a garage, carport or open covered space).

This is all there is, but the reader should note that Part E (sound insulation) contains specific requirements for refuse chutes.

Comment

Although the requirement to provide solid waste storage and removal facilities is new to the Regulations (previously contained only in the Act(s)), there were rules regarding the construction of refuse storage chambers and chutes, when provided, in Part J of the 1976 Regulations. These were a great deal more comprehensive and useful than those now provided in 1.5 and 1.6 above. This must be one of the few cases where the amount of guidance supplied by the new Approved Documents is less than that in the old Regulations. The designer now has no alternative but to consult the BS, and it is perhaps significant that in this case the reference to the BS is part of the provisions (1.3) rather than being placed at the end as an alternative. Because of this a fairly comprehensive illustrated note on this British Standard is included below.

Note on BS 5906: 1980

This replaces CP 306: Part 1 which dealt only with domestic buildings but was intended to be the first of a series dealing with other types of building. This never materialised due to lack of reliable data. A little more is now available.

The new code includes limited information on commercial and hotel buildings. It deals with a variety of alternative possibilities including on-site treatment and piped collection systems, but these are not included in the relevant clauses listed in 1.3. This list however also excludes Clause 9 which deals with chutes. One feels that this must be an error since the Approved Document itself makes reference to chutes (1.2 and 1.5) but provides virtually no information.

Under 'General principles' the BS stresses the importance of adequate storage space, maximum convenience for user and collector, hygiene, amenity, fire risk and sound insulation (also provision for salvageable material).

Storage provision depends on the volume and nature of the waste and frequency of collection. An approximate figure per dwelling per week is 12 kg at a density of 133 kg/m^3 (both figures plus or minus 10 per cent). Individual containers (bins or sacks suitably protected) are recommended for houses. Shelters if provided should be open to the air and large enough to contain two bins, about 0.8 m^3, which is twice the requirement in the Approved Document. Blocks up to 4 storeys should have either chutes or communal containers sited to be within 30 m horizontally from each dwelling. Over four storeys chutes should always be provided. The recommendations for chutes and waste storage chambers are very similar to those previously included in Part J of the 1976 Regulations (illustrated diagramatically in the last edition of the Architectural Press's *Guide to the Building Regulations*). Since there are differences these diagrams have been redrawn, based on the new BS and suitably annotated to take in the recommendations in the text [9.24, 9.25].

It is also recommended that chutes should be not further than 30 m from any dwelling they serve and that hoppers should not serve more than six dwellings.

[9.24] *Requirements for refuse hoppers.*
In addition, hoppers must not be situated in a dwelling, and must be made entirely of non-combustible material.

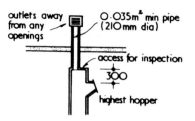

outlets away from any openings

0.035 m² min pipe (210 mm dia)

access for inspection

300

highest hopper

Alternative ventilation

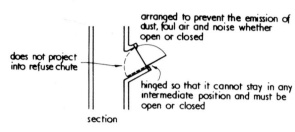

does not project into refuse chute

arranged to prevent the emission of dust, foul air and noise whether open or closed

hinged so that it cannot stay in any intermediate position and must be open or closed

section

Hopper detail

[9.25] *Chutes and storage chambers.*

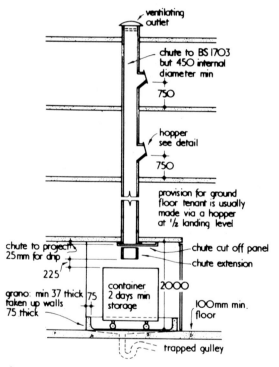

ventilating outlet

chute to BS 1703 but 450 internal diameter min

750

hopper see detail

750

provision for ground floor tenant is usually made via a hopper at ½ landing level

chute to project 25 mm for drip

225

grano: min 37 thick taken up walls 75 thick

chute cut off panel

chute extension

container 2 days min storage

2000

75

100 mm min floor

trapped gulley

Section.

Plan of chamber.

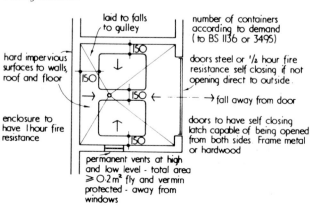

laid to falls to gulley

150

150

150

150

hard impervious surfaces to walls, roof and floor

enclosure to have 1 hour fire resistance

permanent vents at high and low level - total area ≥ 0.2 m² fly and vermin protected - away from windows

number of containers according to demand (to BS 1136 or 3495)

doors steel or ½ hour fire resistance self closing if not opening direct to outside.

fall away from door

doors to have self closing latch capable of being opened from both sides. Frame metal or hardwood

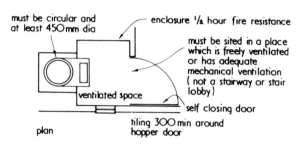

must be circular and at least 450 mm dia

enclosure ½ hour fire resistance

must be sited in a place which is freely ventilated or has adequate mechanical ventilation (not a stairway or stair lobby)

ventilated space

self closing door

plan

tiling 300 min around hopper door

Hopper compartment

NOTES 1 *Both chute and vent pipe must be entirely non-combustible and so constructed as to prevent the ignition of any part of the building in the event of a fire in the chute or refuse chamber.*
2 *Inner surface of chute must be impervious to moisture and arranged so as to prevent lodgement of refuse.*

References

The following British Standards and other documents are referred to in the Approved Document on the page number(s) given after each entry.

BS 65: 1981 *Specification for vitrified clay pipes fittings and joints* Amendment 1: AMD 4328. Amendment 2: AMD 4394. £16·20 (£8·10), pp. 7, 10.

BS 416: 1973 *Cast iron spigot and socket soil, waste and ventilating pipes (sand cast and spun) and fittings* Amendment 1: AMD 3113. £22·80 (£11·40), p. 6.

BS 437: 1978 *Specification for cast iron spigot and socket drain pipes and fittings.* £22·80 (£11·40), p. 7.

BS 864 *Capillary and compression tube fittings of copper and copper alloy.* Part 2: 1983 *Specification for capillary and compression fittings for copper tubes.* £12·20 (£6·10), p. 6.

BS 882: 1983 *Specification for aggregates from natural sources for concrete.* £10·20 (£5·10), p. 8.

BS 1184: 1976 *Copper and copper alloy traps.* £16·20, p. 6.

BS 2868: 1973: *Prefabricated drainage stack units: galvanised steel*

BS 2871 *Copper and copper alloys. Tubes.* Part 1: 1971 *Copper tubes for water, gas and sanitation* Amendment 1: AMD 1422. Amendment 2: AMD 2203. £8 (£4), p. 6.

BS 3656: 1981 *Specification for asbestos-cement pipes, joints and fittings for sewerage and drainage.* £10·20 (£5·10), p. 7.

BS 3868: 1973 *Prefabricated drainage stack units: galvanised steel.* £16·20 (£8·10), p. 6.

BS 3921: 1976 *Clay bricks and blocks.* £22·80 (£11·40), p. 10.

BS 3943: 1979 *Specification for plastics waste traps* Amendment 1: AMD 3206. Amendment 2: AMD 4191. £10·20 (£5·10), p. 6.

BS 4514: 1983 *Specification for unplasticised PVC soil and ventilating pipes, fittings and accessories* Amendment 1: AMD 4517. £12·20 (£6·10), p. 6.

BS 4660: 1973 *Unplasticised PVC underground drain pipe and fittings* Amendment 1: AMD 2514. Amendment 2: AMD 3708. Amendment 3: AMD 4006. Amendment 4: AMD 4081. Amendment 5: 4441. £16·20 (£8·10), p. 7.

BS 5254: 1976 *Polypropylene waste pipe and fittings (external diameter 34.6 mm, 41.0 mm and 54.1 mm)* Amendment 1: AMD 3588. Amendment 2: AMD 4438, £12·20 (£6·10), p. 6.

BS 5255: 1976: *Plastics waste pipes and fittings* Amendment slips nos 1: AMD 3565, 2: AMD 3854, 3: AMD 4472.

BS 5481: 1977 *Specification for unplasticised PVC pipe and fittings for gravity sewers* Amendment 1: AMD 3631. Amendment 2: AMD 4436. £12·20 (£6·10), p. 7.

BS 5572: 1978 *Code of practice for sanitary pipework* Amendment 1: AMD 3613. Amendment 2: 4202. £22·80 (£11·40), p. 6.

BS 5911 *Precast concrete pipes and fittings for drainage and sewerage.* Part 1: 1981 *Specification for concrete cylindrical pipes, bends, junctions and manholes*, unreinforced or reinforced with steel cages or hoops. Amendment 1: AMD 4035. £22·80 (£11·40), p. 7. Part 2: 1982 *Specification for inspection chambers and gullies.* £10·20 (£5·10), p. 10.

BS 8301: 1985 *Code of practice for building drainage.* £26·20, pp. 8, 10.

CP 110: *The structural use of concrete.* Part 1: 1972 *Design, materials and workmanship* Amendment 1: AMD 2289. Amendment 2: AMD 3451. £32·60 (£16·30), p. 10.

BS 6297: 1983 *Code of practice for design and installation of small sewerage treatment works and cesspools.* £22·80, p. 14.

BS 416: 1973 *Cast iron spigot and socket soil, waste and ventilating pipes and fittings* Amendment 1: AMD 3113. £22·80 (£11·40), p. 17.

BS 460: 1964 *Cast iron rainwater goods.* £12·20 (£6·10), p. 17.

BS 882: 1983 *Specification for aggregates from natural sources for concrete.* £10·20, p. 8.

BS 1091: 1963 *Pressed steel gutters, rainwater pipes, fittings and accessories.* £8 (£4), p. 17.

BS 1178: 1982 *Specification for milled lead sheet for building purposes.* £7, p. 17.

BS 1431: 1960 *Wrought copper and wrought zinc rainwater goods.* £10·20 (£5·10), p. 17.

BS 2997: 1958 *Aluminium rainwater goods* Amendment 1: PD 6403. £16·20 (£8·10), p. 17.

BS 4514: 1983 *Specification for unplasticised PVC soil and ventilating pipes, fittings and accessories* Amendment 1: AMD 4517. £12·20 (£6·10), p. 17.

BS 4576 *Unplasticised PVC rainwater goods.* Part 1: 1970 *Half round gutters and circular pipes* Amendment 1: AMD 688. Amendment 2: AMD 1287. Amendment 3: AMD 2720. £10·20 (£5·10), p. 17.

BS 5493: 1977 *Code of practice for protective coating of iron and iron and steel structures against corrosion* Amendment 1: AMD 4443. £29·20 (£14·60), p. 17.

BS 6367: 1983 *Code of practice for drainage of roofs and paved areas.* £26·20 (£13·10), p. 17.

BS 8301: 1985 *Code of practice for building drainage.* £26·20 (£13·10), p. 18.

BS 5906: 1981 *Code of practice for the storage and on-site treatment of solid waste from buildings.* £12·20 (£6·10), p. 20.

Approved Document J
Heat Producing Appliances

This part replaces the two parts L and M of the 1976 Regulations. The subdivision into two parts always seemed illogical and arose only because of the somewhat arbitrary division of previous Regulations into 'buildings' and 'works and fittings'. It is a good deal shorter, mainly because of the omission of clauses concerning flueless appliances, multiple flue connections and appliance ventilation ducts. For all of these matters the user must now look to the relevant British Standards, which in this case are not just an alternative approach. Practically all of these have been revised since 1976 and so there are quite a lot of changes. Some of the existing Regulations based on BS 5440, and BS 5546 and various parts of BS 5258 were introduced in the 1981 Second Amendment, but most of this material which concerned flueless appliances is no longer included.

The requirements are as follows:

	Requirement	Limits on application
	Air supply	
Walls; roofs	J 1. Heat producing appliances shall be so installed that there is an adequate supply of air to them for combustion and for the efficient working of any flue-pipe or chimney.	The requirements in this Part apply only to fixed heat producing appliances which – *(a)* are designed to burn solid fuel, oil or gas; or *(b)* are incinerators.
	Discharge of products of combustion	
Chimneys; flue-pipes.	J 2. Heat producing appliances shall have adequate provision for the discharge of the products of combustion to the outside air.	
	Protection of building	
	J 3. Heat producing appliances and flue-pipes shall be so installed, and fire-places and chimneys shall be so constructed, as to reduce to a reasonable level the risk of the building catching fire in consequence of their use.	

They are followed by a statement of the acceptable level of performance which in this case merely says the same thing in a slightly different way. It is specifically stated that with regard to damage by 'fire' the term includes a chimney fire.

It is also stated that in this document non-combustible means 'able to be classified under BS 476: Part 4', which means that 'materials or limited combustibility' as defined in A 14 of Part B will not do.

Three requirements are here dealt with in one document, but the contents are arranged so as to deal with each separately. One feels that this has resulted in an arbitrary and unnecessary breakdown of material, involving the reader in looking in several places for parts of the same thing. In particular the requirements of J 2 and J 3 are so interlocked that separating them is a surgical operation.

Arrangement

There are two sections:

Section 1   Solid fuel and oil appliances up to 45kW output rating.
Section 2   Gas appliances up to 60kW input rating.
Both are divided into three parts corresponding to the three requirements above.

There is now no mention of 'high rating appliances' which were included in Part M. This does not mean that such appliances are not covered by the requirements of Part J, but clearly one must look elsewhere for the information. The BSS referred to also relate only to appliances in the same size range, so there is no advice at all as to where the information may be found. However appropriate BSS do in fact exist.

Section 1   Solid fuel and oil burning appliances with a rated output up to 45kW

Part A   Provisions for introducing air

1.1   The following are required in rooms containing appliances:

1   Solid fuel open appliances: 50 per cent of the area of the throat opening, but at least 5500 m^2.

2   Other solid fuel appliances: the combined areas of the primary and secondary inlets to the appliance.

3   Oil burning appliances: 550 mm^2 per kW of rated output.

4   Room sealed appliances: none.

NOTES

(*a*)   The entry may be through another room if this has an opening of equal size to the open air.

(*b*)   If a draught stabiliser is fitted in the same room allow an additional 550 mm^2 per kW.

(*c*)   Extract fans should not be fitted unless the appliance is room sealed (this would exclude the use of extract-type cooker hoods over Aga-type cookers).

Part B   Provisions for discharging the products of combustion

1.2/1.3   The following are required, but 1.10 to 1.14 do not apply to a chimney built before 1 February 1966 (ie before the Building Regulations).

Balance flue and low level flued appliances

1.4   These should be installed so that the terminal is:

(*a*)   External, situated to allow free intake of air in the case of balanced flues and dispersal of combustion products.

(*b*)   600 mm from any opening into the building.

(*c*)   Protected with a guard if within reach of people or subject to damage.

(*d*)   Designed to prevent the entry of foreign matter.

Flues

A flue is the passage for combustion products. It can be contained either in a chimney or a flue pipe.

1.5   If the temperature of flue gases from an oil burning appliance will not exceed 260°C a gas appliance type flue is adequate (see Section 2).

1.6   The following are the minimum sizes for flues:

1   Open fire in recess*   Square   185 mm

Circular   225 mm (220 absolute minimum)

2   Other appliances

(*a*)   In a flue pipe: the size of the appliance outlet.

(*b*)   In a chimney: up to 30kW – 150 mm square or diameter.

(*c*)   In a chimney: up to 45kW – 175 mm square or diameter.

* Open fires larger than those specified in BS 1251: 1970 may need a larger flue.

1.7   Openings: there must be none except for:

(*a*)   Inspection and cleaning: fitted with a non-combustible, rigid double cased, gas-tight cover.

(*b*)   A draught stabilizer or explosion door in the same space as the appliance.

1.8   No flue should have an opening into more than one room except for inspection and cleaning.

1.9   Outlets: the height should be as shown in diagram [10.1].

*1.9 [**10.1**] Details of outlets for class 1 appliances.*

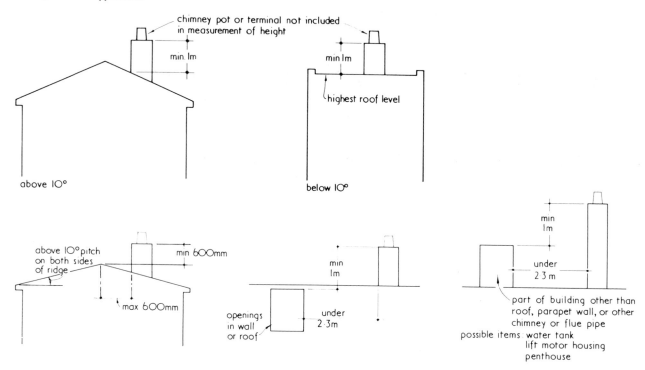

NOTE   Section 73 of the Building Act 1984 gives Local Authorities special powers when a building is erected or raised to overreach existing chimneys. If these are in a party wall or within 6 feet of the new building, the owner may be required to raise them to the same height as his building or its chimneys.

1.10   Bends: flues should be vertical, but if a slope is necessary it should be restricted as shown in diagram [10.2].

1.11   Access: this should be provided for inspection and cleaning of an appliance, flue pipe and chimney. Unless a fluepipe is directly above the appliance a soot box should be provided (see diagram [10.3]).

*1.10 [**10.2**] Bends in flues.*

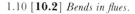

*1.11 [**10.3**] Access to flues.*

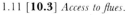

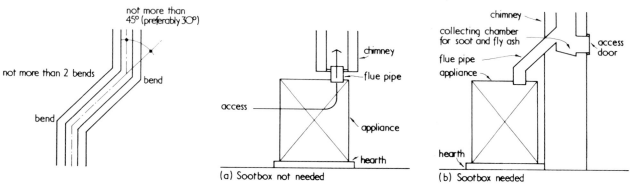

Chimneys

1.12   These should be either built of masonry or be factory-made insulated chimneys.

1.13   Masonry chimneys: these may be of any type of masonry with a refractory lining or built of refractory material unlined.

1.14   Linings: these can be:

(*a*)   Clay flue liners with rebated or socketed joints to BS 1181: 1971.

(*b*)   Clay pipes with socketed joints to BS 65: 1981 (NOTE   Apart from diameters, this no longer gives size details which must now be obtained from manufacturers).

(c)   Pipes of high alumina cement and kiln burnt aggregate with rebated, socketed or steel collar joints.

Linings should be fitted with sockets upwards to prevent condensate running out or caulking being affected. Joints and any space between liners and masonry to be filled with weak mortar or insulating concrete.

Some details of types (a) and (b) are illustrated [10.4].

1.14 [**10.4**] *Chimney linings to BS 1181: 1971.*
The BS also includes terminals. It also gives
maximum external diameters for circular pipes. These,
with tolerances allowed for internal diameters, are
based generally on a pipe wall thickness of about
20 mm. Linings of type (b) (mentioned above) are
normal BS 65 Drain pipes, available in a wider range
of diameters and bends.

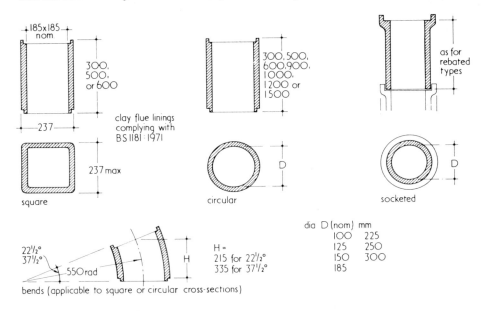

British Standard approach

1.15   Alternatively the relevant recommendations of BS 6461: Part 1: 1984 *Code of Practice for masonry chimneys and flue pipes (solid fuel)* may be followed. This is clearly the basis for the provisions in the Approved Document regarding flues and flue pipes, including those in Part C. A note describing its main recommendations follows at the end of this section.

Factory made insulated chimneys

1.16   Factory made insulated chimneys should be constructed and tested in accordance with BS 4543 as follows:

Method of test   Part 1: 1976
Solid fuel appliances   Part 2: 1976
Oil fired appliances   Part 3: 1976

These deal with prefabricated chimneys suitable for industrialised housing for use with appliances up to 45kW output. They consist of an internal corrosion and heat resistant pipe surrounded by insulation and a weather resistant casing (although some are designed for internal situations).

Chimneys complying with Part 2 are also suitable for oil and both Parts 2 and 3 may be suitable for gas appliances.

Linings are either stainless steel of a specific composition or vitrified clay to BS 1181. Outer casings are aluminium, stainless steel or galvanised or aluminium coated sheet steel.

They must be designed for assembly and erection on site without any cutting, drilling or alteration (ie purpose made for each situation). They must be properly supported and provided with firestops.

For details of these recommendations and sizes see diagram below [10.5].

[**10.5**] *Factory made chimney detail.*

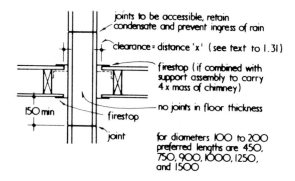

joints to be accessible, retain condensate and prevent ingress of rain

clearance = distance 'x' (see text to 1.31)

firestop (if combined with support assembly to carry 4 x mass of chimney)

no joints in floor thickness

150 min

firestop

joint

for diameters 100 to 200 preferred lengths are 450, 750, 900, 1000, 1250, and 1500

A sequence of 8 tests must be carried through (one occurs three times) for support, joint leakage, flue draught, thermal shock, thermal insulation and strength. A minimum standard for each is specified. The test procedures are laid down in Part 1.

The specifications in Parts 2 and 3 appear virtually identical except that the tests for draught and thermal shock are not required by Part 3 and in Part 2 a second insulation test using a higher initial temperature is required.

1.17   Access for repair or replacement must be possible throughout its length. If this is difficult (eg in flats or maisonettes) these chimneys should not be used. Joints should not be made within a wall unless sleeved.

1.18   Installation should comply with 1.17 and the manufacturers' instructions.

Flue pipes

1.19   These should only be used to connect an appliance to a chimney (not carried to a final outlet). This is a new rule since the 1976 Regulations and comes from BS 6461: Part 1: 1984. Previously it was not uncommon to find flue pipes with suitable terminals used as the whole flue for closed or closable appliances in rooms which were not below a roof space.

They should not pass through any internal wall or partition, floor or roof space. Passage through a roof is not prohibited, but there would now seem to be little need of this in view of the necessity of connecting to a chimney.

Angles over 45° to the vertical are not permitted except as shown in diagram [10.6].

1.19 [**10.6**] *Spaces and elements of structure through which flue pipes may not pass.*

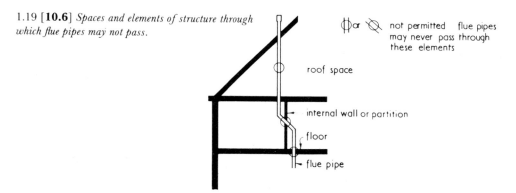

or   not permitted   flue pipes may never pass through these elements

roof space

internal wall or partition

floor

flue pipe

flue pipes may pass through roofs and external walls subject to placing and projection (see 1.32)

Flue pipe connections to chimney.

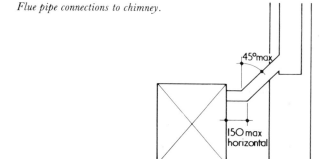

45°max

150 max horizontal

back outlet

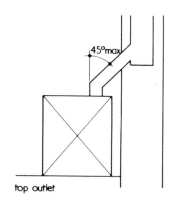

45°max

top outlet

Materials

1.20 Any of the following may be used:

(*a*)   Cast iron as described in BS 41: 1973 (1981) *Cast iron spigot and socket flue or smoke pipes and fittings*, or

(*b*)   Mild steel with a wall thickness of at least 3 mm, or

(*c*)   Stainles steel with a wall thickness of at least 1 mm and as in BS 1449: *Steel plate, sheet and strip*, Part 2: 1983 *Specification for stainless and heat resisting steel plate, sheet and strip* for Grade 316 S 11, 316 S 13, 316 S 16, 316 S 31, 316 S 33, or equivalent Euronorm 88–71 designation

(*d*)   Vitreous enamelled steel of low carbon content, coated internally and externally with acid-resistant enamel

The nominal thickness of the steel should be at least 0.9 mm for pipes up to 113 mm diameter and 1.2 mm if larger. The vitreous enamel should be resistant to thermal shock, combustion products and heat when tested to the relevant recommendations of BS 1344 *Methods of testing vitreous enamel finishes*, Part 1: 1965 *Resistance to thermal shock of coatings on articles other than cooking utensils*, Part 3: 1967 *Resistance to products of combustion containing sulphur compounds*, and Part 7: 1967 *Resistance to heat*. In the test for resistance to combustion products, the enamel should achieve a classification of at least SA.

1.21 Joints; pipes should be fitted with sockets upwards and with sufficient gap to allow for expansion.

Part C   Provisions for protection against fire and heat

1.22/1.23 The following rules are designed to avoid danger from fire in structure adjacent to appliances, flues etc but:

(*a*)   If the temperature below the appliance will not exceed 100°C it may stand on a rigid, non-combustible, imperforate shield instead of a constructional hearth

(*b*)   If the temperature of the side or back panels will not exceed 100°C the rules regarding proximity to walls do not apply.

Constructional hearths, fireplace recesses and location of appliances

1.24/1.28 and **1.33**   As these various aspects are so closely interrelated they are dealt with here together.

They are a revised version of the old L 3, 4, 5 and M 4, but some of those provisions are no longer included.

There are now no rules concerning the level of the hearth in relation to the floor or the construction of pits for ash containers below grates or the use of superimposed hearths. The last item will probably not be missed, but it is difficult to understand the omission of the other two. In particular it is surely not intended to rule out the use of the controlled draught type of solid fuel fire with below floor level ash collection and disposal arrangements (the ubiquitous Baxi) and if not, the need for regulation must still be there.

Constructional hearths must now always be provided. The rules regarding these, and also fireplace recesses and walls adjacent to free standing appliances are illustrated below. These are not the diagrams in the Approved Document, which are somewhat less than satisfactory.

1.27 [**10.7**] *Permitted constructions of fireplace recesses.*

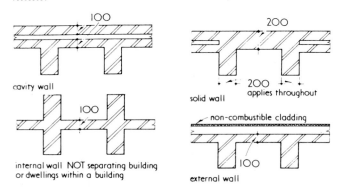

All dimensions are minima.
Construction to be solid non-combustible material.
Thickness of wall at back must extend to full height of recess.

1.24/1.25 [**10.8**]
Constructional hearths.

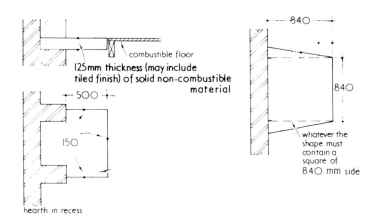

125mm thickness (may include tiled finish) of solid non-combustible material

hearth in recess

whatever the shape must contain a square of 840 mm side

NOTES All dimensions are minima.
Hearths to be of non-combustible material.
If a class 1 appliance is installed over a constructional hearth built before 1/2/66 that hearth need not comply with the minimum dimensions for projection (500 mm) and square size (840 mm) shown here.

1.33 [**10.9**] *Appliance on constructional hearth.*

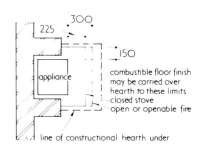

combustible floor finish may be carried over hearth to these limits
closed stove
open or openable fire
line of constructional hearth under

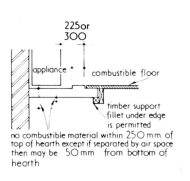

appliance
combustible floor
timber support fillet under edge is permitted
no combustible material within 250 mm of top of hearth except if separated by air space then may be 50 mm from bottom of hearth

1.28 *and* 1.33 [**10.10**] *Walls and partitions adjoining hearths for class 1 appliances.*

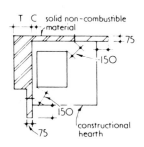

T C solid non-combustible material
constructional hearth

if clearance C is less than 50 mm thickness T is at least 200 mm

C more than 50mm thickness T at least 75 mm

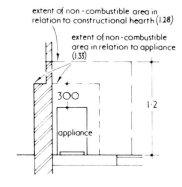

extent of non-combustible area in relation to constructional hearth (1.28)
extent of non-combustible area in relation to appliance (1.33)
appliance

Chimneys

1.29 Masonry chimneys: these must have the minimum thicknesses (excluding linings) shown in diagram [10.11], depending on their location; (for linings see 1.14).

1.30 Combustible material must not be placed in the zones indicated in diagram [10.12]. Previously there was a rule about wooden plugs being permitted up to 150 mm from a flue or inner face of a fireplace recess but this seems to have been discarded, so that the general 200 mm exclusion zone applies universally.

Part L also contained rules regarding the proximity of combustible material to flue pipes at the point of entry into a flue in a chimney. These are no longer included but the need may be said to be covered by the general rules regarding flue pipes which follow. The diagram below is taken from the AD with slight alteration.

According to the text the rule illustrated in (*c*) also applies in relation to the outer face of a fireplace recess but not those in (*a*) and (*b*). This seems quite illogical and in the old L 10 the rules in (*a*) and (*b*) also applied in relation to the inner face of the fireplace recess. It seems likely that this is the intention and that the omission is inadvertent.

The exceptions referred to in (*c*) are a floorboard, skirting, dado, picture rail, mantelshelf or architrave. Any metal fixings in contact with combustible material to be at least 50 mm from a flue.

1.29 [**10.11**] *Masonry chimneys: construction.*

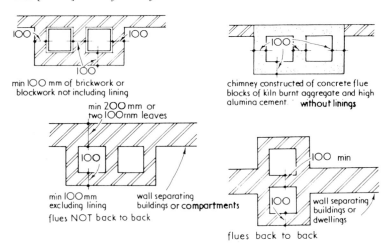

min 100 mm of brickwork or blockwork not including lining

chimney constructed of concrete flue blocks of kiln burnt aggregate and high alumina cement **without linings**

min 200 mm or two 100mm leaves

min 100mm excluding lining
flues NOT back to back

wall separating buildings or **compartments**

100 min

wall separating buildings or dwellings

flues back to back

1.31 Factory made insulated chimneys: these should not:

(*a*) Pass through a separate compartment unless cased in non-combustible material with at least half the fire resistance of the compartment wall or floor. The illustration [10.13] shows a possible situation in relation to a compartment wall.

(*b*) Be positioned nearer to combustible material than 'x'.

(*c*) Pass through a cupboard, storage space or roof space unless cased in non-combustible material placed at least 'x' from the outer casing of the chimney (see also diagram [10.5]).

The value of 'x' is explained in BS 4543: Part 1 and is either 40 mm or the distance stated by the manufacturer whose product is under test.

NOTE   L 22 (1976) also had a prohibition against passing through any part of a building not in the same occupation.

1.30 [**10.12**] *Combustible material adjacent to flues.*

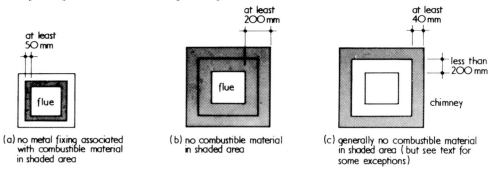

at least 50 mm

at least 200 mm

at least 40 mm

less than 200 mm

flue

flue

chimney

(a) no metal fixing associated with combustible material in shaded area

(b) no combustible material in shaded area

(c) generally no combustible material in shaded area (but see text for some exceptions)

Flue pipes

1.32 This very short clause simply requires that flue pipes passing through or near to combustible material should be separated from it, as shown in the diagrams here [10.14]. This is very unsatisfactory for a number of reasons:

1   No indication is given of what the elements are through which the flue is passing. 1.19 prohibits these from passing through any floor, internal wall, partition or roof space. This only leaves external walls and flat or open pitched roofs. This was the clear situation in Part L (1976). Now however 1.19 states that flue pipes should only be used to connect an appliance to a chimney, which really leaves no reason for them to pass through these elements either, so that the whole point of the first diagram disappears.

2   Even if this were not so a passage through a roof would sometimes have been through a pitched roof which leaves areas of doubt about where measurements are taken from which are not illustrated.

3   The second diagram gives a misleading impression of how the rule would work. Diagram [10.15] which gives a plan view is more satisfactory. It also shows the width of the shield (taken from BS 6461).

Corrections issued later by the DOE state that the top diagram is intended to illustrate plans through an external wall. However, this still leaves the question of where the flue pipe is going, since it is only supposed to connect an appliance to a chimney (1.19).

1.31 [**10.13**] *Factory-made chimney passing through compartment wall.*

NOTE   This rule also applies to masonry chimneys (see AD B, Appx F 18/19) but this is not mentioned in 1.29 although it is in Section 2 in relation to gas flues.

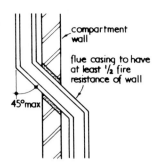

J 1.32 [**10.14**] *Flue pipes passing through or adjacent to combustible material.*

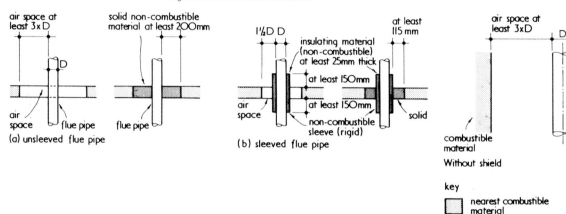

1.32 [**10.15**] *Flue pipes passing close to combustible material.*

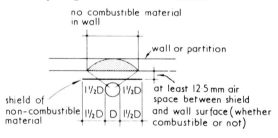
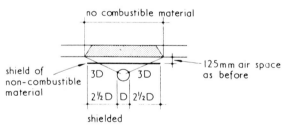

Note on BS 6461: Part 1: 1984

This deals with the installation of chimneys and flues for domestic appliances burning solid fuel (including wood and peat). Part 1 gives recommendations for flues whether in chimneys or flue pipes. It replaces CP 131: 1974.

It includes recommendations for chimneys of brick, stone, concrete or flue blocks and also on materials for flue pipes and their installation, serving appliances up to 45kW. The flue gas temperatures are assumed generally not to exceed 500°C but it is accepted that this may be exceeded for short periods. More information is available in CP 403 with regard to chimney height and fireplace recess construction.

Flues built to this standard are also suitable for oil or gas appliances.

The BS does not conflict in any way with Approved Document J, which is clearly based upon it, but it provides more detail, particularly by way of explaining the basis of the recommendations.

It gives general principles for chimney design which include:

(*a*)   Totally non-combustible, durable, temperature and corrosion resistant construction.

(*b*)   Chimneys to be lined unless of special flueblocks.

(*c*)   Area and height chosen in relation to appliance.

(*d*)   Prevention of air leakage and excessive heat loss.

(*e*)   Avoidance of rough interiors, flat gradients and sudden changes of direction.

(*f*)   Limit the number of bends and keep angles as small as possible.

(*g*)   Locate terminals to avoid pressure zones and away from openings.

(*h*)   Build stacks in materials to suit exposed conditions (eg the bricks may need to be different from those used in general building).

(*i*)   Site chimneys on internal walls if possible (to conserve heat).

Size

The recommendations follow the Approved Document for open appliances with openings up to 500 × 550 mm. For larger sizes the flue area should be 14 to 16 per cent of the free area of the fire opening. For closed appliances a flue of 150 nominal diameter is suitable.

A total height of 4.5 m is usually adequate for draught.

Fireplace recesses: there are diagrams showing recommended dimensions and construction.

Other details: Flues are best vertical, but if bends are necessary they should be limited to two and angles of 45° (preferably 30°) to the vertical. A flue should serve only one appliance and there should be no openings except for cleaning and inspection or a draught stabiliser.

External: the recommendations for projection above roofs are as in the Approved Document, but there are also notes on the design of flue terminals and chimney terminals (the top of the stack).

Structural: there is a rule about the height of chimneys above roofs in relation to width (4.5 × the least dimension) which is as laid down in Approved Document A Part D. There is also a lot more advice on foundations, general structural design and stays.

Fire precautions: the outside surface should not exceed 70°C under working conditions (usually achieved by 100 mm of masonry). Other recommendations are as those in the AD.

There are sections on flue linings, brickwork, stonework, blockwork and concrete construction, and also on the use of purpose made flue blocks which do not need lining and which should have rebated joints and rounded internal angles.

Flue pipes: There are the same recommendations as in the AD and in addition they should be as short as possible, contain not more than two bends and be accessible for inspection throughout. For pipes close to surfaces the effects of radiation may be reduced by insulation as well as by shielding. Access for cleaning should be provided where this cannot be done through the appliance or chimney soot door.

There are sections on site inspection and testing and appendices on remedial action, cleaning and maintenance, as well as a number of diagrams.

Section 2   Gas burning appliances with a rated input up to 60kW

2.1   The section gives provisions for:

(*a*)   Cooking appliances.

(*b*)   Balanced flue appliances.

(*c*)   Decorative solid fuel effect gas appliances.

(*d*)   Other individual natural draught open flued appliances.

NOTE   This does not include flueless appliances, incinerators or appliances connected to common flue or duct systems which were previously included in Parts L and M. For those it is now necessary to look to the following.

2.2   For all other appliances follow the relevant recommendations of BS 5440: *Code of Practice for flues and air supply for gas appliances of rated input not exceeding 60kW*: Part 1: 1978: *Flues* and Part 2: 1976: *Air supply*, and in addition for flueless water heaters of BS 5546: 1979: *Code of Practice for the installation of gas hot water supplies for domestic purposes*. Notes on these will be found at the end of this section.

Part A   Air supply

2.3   The following will meet the provisions:

(*a*)   Cooker: must be installed in a room of at least 6 m^3 having an openable window or some other opening to the outside air.

Additionally a permanent free opening of:

6500 mm^2 in rooms less than 9 m^3

3500 mm² in rooms between 9 and 11 m³.

(*b*)   Balanced flued appliances: no requirement.

(*c*)   Open flued appliances – the room to have permanent free opening of:

(i) decorative (type (*c*) above) 1800 mm² for each kW of rated input over 2kW.
NOTE   These have similar demands to solid fuel open fires.

(ii) Any other: 450 mm² for each kW over 7kW.

(*d*)   The appliance is installed in a sealed balanced compartment as described in BS 5440: Part 2: Air supply. This is an error, because these recommendations are actually contained in Part 1 of the BS. When an open flued appliance is installed in this way it becomes technically a balanced flued appliance because it draws its combustion air from a point adjacent to the point at which the combustion products are discharged. The advantage over the ordinary balanced flued arrangement is that this point may be remote from the appliance. The BS gives recommendations for suitable arrangements in the compartment and at the inlet/outlet position (see note on BS 5440: Part 1).

These provisions are all different from those in Part M (1976) and (*d*) above is entirely new.

Part B   Discharging combustion products

2.4/2.5   The requirements are described below but if the chimney was built before 1 Feb 1966 2.13 to 2.16 (flue construction) and 2.26 (fire resistance) do not apply.

2.6   Only balanced flued appliances are allowed in bath or shower room or in private garages (the latter is new).

2.7   Balanced flued appliances; the requirements for these are illustrated in [10.16].

2.8   Open flued appliances – the sizes should be as illustrated in [10.17].

2.9/2.10   Openings: the only openings into a flue should be for inspection and cleaning (fitted with a non-combustible gas-tight cover) or a draught diverter.

No flue must have an opening into more than one room except for inspection and cleaning.

2.11   Outlets: these should be arranged as in diagram [10.18].

2.7 [**10.16**] *Balanced flue terminals.*

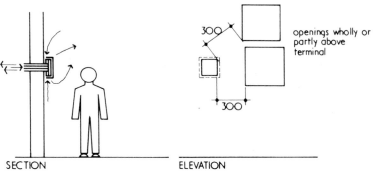

SECTION   ELEVATION

- situated to allow free intake of air and dispersal of products
- protected by guard if it may be in contact with people or be damaged
- designed to prevent entry of matter which may restrict flue

2.8 [**10.17**] *Open flued appliances: flue sizes.*

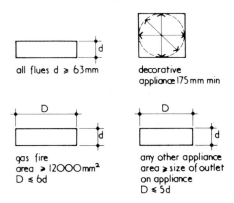

all flues d ⩾ 63mm

decorative
appliance 175 mm min

gas fire
area ⩾ 12000 mm²
D ⩽ 6d

any other appliance
area ⩾ size of outlet
on appliance
D ⩽ 5d

NOTE   Flues may be circular.

2.11 [**10.18**] *(a) detail of outlet terminal. (b) siting of outlet terminals in respect of openings.*

NOTE   Terminal not required if flue outlet exceeds 200 mm across the axis.

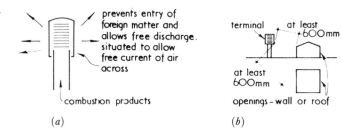

(a)   (b)

| **Chimneys** | **2.12/2.13**   These may be of masonry or factory made components. |

2.12/2.13   These may be of masonry or factory made components.

2.13   Masonry chimneys: these may be of any masonry with a lining or of flue blocks without a lining.

2.14/2.15   Linings may be of any material and fixed as described in Section 1.

2.16   Flue blocks may be as described in BS 1289: 1975: *Precast concrete flue blocks for domestic gas appliances*, or of any material described in Section 1; however, Section 1 contains no reference to flue blocks, so we are left with BS 1289, a brief description of which follows.

Note on BS 1289: 1975

Because of difficulties over dimensional co-ordination with bricks and blocks, this standard no longer give tables of detailed sizes which must now be obtained from manufacturers. Certain basic dimensions only are given and these are as follows:

* The AD permits slightly lower standards than these for gas fires.

(a)   Area of flueway to be at least 1300 mm^2 and remain constant.*

(b)   Flueway length/width ratio to be no more than 5:1.*

(c)   Minimum flueway width to be 63 mm.

(d)   Outer wall thickness to be at least 25 mm.

These dimensions tie in generally with the requirements of the Approved Document and BS 5440.

Specifications are given for materials and mixes. Joints should be rebated or grooved. PC terminals should have discharge outlets on two opposite sides each at least equal to the area of the flue with suitable guards to exclude birds.

Most of the BS is taken up by Appendices describing methods of measurement and tests for compressive strength, shrinkage, expansion and flue performance as well as a series of diagrams illustrating several types of installation including a multi-storey range.

2.17   Flexible flue liners complying with BS 715: 1970 may be used if the chimney was built before 1 February 1966 or is already lined.

NOTE   These are no longer permissible for Section 1 appliances.

2.18   Chimneys which are not lined or constructed in accordance with 2.13 to 2.17 above must have a debris collecting space at the base of at least 0.012 m^3 and a depth of 250 mm below the point of connection of the appliance. Ready access for debris clearance must be available by removal of the appliance or otherwise.

2.19   Factory made insulated chimneys described in Section 1 may also be used for gas.

Flue pipes

2.20   The following materials may be used:

(a)   Sheet metal as described in BS 715: 1970 *Sheet metal flue pipes and accessories for gas fired appliances*, or

(b)   Stainless steel, or

(c)   Asbestos cement as described in BS 567: 1973 (1984) *Asbestos-cement flue pipes and fittings, light quality*, or

(d)   Cast iron as described in BS 41: 1973 (1981) *Cast iron spigot and socket flue or smoke pipes and fittings*, or

(e)   Any material described in Section 1 for a solid fuel or oil burning appliance.

Flue pipes with spigot and socket joints should be fitted with the sockets uppermost.

NOTE   Vitrified clay pipes to BS 65, which were permitted by Part L (1976) are no longer allowed.

Part C   Protection against heat

2.21   For decorative appliances the appropriate provisions of Section 1 apply (1.22 to 1.33). They are in other words treated like solid fuel open fires. Otherwise the following apply.

Hearths

2.22   These must always be provided unless:

(*a*)   Any flame or incandescent material is not less than 225 mm above the floor (see below) [10.19] or

(*b*)   The appliance complies with the recommendations of the appropriate parts of BS 5258: *Safety of domestic gas appliances* or BS 5386: *Specification for gas burning appliances* which refer to installation without a hearth.

BS 5258 has a number of parts (12 with more to come) each dealing with a different type of appliance. They are mostly concerned with the safety standards of the appliances themselves, but include in each case a test rig to simulate the complete installation, designed to establish that floor and wall temperatures in the immediate vicinity do not rise by more than 50°C during operation. In such circumstances special provisions for protecting adjacent combustible material are not necessary.

2.23/2.24   If these conditions are not met a hearth at least 12.5 mm thick of solid non-combustible material must be provided, as shown in diagram [10.20]. The reference to a wall intervening at the back is taken from the old M 8 and not mentioned in the new Approved Document, but it seems such a likely situation that it has been left in (in any case 2.25 below shows that a separation of only 75 mm is required between an appliance and adjacent combustible material).

2.22 [**10.19**] *Appliance fixed above floor.*

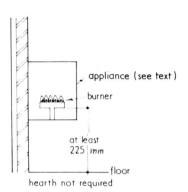

2.24 [**10.20**] *Hearth (general).*

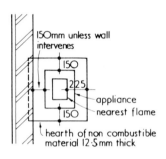

Back boilers require special attention. The Approved Document refers loosely to a 'back boiler whether installed alone or with another appliance' and the accompanying diagram (illustrated in [10.21] to demonstrate the degree of ambiguity) is quite unsatisfactory, as is the terminology. A 'back boiler', by definition, is behind something else and cannot therefore be installed on its own. The usual arrangement is a combination of gas fire and small central heating boiler behind. Such boilers may however also be fitted in a fireplace recess behind a decorative closure screen (when they are usually known as circulators). In such cases the front projection of the hearth may be measured from the front of the boiler. If however there is a fire in front of the boiler, the 225 mm front projection must clearly be taken from the flame position of the fire, as for other appliances. Diagram [10.21] illustrates the situation.

2.23 [**10.21**] *Hearth for backboiler.*

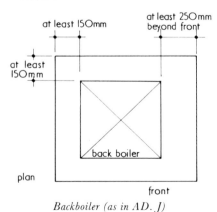

Backboiler (as in AD. J)

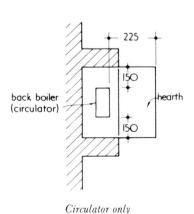

Circulator only

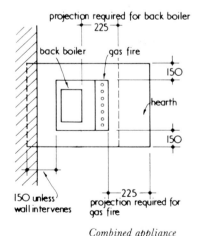

Combined appliance

In both cases the construction of the hearth for these appliances must be solid non-combustible material either:

125 mm thick (ie as for Section 1 hearths) or

25 mm thick on non-combustible supports at least 25 mm high.

Shielding of appliances

2.25 This really should be headed 'proximity to combustible material' because unless the appliance is within 75 mm no shield is needed. Diagram [10.22] shows the requirement. This does not apply to appliances which comply with the relevant recommendations of BS 5258: *Safety of domestic appliances* or BS 5386: *Specifications for gas burning appliances.*

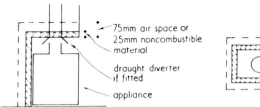
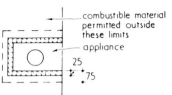

2.25 [**10.22**] *Appliances: separation from combustible material.*

Chimneys

2.26 This again is far from explicit and the diagram not at all helpful. Its predecessor is L 14(2) of the old Regulations, which simply required a surround of solid material at least 25 mm thick to each flue (in addition to the lining). Additional matter has however been brought in which is actually part of B 3 (structural fire precautions). The intentions are better illustrated in [10.23].

2.26 [**10.23**] *Chimney walls.*

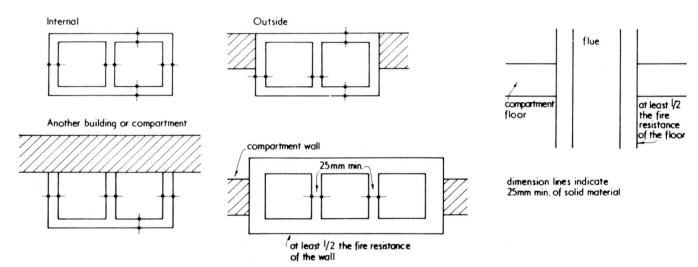

The diagram in the Approved Document also shows a chimney penetrating a compartment wall at an angle which could really only apply to a factory made insulated chimney, for which see illustration [10.13].

Flue pipes

2.27 These must not be nearer than 25 mm to any combustible material and be sleeved where passing through the same; diagrams [10.24–26]. Here again the provisions of B 3 are repeated with regard to compartment walls or floors. What is not explained is that in the case of flue pipes a duct is necessary to enclose one or more pipes (see F 18/F 19 of Approved Document B).

2.27 [**10.24**] *Flue pipes through structure containing combustible material.*

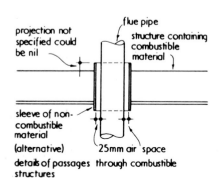

2.27 [**10.25**] *Flue pipes adjacent to combustible material.*

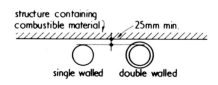

2.27 [**10.26**] *Flue pipes passing through compartment wall or floor.*

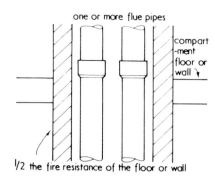

one or more flue pipes

compart-ment floor or wall

½ the fire resistance of the floor or wall

Notes on the three BS documents which contain the information for appliances not covered by the Approved Document are given below. It is a little difficult to understand why these requirements have been dealt with in this way.

BS 5440: Flues and air supply for gas appliances of rated input not exceeding 60kW

This is in two parts, the first dealing with flues and the second with air supply. It is a revision of CP 367: 1963.

Part 1: 1978: Flues

Flue systems are classified as follows:
1   Individual room-sealed.
2   Individual open flued.
3   Shared room sealed (Se ducts and U ducts).
4   Shared open flue.
All except item 3 may be natural or fan draught.

A balanced flued appliance is a room sealed appliance where the air intake is adjacent to the discharge point, arranged so that the wind effects are balanced. This is usually on an outside wall behind the appliance, but an arrangement known as a 'natural draught balanced compartment' is possible where an open flued appliance is installed in a sealed chamber which draws its air from a point adjacent to the flue outlet (see diagram [10.28]).

Generally room-sealed systems are to be preferred where possible.

All flues comprise 4 parts arranged in the following order:
(*a*)   Primary flue: usually integral with the appliance.
(*b*)   Draught diverter: may also be integral.
(*c*)   Secondary flue: the main and longest part.
(*d*)   Terminal.

Draught diverters prevent downdraughts reaching the burners and also dilute the flue gases by drawing air from the room. They must always be in the same room as the appliance: diagrams [10.27, 10.28]).

[**10.27**] *Parts of flue.*

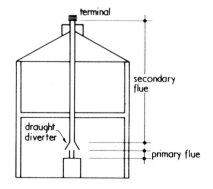

terminal

secondary flue

draught diverter

primary flue

[**10.28**] *Natural draught balanced compartment.*

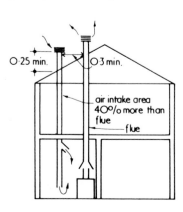

0·25 min.   0·3 min.

air intake area 40% or more than flue

flue

The recommendations for individual natural draught appliances conform with those in the Approved Document but there are more details. Circular flues serving gas fires should generally be 125 mm diameter which is equivalent to a 1300 mm^2 rectangular flue in a block. The avoidance of condensation is important, not only because of the need to dispose of the water, but also because of its corrosive effect. It can be avoided by limiting the length of flues or by insulation. A table and chart are given for determining the lengths of various kinds of flue which would normally be condensate-free. (The old L 14 contained a table showing the maximum lengths of flue which could be constructed using ordinary cement and bricks: ie those that would be condensate-free).

Minimum heights for flues are specified based on the concept of 'equivalent height' which makes allowance for bends, offsets etc. The route of a flue is less important than with Section 1 flues, but the rise should be continuous and the first 600 mm above the draught diverter should be vertical. With fanned systems any route can be taken.

Shared room-sealed systems consist of a vertical shaft, usually of prefabricated sections, which both supplies the combustion air and takes away the products of combustion from the room sealed appliances. They may be in either Se duct or U duct form (diagram [10.29]). Tables are given for sizing these for various combinations of appliances. They are suitable for continuous burning appliances and instantaneous water heaters.

Shared open flued systems serving appliances in different rooms can be used for the same type of appliance subject to certain conditions (diagram [10.30, 10.31]). These can also be used for gas fires, but these must have their own separate system and the minimum required height for the branch flues is greater. A table for sizing based on rated input is provided.

[**10.29**] *Shared room sealed systems.*

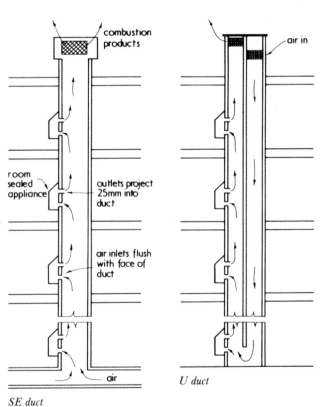

[**10.31**] *Shared flue.*

[**10.30**] *Appliances sharing a common flue.*

NOTE All appliances to be of the same type and limited in number and aggregate input rating.

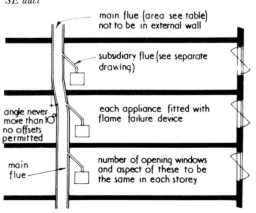

[**10.32**] *Detail of subsidiary flue*

NOTE   All appliances to be the same type.

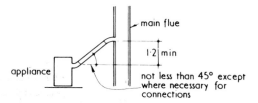

Recommendations are given for catering appliances, incinerators and drying appliances all of which have special requirements. Fire precautions are the same as in the Approved Document but include a further recommendation that where flue pipes pass through spaces outside the room in which the appliance is installed they should be protected from contact or damage by a suitable non-combustible guard at least 25 mm clear of the pipe (this was also in Part L of the 1976 Regulations).

The following general comments might aid understanding.

1   Gas fires are a special case because, being open, they behave to some degree like ordinary open solid fuel fires and induce a greater airflow than is needed for combustion.

2   Incinerators are a special case because of the possibility of debris in the flue gases: flues must be fully sealed and draught diverters cannot be used.

3   Drying cabinets are a special case because of the quantity of moisture-laden air.

Most importantly the BS stresses that apart from the simplest installation it is always essential to seek the advice of the local gas undertaking. This applies especially to all multiple installations and incinerators.

Part 2: 1976 Air supply

This is a much shorter document and includes some advice on flueless heaters.

Recent work by the British Gas Corporation shows that it is impossible to reduce the area of adventitious openings (cracks around doors etc) to less than 3500 mm^2 and this has been allowed for in determining the additional requirement, if any.

The area of ventilation given for appliances covered by the Approved Document are the same, but there is additional information as follows:

1   Where a room-sealed or open flued appliance is fitted in a compartment, the compartment should be ventilated at both high and low level with grilles of the following free areas:

Compartment ventilated to a room   900 mm^2/kW
Compartment ventilated to the outside   450 mm^2/kW

If the appliance is open flued these figures should be doubled for the low level only.

2   Where an open flued appliance is in a room the vents should be arranged as shown in diagram [10.33] where two vents are in series as illustrated on the right of the diagram no additional area is needed, but if more than two add 50 per cent. If there are several appliances of different types add the total of the space heating appliances and add the total of the flueless appliances and use the larger of the two totals to determine the area required.

[**10.33**] *Air supply arrangements.*

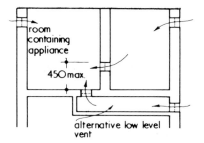

3   Flueless appliances should be installed in a room with an openable window plus the following permanent vents.

Type of flueless appliance	Input rating limit	Vol of room or space (m^3)	Area reqd (mm^2)	Comment
1 Cooker	none			
2 Inst water heater	12kW	6 to n/e 11	3500*	over 11 no requirement
3 Storage water heater	3kW	6 to n/e 11	9500	over 21 no
4 Washer or wash boiler	6kW	11 to n/e 21	3500	requirement
5 Space heater in room†	50W/m^3			
6 Ditto not in room‡	100W/m^3	no limit	9500	applies universally

NOTES

* If the room is less than 9 m^3, 6500 m^2 is needed for a cooker but if there is a door direct to the external air there is no requirement.

† Increased by 3500 for every kW (or part) over 3kW.

‡ Increased by 3500 for every 2kW (or part) over 6kW.
If two or more appliances are installed in one room, the total ventilation area required is the aggregate of those for each.

The introduction states that these are taken from the 1972 Building Regulations (a reversal of the usual process). The 1981 Second Amendment introduced a lot of changes to M 9 but the ventilation requirements remained very similar. M 9 also contained a lot of provisions regarding the location of flueless appliances (eg not in bathrooms, bed-sits or bedrooms) and the items they serve. Most of this material is to be found in BS 5546, a note on which follows.

BS 5546: 1979: Gas hot water supplies

This covers appliances for supplying hot water to individual dwellings.

The Approved Document gives this as a reference for flueless water heaters, but it also deals with flued appliances and it is recommended that all large water heaters (those dealing with a whole house supply) whether instantaneous or storage, should be flued.

The storage range includes circulators which may be located remote from the storage cylinder in combination with a living room gas fire (ie a back boiler).

Small water heaters are intended to supply only a sink or wash basin and this type may be flueless. They may be instantaneous or storage type and in the latter case they are usually integral with the storage vessel.

Location – the following points are made:

1   Room sealed water heaters are allowed anywhere.

2   Open flued or flueless heaters must never be installed in bath or shower rooms.

3   Bedrooms and bed-sits exceeding 21 m^3 may contain:

(*a*)   A flueless instantaneous heater up to 12kW.

(*b*)   A flueless storage heater up to 9 litres and 3kW in each case serving only a wash basin or sink.

(*c*)   An open flued circulator not exceeding 4.5kW.

4   Any type of water heater may be installed in kitchens, circulation spaces, cloakrooms and wcs (but large instantaneous water heaters are not considered suitable for single-house use).

5   Flued water heaters may be installed in a compartment (such as an airing cupboard) with suitable guarding.

Air supply requirements are given in BS 5440: Part 2.

NOTE   Most of the recommendations of these BSS will also be found in the Gas Safety Regulations 1972 which are obligatory. (British Standards, of course, are not).

References

The following British Standards and other documents are referred to in the Approved Document with the page number on which the reference is made.

BS 41: 1973 *Cast iron spigot and socket flue or smoke pipes and fittings.* £10·20 (£5·10), p. 5, 10.

BS 65: 1981 *Specification for vitrified clay pipes, fittings and joints* Amendment slip no 1: AMD 4328. Amendment slip no 2: AMD 4394. £16·20 (£8·10), p. 5, 10.

BS 476 *Fire tests on building materials and structures.* Part 4: 1970 *Non-combustibility test for materials* Amendment slip no 1: AMD 2483. Amendment slip no 2: AMD 4390. £16·20 (£8·10), p. 1.

BS 567: 1973 *Asbestos-cement flue pipes and fittings, light quality.* £16·20 (£8·10), p. 5, 10.

BS 715: 1970 *Sheet metal flue pipes and accessories for gas fired appliances* Amendment slip no 1: AMD 3284. Amendment slip no 2: AMD 3517. £12·20 (£6·10), p. 10.

BS 1181: 1971 *Clay flue linings and flue terminals* £10·20 (£5·10), p. 5, 10.

BS 1251: 1970 *Open fireplace components* Amendment slip no 1: AMD 903. Amendment slip no 2: AMD 1651. £10·20 (£5·10), p. 4.

BS 1289: 1975 *Precast concrete flue blocks for domestic gas appliances.* £16·20 (£8·10), p. 10.

BS 1344 *Methods of testing vitreous enamel finishes.* Part 1: 1965 *Resistance to thermal shock of coatings on articles other than cooking utensils* Amendment slip no 1: AMD 2152. £5·20 (£2·60). Part 3: 1967 *Resistance to products of combustion containing sulphur compounds.* £5·20 (£2·60). Part 7: 1984: Resistance to heat. £5·20 (£2·60), p. 5.

BS 1449 *Steel plate, sheet and strip.* Part 2: 1983 *Specification for stainless and heat resisting steel plate, sheet and strips.* £12·20 (£6·10), p. 5.

BS 4543 *Factory-made insulated chimneys.* Part 1: 1976 *Methods of test.* £10·20 (£5·10), p. 5, 7. Part 2: 1976 *Specification for chimneys for solid fuel appliances* Amendment slip no 1: AMD 2794. Amendment slip no 2: AMD 3475. Amendment slip no 3: AMD 3878. £7 (£3·50), p. 5. Part 3: 1976 *Specification for chimneys for oil fired appliances* Amendment slip nos 1: AMD 2981, 2: AMD 3476. £7 (£3·50), p. 5.

BS 5258 *Safety of domestic gas appliances.* Part 1: 1975 *Central heating boilers and circulators* Amendment slip no 1: AMD 3348. Amendment slip no 2: AMD 4228. £16·20 (£8·10). Part 1: Supplement 1: 1983 *Fan-powered appliances.* £12·20 (£6·10). Part 2: 1976 *Cooking appliances* Amendment slip no 1: AMD 3285. £16·20 (£8·10). Part 4: 1977 *Fanned circulation ducted air heaters.* £16·20 (£8·10). Part 5: 1975 *Gas fires* Amendment slip no 1: AMD 4076. £16·20 (£8·10). Part 7: 1977 *Storage water heaters.* £16·20 (£8·10). Part 8: 1980 *Combined appliances: gas fire/back boiler.* £16·20 (£8·10). Part 12: 1980 *Decorative gas log and other fuel effect appliances (second and third family gases).* £16·20 (£8·10), p. 11.

BS 5386 *Specification for gas burning appliances.* Part 1: 1976 *Gas burning appliances for instantaneous production of hot water for domestic use* Amendment slip no 1: AMD 2990. £22·80 (£11·40). Part 3: 1980 *Domestic cooking appliances burning gas* Amendment slip no 1: AMD 4162. Amendment slip no 2: AMD 4405. £22·80 (£11·40). Part 4: 1983 *Built-in domestic cooking appliances.* £10·20 (£5·10), p. 11.

BS 5440 *Code of practice for flues and air supply for gas appliances of rated input not exceeding 60 kw (first and second family gases).* Part 1: 1978 *Flues* Amendment slip no 1: AMD 4639, £22·80 (£11·40). Part 2: 1976 *Air supply.* £10·20 (£5·10), p. 9.

BS 5546: 1979 *Code of practice for installation of gas hot water supplies for domestic purposes (second family gases).* £16·20 (£8·10), p. 9.

BS 6461 *Installation of chimneys and flues for domestic appliances burning solid fuel (including wood and peat).* Part 1: 1984 *Code of practice for masonry chimneys and flue pipes.* £16·20 (£8·10), p. 5.

Approved Document K
Stairways, Ramps and Guards

This Document is divided into two parts:

K 1   Stairways and ramps

K 2/3   Pedestrian and vehicle barriers

These requirements replace Part H of the 1976 Regulations and cover much the same ground. A few of the more detailed requirements of Part H seem to have been omitted, but the principal provisions remain the same. Three notable omissions are:

○   The rule prohibiting flights of less than 2 risers in domestic stairs or 3 in others.

○   The 75 mm minimum for risers, and

○   The limiting of flights to 16 risers (but retained for shop and assembly areas).

The first of these caused some controversy in the past, especially in relation to gangways between raked seating in theatres etc. The reference to lighting on escape stairs is also omitted, presumably because it is now included in B 1 *Means of Escape*. There is also now no prohibition or conditions on the use of perforated treads, or limit on the total rise of stairs exposed to the weather.

Although the question of guarding is dealt with generally under K 2/3, the guarding of stairways and ramps is dealt with under K 1. The need for this segregation is far from apparent but is no doubt the result, as we have already seen so often, of the effort to define the regulations in terms of functional requirements which tends to lead to an artifical separation of related elements and inevitably results in repetition.

K 1   STAIRWAYS AND RAMPS

The requirement of Schedule 1 is as follows:

	Requirement	Limits on application
	Stairways and ramps	
Stairways; ramps	K 1. Stairways and ramps shall be such as to afford safe passage for the users of the building.	The requirements of this Part apply to stairways and ramps which form part of the structure of the building.

After an introduction this is divided into two sections:

Section 1   Stairways

Section 2   Ramps

Introduction   **0.1/0.3**   The point is made that the Regulations do not require buildings to have stairs or ramps, but that they do apply to any building which has them.

They do not apply to stairs or ramps outside a building unless these are part of the building structure. They do not apply to ladders which are defined as any flight, fixed or not, steeper than 55°. This clears up a point sometimes raised in the past about the status of loft ladders.

Stairways and ramps which are part of an escape route and those which form the only means of access for disabled persons may need to meet additional requirements (see B 1 and Schedule 2).

Section 1   Stairways

1.1/1.2   The provisions apply if the stairway:

(*a*)   Is part of a means of escape (see B 1 Mandatory rules), or

(*b*)   Has a rise of more than 600 mm, or

(*c*)   Has a drop at the side of more than 600 mm.

1.3   Definitions: The following are defined:

Stairway   Includes flights and landings.

Private stairway   Intended to be used only by one dwelling.

Common stairway   Intended to be used by more than one dwelling.

Going and rise   See diagram [11.1].

Flight   Part of a stairway or ramp which has consecutive steps.

1.3 [**11.1**] *Going and rise.*   1.4 [**11.2**] *Pitch.*

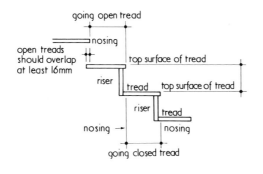
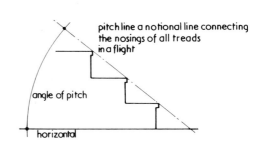

Steepness

1.4   This is defined as the angle of pitch (see diagram [11.2]). It is generally controlled by the limits set later for maximum rise and minimum going, but over-riding limits are set on the pitch.

These are: Private stair 42°

Common stair 38°

The first of these shows up as a cut-off line on the chart for private stairs here, but for common stairs the limit is, in fact, unnecessary because, despite what the Approved Document says, even combining the maximum permitted rise with the minimum going, the angle would still be below 38° (because Tan 38° is less than 190/240).

Rise and going

1.5   All steps in a flight should have the same rise and going (for tapered steps see 1.16 to 1.18).

NOTE   Although not mentioned in the Approved Document this does not prohibit the use of curved nosings provided the going stays the same across the width of the stair (diagram [11.3]).

1.6   Where the landing is formed by ground which slopes across the stair the depth of the riser should be taken at the centre (diagram [11.4]).

1.5 [**11.3**] *Possible use of curved nosings.*   1.6 [**11.4**] *Sloping ground.*

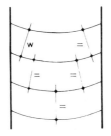
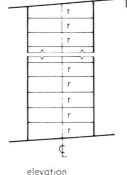

elevation

1.7/1.8   The basic relationship between rise and going is represented by the formula

$$2R + G \geq 550 \text{ mm} \leq 700 \text{ mm}$$

In addition there are limitations on the maximum rise and minimum going for four types of stairway as shown in the table below and in diagram in [11.5].

*Table to 1.7 [**11.5**]*
Comparison of gradients
resulting from the use of
maximum rise and minimum
going in the four types, also
the maximum angle of pitch
in types 1 and 2.

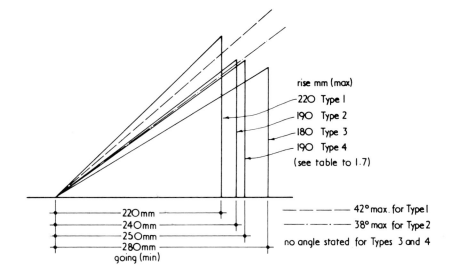

Table to 1.7

	Rise (max)	Going (min)
1 private stair	220 mm	220 mm
2 common stair	190 mm	240 mm
3 stairway in: (a) an institutional building (unless it will only be used by staff) (b) an assembly building and serving an area used for assembly purposes (unless the area is less than 100 m²)	180 mm	280 mm
4 stairway not described in 1, 2 and 3 above	190 mm	250 mm

The possible combinations which may be used within these limits are within the heavy lines on the following three charts [11.6, 11.8].

[**11.6**] *Private stairways within one dwelling.*

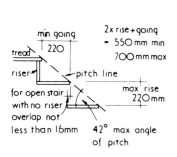

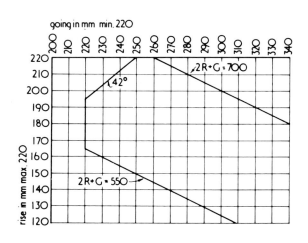

[**11.7**] *Common stairways: two or more dwellings.*   going in mm min 240

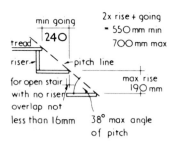

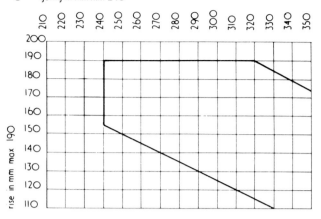

[**11.8**] *Non-domestic buildings. No specific requirement for angle of pitch.*

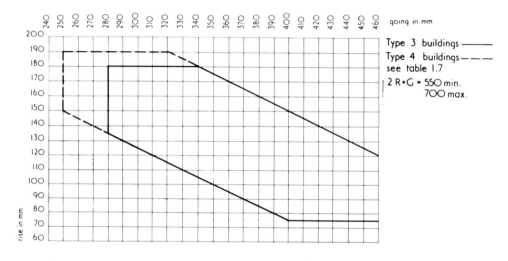

Type 3 buildings ————
Type 4 buildings — — —
see table 1.7
2 R+G = 550 min.
          700 max.

Headroom

1.9   There must be a minimum of 2 m headroom measured vertically from the pitch line at all places (diagram [11.9]).

Steps

1.10/1.11   All steps must be level. If they have open risers they must overlap by at least 16 mm. If they have open risers in a flight which:

(*a*)   Forms part of a private or common stair, or

(*b*)   Is in an institutional building likely to be used by children under 5 years old, or

(*c*)   Is in any other residential building

The open risers must be so constructed as to prevent the passage of a 100 mm diameter sphere (diagram [11.10]).

1.9 [**11.9**] *Headroom.*   1.11 [**11.10**] *Open risers in certain buildings.*

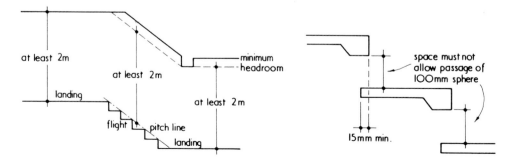

Width of flights   **1.12/1.13**   The Approved Document says that there are three minimum widths of flight and then refers to a table which gives four (since corrected). There is also a diagram showing how widths are measured: see Table below and diagram [11.11].

Table to 1.12   Widths of stairways

	Unobstructed width (min)
1(a) private stair providing access only to one room (not being a kitchen or living room) or to a bathroom, a closet, or both	600 mm
1(b) private stair other than **1**(a) above	800 mm
2 common stair	900 mm
3 stairway in: (a) an institutional building (unless it will only be used by staff) (b) an assembly building and serving an area used for assembly purposes (unless the area is less than 100 m²) (c) any other building and serving an area which can be occupied by more than 50 people	1000 mm
4 Any stairway not described in **1, 2m 3** or **4** above	800 mm

NOTE   This is the unobstructed width which is not the same as that given in the British Standards relating to means of escape.

A stair wider than 1800 mm, other than a private or common stair, must be divided into flights not wider than 1800 mm. In buildings where the minimum width is 1000 mm this exercises a certain limitation as illustrated in [11.12].

1.12 [**11.11**] *Width of stairways.*

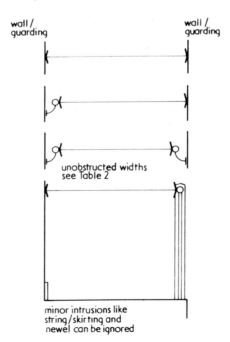

wall / guarding   wall / guarding

unobstructed widths see Table 2

minor intrusions like string/skirting and newel can be ignored

1.13 [**11.12**] *Rule regarding the subdivision of stairs over 1 m wide.*
NOTE   The effect of this, whether intentional or not, is to rule out the use of stairways between 1.8 m and 2.0 m wide, since anything over 1.8 m must be divided, but the minimum width of any subdivision is 1.0 m.

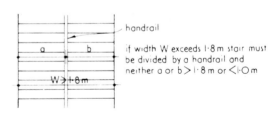

handrail

if width W exceeds 1·8 m stair must be divided by a handrail and neither a or b > 1·8 m or < 1·0 m

Where a stairway forms part of a means of escape increased width may be needed to comply with B 1.

Length of flights

1.14   There should be no more than 16 risers to a flight in areas used for *shop or assembly purposes.*
This rule used to be universal and designers will clearly decide for themselves on the advisability of using long uninterrupted flights.
1.15   Stairways of over 36 risers must have a change of direction of at least 30° (diagram [11.13]).

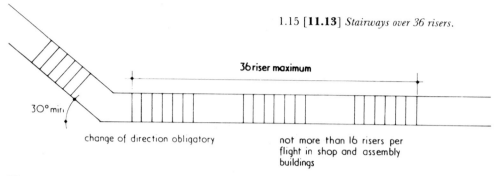

1.15 **[11.13]** *Stairways over 36 risers.*

36 riser maximum

30° min

change of direction obligatory

not more than 16 risers per flight in shop and assembly buildings

There was also a rule in the old Part H that on an escape route flights nearer to the exit should not have a pitch greater than those further away but this has now been omitted, no doubt because matters relating to Means of Escape are now dealt with elsewhere.

Tapered treads

1.16   The going of tapered treads should be measured:
(*a*)   If the flight is less than 1 m wide, in the middle.
(*b*)   If the flight is 1 m or wider, 270 mm from each side.
The rise and going should be within the same limits as shown in the table for parallel steps (see 1.8) and going should measure at least 50 mm at the narrow end.
1.17   Consecutive steps should have uniform going (see diagrams [11.14, 11.15]).

Comment
These are the same rules as in the old Part H, but omitting what might be termed the 'small print' ie careful specification of what exactly is meant by the various terms in relation to circular stairs.
It is not however specifically stated (as it was in Part H) that the 2R + G formula and gradient rules also apply to tapered steps. It is none the less logical to assume that they do (in the absence of anything to the contrary), since if they did not, the requirement that the going be measured as in 1.16(*b*) above (270 mm from each side) would have no purpose, as the going at the wider side must be a maximum (the inner side being a minimum) and without the formula 2R + G there is no way of establishing a maximum going.
Diagram [11.16] shows how these rules are applied to a spiral or helical stair and also to winders forming part of an otherwise parallel stair.

1.17 **[11.14]** *Tapered treads: width 'w' changes at constant rate.*

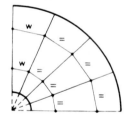

[11.15] *Taper steps can have curved nosings providing the width reduces at a constant rate.*

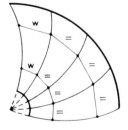

1.16 [**11.16**] *Spiral stairs and winders.*

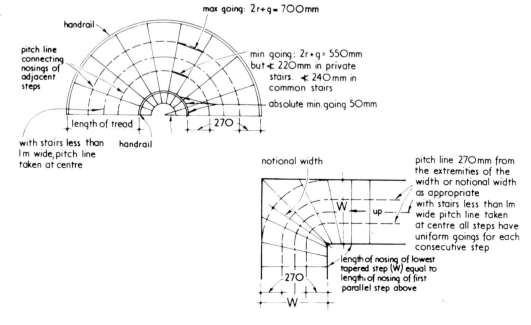

max going: 2r+g= 700mm

handrail

pitch line connecting nosings of adjacent steps

min going: 2r+g= 550mm but ≮ 220mm in private stairs. ≮ 240mm in common stairs

absolute min. going 50mm

length of tread

270

with stairs less than 1m wide, pitch line taken at centre

handrail

notional width

pitch line 270mm from the extremities of the width or notional width as appropriate with stairs less than 1m wide pitch line taken at centre all steps have uniform goings for each consecutive step

W   up

length of nosing of lowest tapered step (W) equal to length of nosing of first parallel step above

270

W

To assist the reader in understanding how these controls affect the design of stairs in practice, diagrams [11.17-19] show three examples of tapered steps in different types of building with varying widths or riser dimensions. In cases 1 and 3 it can be seen that the height of the riser controls the maximum going and hence the degree of taper and thus the minimum radius. In Case 2 this does not apply and the taper is controlled only by the minimum going at the centre and narrow end.

If the 2R + G formula did not apply to tapered steps at all, this would be the same for the other two cases except that the going would be measured only 270 mm from the narrow end and the outer measurement, as stated earlier, would have no significance (see also note on BS 5395 below).

[**11.17**] *The diagram shows the effect of rise and width on taper and radius. The formula 2 × rise + going = 700 mm max or 550 mm min, together with the absolute minimum for going, controls the angle of taper and hence the minimum radius of the stair for any given width. The calculation is affected by the selected rise, which controls the maximum going on the outer pitch line. The examples are based on a common stairway.*

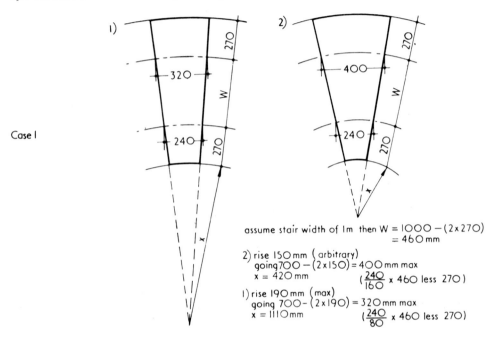

Case I

assume stair width of 1m then W = 1000 − (2 x 270)
= 460 mm

2) rise 150 mm (arbitrary)
going 700 − (2 x 150) = 400 mm max
x = 420 mm ($\frac{240}{160}$ x 460 less 270)

1) rise 190 mm (max)
going 700 − (2 x 190) = 320 mm max
x = 1110 mm ($\frac{240}{80}$ x 460 less 270)

1.16 [**11.18**] *Tapered treads: method specified for stairways less than 1 m wide (example based on private stair). The rises in both cases will be the same – between 165 mm and 195 mm.*

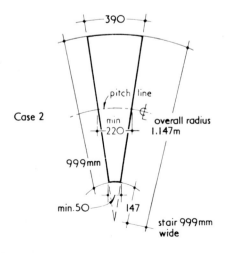

Case 2

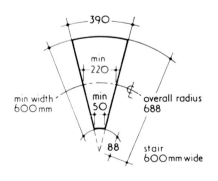

[**11.19**] *This example is based on a Type 3 building (see Table to 1.7). Type 4 buildings are similar but the minimum going is 250 mm and maximum rise 190 mm.*

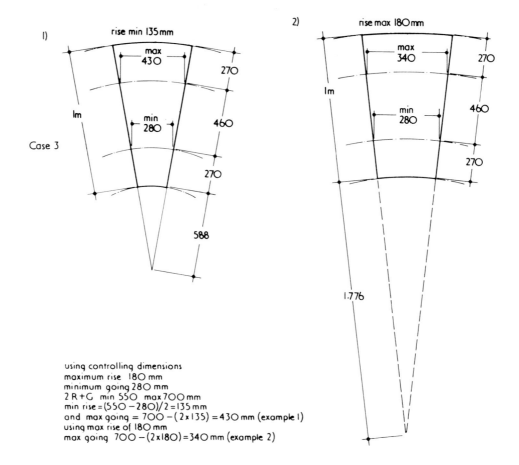

using controlling dimensions
maximum rise 180 mm
minimum going 280 mm
2 R + G min 550 max 700 mm
min rise = (550 − 280)/2 = 135 mm
and max going = 700 − (2 x 135) = 430 mm (example 1)
using max rise of 180 mm
max going 700 − (2 x 180) = 340 mm (example 2)

Alternative approach	**1.18** BS 5395: *Stairs ladders and walkways* Part 1: 1977 *Code of practice for stairs* and Part 2: 1984 *Code of practice for helical and spiral stairs* give additional information which may be useful for setting out stairways. NOTE Although this is headed 'alternative approach' the Approved Document does not say, as in most other cases, that it may be used instead of the rules in the Document, but merely that it provides 'additional information'. This is important, as may be seen in the note on the BS which follows.
BS 5395: 1977 Stairs, ladders and walkways	Stairs seem to be only a recent subject for British Standard attention and Part H of the 1976 Regulations could not therefore have been based on them. The standard itself draws on a lot of other sources which must have also been used for earlier Regulations, because the principal recommendations are the same.
Part 1 CP for straight stairs	Originally BS 5395 covered all types of stairs but subsequently all reference to circular stairs was transferred to a new Part 2. Part 1, however, still covers the use of winders in straight stairs. The geometry of stairs is covered rather more comprehensively than in the Approved Document. In addition the BS deals with structural systems, materials, components, finishes, safety aspects, fire protection and lighting.
Part 2 CP for helical and spiral stairs	The defined difference between these is that a spiral stair is one describing a helix around a central column, whereas a helical stair has no central column. The rules for determining the setting out vary a little from the Approved Document. The lines on which measurements are to be taken for going and rise are given as 270 mm from the inner and outer edges, as in the Approved Document, but there is no mention of measuring

on the centre line for stairs less than 1 m wide. Furthermore the relationship between rise and going is given as:

$$2R + G \geq 480 \text{ mm} \leq 800 \text{ mm}$$

which gives a wider range than the normal rule for parallel steps which is assumed to apply in the Approved Document (see above). A table also gives a range of minima and maxima for goings (instead of only minima) which vary from those for parallel treads given in Part 1 although the risers remain unchanged. Thus following these rules would not necessarily comply with the Approved Document.

Limited advice is given on construction and testing.

Handrails

1.19/1.20   All flights must have a handrail at one side and if over 1 m wide at both sides, but they need not extend beside the two bottom steps. If the heights match up the handrails may form the top of the guarding (the usual balustrade and handrail). The diagram illustrates the requirements (see diagram [11.20].

1.20 [**11.20**] *Handrails and guarding of stairways, ramps, landings etc*

NOTES   No handrail is required for flight or ramp formed by fixed seating.

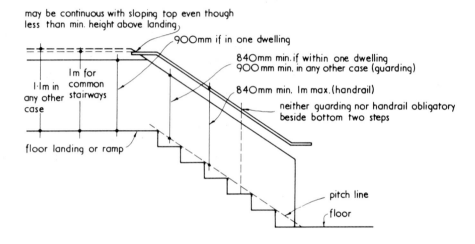

Landings

1.21   There must be a landing at the top and bottom of every flight and its width and depth must be at least equal to the width of the stair.

1.21/1.22 [**11.21**] *Landings.*

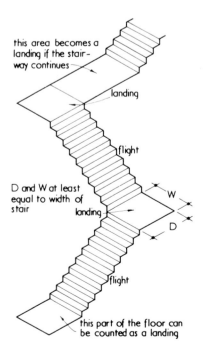

1.23 [**11.22**] *Landings: obstruction.*

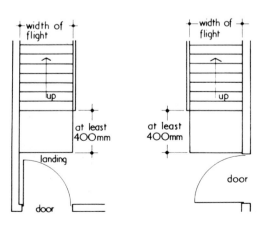

1.22/1.23   Part of the floor may count as a landing, but all landings must be clear of obstruction. A door may however swing across part of a landing at the *bottom* of a flight only, if certain clearances are maintained (see diagram [11.21, 22].

1.24/1.25   These are two exceptions to the general rule, namely that there may be a door at the top of a flight which does not rise more than 600 mm if it opens away from the steps, and landings may slope up to 1:12 if they form part of the ground and are paved (diagram [11.23]).

1.24/1.25 [**11.23**] *Exceptions to general rule*
(landings)

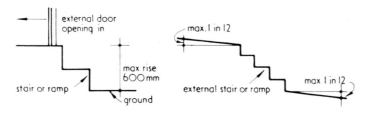

Guarding

1.26   Flights and landings should be guarded wherever there is a drop exceeding 600 mm. Suitable forms include walls, screens, railings and balustrades (a somewhat overlapping series of definitions).

1.27   As in the case of open risers, there must be no openings which would pass a 100 mm diameter sphere if the stair is:

(*a*)   A private or common stair.

(*b*)   In an institutional building likely to be used by children under 5 years old.

(*c*)   In any other residential building.

It should also not be readily climbable by children.

1.28   The height should be as shown in diagram [11.24] and it should be able to resist at this height a horizontal force as illustrated in the diagram.

If glazing is used it should be of glass blocks, toughened or laminated safety glass. Wired glass should not be used.

1.28 [**11.24**] *Guarding.*

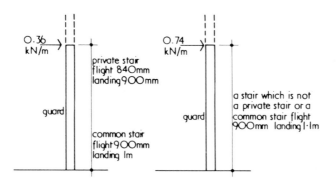

Section 2   Ramps

2.1   Ramps should not have a slope steeper than 1:12.

2.2/2.6 and **2.8**   These rules cover headroom, widths, obstruction, handrails, guarding and landings and are identical with those for stairways except that handrails are not essential if the rise of the ramp does not exceed 600 mm.

Stepped ramps

2.7   Where ramps and stairs are combined the length of the ramps should be between 1 and 2 m (diagram [11.25]) and intermediate steps should be level.

2.7 [**11.25**] *Stepped ramps.*

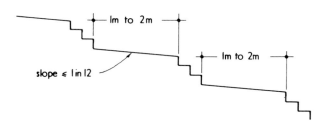

slope ≤ 1 in 12

K 2/3   PEDESTRIAN AND VEHICLE BARRIERS

This covers the provision of barriers for the protection of people and the containment of vehicles. The requirements of Part K of Schedule 1 are as follows:

	Requirement	Limits on application
	Protection from falling	
	K 2. Stairways, ramps, floors and balconies, and any roof to which people normally have access, shall be guarded with barriers where they are necessary to protect users from the risk of falling.	
	Vehicle barriers	
Vehicle ramps; floors; roofs.	K 3. Vehicle ramps, and any floor and roof to which vehicles have access, shall be guarded with barriers where they are necessary to provide protection for people in or about the building.	

This is backed up by an acceptable performance level which states:
(*a*)   Pedestrian guarding to prevent people being injured by falling from a height of more than 600 mm. (Presumably this is accepted as being the minimum height from which people are likely to sustain significant injury).
(*b*)   Vehicle barriers capable of resisting or deflectng the impact of vehicles. (This means nothing without some definition of weight speed etc, and these are more clearly defined in the document).

Pedestrian guarding

1.1   This must be provided wherever reasonably necessary to meet criterion (*a*) above. This includes the edges of any part of a raised floor or gallery, balcony, roof (including rooflights etc), lightwell, basement area or sunken area next to a building, unless in a space used only for maintenance and repair. Diagram [11.26] illustrates some examples.
1.2/1.3   The same rules as to height, horizontal forces, glazing and the 100 mm diameter sphere apply as for stairs and landings but there is a relaxation for balcony guarding in front of fixed seating (diagram [11.27]).
NOTE   BS 6180 gives much more detail with regard to protection of balconies in assembly buildings and recommends minimum widths across the top of these, as well as heights and loadings.

1.1 [**11.26**] *Location (guarding).*

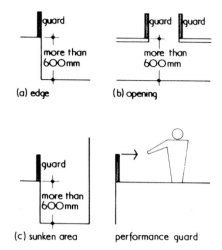

1.2 [**11.27**] *Height and strength (guarding): this is for pedestrian protection. For audience, spectator and crowd protection see BS 6180: 1982.*

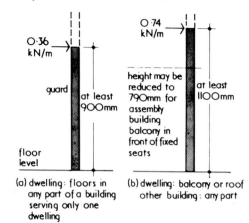

Vehicle barriers

1.4   Where vehicles have access to any part of a building barriers should be provided to all edges which are above the floor, ground or any other vehicle route.

1.5/1.6   Barriers should be at least the height shown in diagram [11.27]. In vehicle parks to be used by vehicles of less than 2.5 tonnes (cars and light vans) they should be able to resist the horizontal force shown in diagram [11.28].

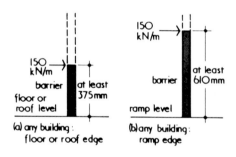

1.5/1.6 [**11.28**] *Barrier heights and strengths.* NOTE   *These loads do not agree with those quoted in BS 6399: Part 1: 1984, CP for dead and imposed loads (previously CP3: Ch V: Part 1) which were quoted in Approved Document A (see AD A Section 2 and note on BS 6180 below).*

In vehicle parks to be used by heavier vehicles, or those moving in excess of 16 km/hr the relevant recommendations of BS 6180: 1982 should be followed (see below).

Alternative approach

1.7   This states that the requirements can be met by following the recommendations of BS 6180: 1982, *Code of practice for protective barriers in and about buildings*, which includes provisions for heavier vehicles at greater speeds. However as may be seen above and below, these do not coincide with the Approved Document.

BS 6180: 1982: Protective barriers in and about buildings

This deals with all guard barriers in buildings and places of assembly including vehicle barriers.

In the latter type it is mainly concerned with vehicles within the 2500 kg/16 km/hr range mentioned in the Approved Document, but Appendix B does give a method of calculation for vehicles outside these limits.

The use of either method depends on establishing an estimated acceptable total displacement figure for the vehicle and barrier combined, as a starting point.

Reference is also made to a method for use within the limitations of mass and speed stated above in BS 6399: Part 1 (previously CP3: Ch V: Part 1) which should suffice for most cases (see AD A, Section 2). Strangely however, these recommendations are not the same as those given in this Document to fulfil the requirements of K 3 (see 1.6 above and note on BS 6399 below). On pedestrian barriers the BS recommends heights and minimum horizontal design loads, applied at design level as in the Approved Document, but also gives two other figures of a UDL per m^2 for infil panels and a point load on any part of the infil. In addition to normal building usage, there is an additional table for audience, spectator and crowd protection. For external situations, wind loading must also be taken into account. There is advice on the various available materials including concrete, masonry, various metals and plastics for railings, handrails etc. Safety aspects apart from strength are dealt with, also fabrication, corrosion protection and fixing methods.

Note on BS 6339: Part 1: 1984

This is referred to in Approved Document A as the guide for dead and imposed loads. It has recently replaced CP 3: Ch V: Pt 1. It looks as though its recommendations for vehicle barriers have been misinterpreted in Approved Document K. The BS gives a load of 150 kN on *any 1.5 m length of barrier (not per m)* at 375 mm above floor level and half this load at 610 mm above floor level along ramp edges (but twice this load at ramp bottoms in certain circumstances). See Approved Document A, Section 2.

References

The following British Standards and other documents are referred to in the Approved Document on the page number(s) given after each entry.

BS 5395 *Stairs, ladders and walkways.* Part 1: 1977 *Code of practice for stairs* Amendment slip no 1: AMD 3355. Amendment slip no. 2: AMD 4450. £22·80. Part 2: 1984 *Code of practice for the design of helical and spiral stairs.* £12·20, p. 4.

BS 6180: 1982 *Code of practice for protective barriers in and about buildings.* £16·20, p. 11.

Department of the Environment/Welsh Office *Mandatory Rules for means of escape in case of fire* (*Document B*1). HMSO. 1985. £1·60, p. 2, 3.

Approved Document L
Conservation of Fuel and Power

Part L of Schedule 1 of the Regulations replaces several parts of the 1976 Regulations. These are:

Part F   Thermal insulation of dwellings.

Part FF   Conservation of fuel and power in buildings other than dwellings.

Part Q   Control of space and water heating systems.

Part R   Thermal insulation of pipes, ducts and storage vessels.

Parts F, Q and R all formed part of the Second Amendment, 1981, Part F being a revised version of the original and Parts Q and R entirely new. Part FF constituted the whole of the First Amendment 1978.

They were all the result of a long period of study and consultation at the DoE following the introduction of enabling powers in the Health and Safety at Work Act 1974, which for the first time made conservation of fuel and power a basis for Building Regulations (prior to that they were restricted to Public Health and Safety). In various consultation documents the DoE expressed its ultimate intention of rationalising and bringing together all aspects of this legislation, and the chance offered by the revision of the whole of the regulations has clearly been taken. In addition a procedure has been introduced to allow account to be taken of useful heat gains and the use of energy demand targets (previously only possible by applying for a relaxation).

The document is divided into three parts:

L 2/3   Resistance to the passage of heat.

L 4   Heating system controls.

L 5   Insulation of heating services.

L 2/3   differ from all the other parts of Schedule 1, in as much as they are not simply a statement of functional requirements couched in terms such as 'thermal insulation shall be adequate . . . etc', but are a statement of specific required performance standards.

L 1 is not included in the Approved Document, as it is simply a list of interpretations, some of which are included elsewhere. There are gaps however which should be filled, and so a description of the contents of L 1 is included here. One of these definitions, 'exposed', is explained diagrammatically in an Appendix to L 2/3 and a modified version of those diagrams is therefore included here.

L 1   INTERPRETATIONS

The following terms are defined:

Element   A wall, floor or roof.

Exposed   (in a dwelling):

(*a*)   Exposed to the outside air, or

(*b*)   Separating the dwelling from a part of the building which has permanent ventilation exceeding 5 per cent of the area of the enclosing walls.

Exposed   (in buildings other than dwellings):

(*a*)   Exposed to the outside air or

(*b*)   Separating part of the building which is heated from a part which is both unheated and exposed to the outside air.

Diagrams [12.1, 2, 3], which are drawn from the Appendix illustrate the situation in relation to houses (1), flats (2) and other buildings (3) The heavy lines indicate the 'exposed' areas.

NOTE   The old definitions of ventilated, partially ventilated and partially heated spaces have been abandoned.

(1) [**12.1**] *Dwellings.*

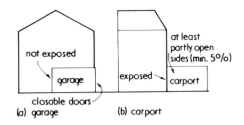

(a) garage   (b) carport

(2) [**12.2**] *Flats.*

Total area of permanent vents exceeds 5 per cent of wall area ABCD.

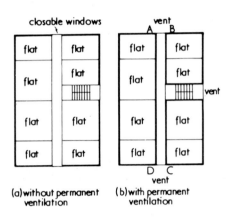

(a) without permanent ventilation   (b) with permanent ventilation

(3) [**12.3**] *Buildings other than dwellings.*

(b) and (c) are alternative ways of treating an unheated space on the perimeter of a building.

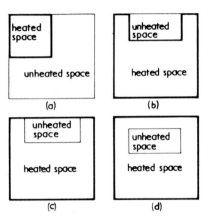

Industrial building a factory within the meaning of the Factories Act 1961, Section 175 (but not including slaughterhouses and associated premises).

Residential building a building used for residential purposes including a hotel or institutional building, but not any part of such building used as a dwelling (which must be treated as a dwelling).

Solid parts see diagram [12.4].

U-value the thermal transmittance coefficient in watts per square metre per kelvin (W/m^2K).

NOTE   The kelvin is a unit of absolute temperature but to all intents and purpose is the same as the °C.

Wall and window: see diagrams [12.5, 12.6].

L 1 [**12.4**] *Definition of 'solid parts'.*   *These include all parts of an exposed element except the items shown on the sketch but NOTE: doors, meter cupboards and other openings do not count as part of the window area, but do not need to have the same U-value as the solid parts Glazed doors with over 2 m^2 of glazing count as windows.*

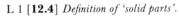

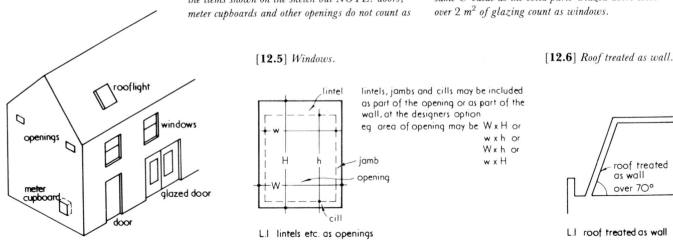

[**12.5**] *Windows.*

lintels, jambs and cills may be included as part of the opening or as part of the wall, at the designers option
eg area of opening may be W x H or
w x h or
W x h or
w x H

L.I lintels etc. as openings

[**12.6**] *Roof treated as wall.*

roof treated as wall over 70°

L.I roof treated as wall

The significance of the choice given regarding the area around window openings is that if treated as solid wall it must have the U-value required for that wall and if treated as window it need not have this U-value but counts against the window area allowance (or rooflight area in roofs).

COMMENT   As may be seen above, the definition of 'exposed' varies for residential and non-residential buildings. In the first case it is determined by the degree of ventilation of the adjoining space and in the second by whether the adjoining space is heated or unheated. Two situations come to mind where a designer may be in doubt and there may indeed be others. The cases in mind are:

(1) A dwelling attached to a building of a different purpose group. Here one would tend to think that the treatment of the wall between would depend on whether that building were to be heated or unheated. However, as its function might change in the future it would be safer to treat the wall as exposed in any case.

(2) A room in the roof space of a dwelling separated by a partition from unoccupied roof space. Under the rules the space is treated as outside air if it has permanent ventilation exceeding 5% of the area of the enclosing walls. Being a roof space there may be no enclosing walls, only a roof or possibly a combination of roof slopes and gable wall. A calculation could be made using the areas of these surfaces instead of walls. F2 does require a minimum degree of ventilation to avoid condensation in cold roofs, but this would not exceed 5% of the area of the enclosing surfaces, so that in general one would expect to be entitled to treat the partition separating the room from the roof space as not exposed. This, of course, would not alter the desirability of providing adequate insulation in any case.

L 2/3   RESISTANCE TO THE PASSAGE OF HEAT

The requirements of Schedule 1 are as follows:

	Requirement	Limits on application
	Resistance to the passage of heat (dwellings)	
Exposed fabric	L 2. – (1) Subject to sub-paragraph (3), the calculated rate of heat loss (W/K) through any windows and roof-lights shall be no greater than it would be if –	This requirement applies only to dwellings.
	(a) the aggregate of the areas of windows and rooflights were 12% of the area of the walls bounding the dwelling, and	
	(b) the windows and rooflights had a U-value of 5.7.	
	(2) The calculated rate of heat loss through the solid parts of the exposed elements shall be no greater than it would be if –	
	(a) the exposed walls and exposed floors had a U-value of 0.6, and	
	(b) the roof had a U-value of 0.35.	
	(3) To the extent that the calculated rate of heat loss through the solid parts of the exposed elements is less than the maximum permitted under sub-paragraph (2), the calculated rate of heat loss through the windows and rooflights may be greater than the maximum permitted under subparagraph (1).	

(Table continued over page)

	Requirement	Limits on application
	Resistance to the passage to heat (buildings other than dwellings)	
Exposed fabric	L 3. – (1) Subject to sub-paragraphs (3) to (5), the calculated rate of heat loss (W/K) through any windows and rooflights shall be no greater than it would be if –	This requirement applies only to a building having a floor area greater than 30 m^2 which is –

<table>
<tr><td>

L 3. – (1) Subject to sub-paragraphs (3) to (5), the calculated rate of heat loss (W/K) through any windows and rooflights shall be no greater than it would be if –

(a) the aggregate area of the rooflights were 20% of the roof area,

(b) the aggregate area of the windows were –
  (i) in the case of a residential building, 25%,
  (ii) in the case of a shop, office or assembly building, 35%,
  (iii) in the case of an industrial or any other building, 15%,
of the exposed wall area; and

(c) the windows and rooflights had a U-value of 5.7.

(2) Subject to sub-paragraphs (4) and (5), the calculated rate of heat loss through the solid parts of the exposed elements shall be no greater than it would be if those parts had a U-value –

(a) in the case of a residential building, shop, office or assembly building, of 0.6, and
(b) in the case of an industrial or any other building, of 0.7.

(3) Where the building consists of a shop with a display window, the storey in which the window is situated shall be disregarded in considering compliance with the requirements in sub-paragraph (1).

(4) An alternative requirement to those specified in sub-paragraphs (1) and (2) is that the calculated heat loss from the building in the conditions in which it is likely to be used, taking account of any useful gain, shall be no greater than it would be if those requirements were met.

(5) Where the building is divided into parts used for different purposes, separate calculations shall be made for each part falling within a description in *(a)* to *(f)* in the limits an application to this requirement, but a building not so divided which is used for more than one purpose shall be regarded as used for its main purpose and not for any ancillary purpose.

</td><td>

This requirement applies only to a building having a floor area greater than 30 m^2 which is –

(a) a residential building,

(b) a shop,

(c) an office,

(d) a building, whether public or private, in which people assemble for recreational, educational, business of other activities ('an assembly building'),

and which is likely to be heated by a space heating system having an output exceeding 25 watts per square metre of floor area, or which is –

(e) an industrial building, or

(f) a building used for a purpose not referred to above, ('any other building'),

and which is likely to be heated by a space heating system having an output exceeding 50 watts per square metre of floor area.

</td></tr>
</table>

The basic requirements are illustrated in the Approved Document a diagram reproduced here as [12.7].

L 2/3 [**12.7**] *Basic requirements for resistance to the passage of heat.*

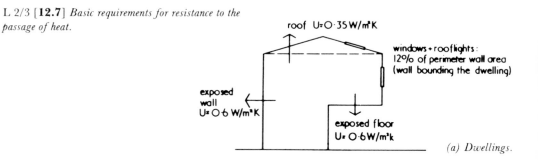

roof U=0·35 W/m²K

windows + rooflights:
12% of perimeter wall area
(wall bounding the dwelling)

exposed wall
U= 0·6 W/m²K

exposed floor
U= 0·6 W/m²k

(a) Dwellings.

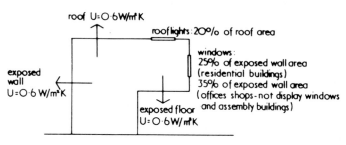

(b) Residential, offices, shops and assembly buildings.

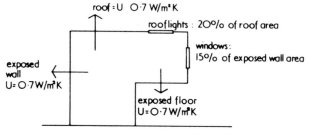

(c) Industrial, storage and other buildings.

It should be noted that the wording of L 2(1) and (2) and L 3(1) and (2) states that the calculated rate of heat loss in each case shall 'be not greater than it would be if . . .' the areas and U-values of windows and the U-values of the solid parts were as stated. This allows a degree of flexibility such as increased window areas by the use of double glazing, or some of the solid parts to be above the limit if compensated for by a better standard elsewhere. In dwellings a trade-off is also allowed between glazed and solid parts L 2(3), and in other buildings a totally different approach may be used taking into account available heat gains L 3(4).

L 3(3) is a relaxation for shops which have a display window which allows the whole storey in which the window is situated to be disregarded. This is a considerable concession, since there is no statement to the effect that the relaxation is limited to the ground storey.

L 3(5) requires separate calculations for parts of buildings (except dwellings) used for different purposes (as defined in the limits on application) where these are divided. If not divided the main purpose applies throughout.

Note that the limits on application exclude all buildings with a floor area of less than 30 m². Buildings with a low heat demand are also excluded and the minimum limits for the likely required output of the space heating system are:

Residential, shop, office and assembly building (public or private)	25W/m² of floor area
Industrial or any other purpose not included above	50W/m² of floor area

These buildings are defined in Regulation 2 of the principle Regulations, some by reference to L 1.

Introduction

0.1/0.3   Four procedures are given divided into two sections.

Section A   Two procedures to limit heat loss by imposing maximum glazing areas and minimum standards for solid parts

Procedure 1   Specified insulation thickness

This makes life simple for the designer by cutting out all reference to U-values and simply giving the thickness of insulation required for each of the three standards, based on the thermal conductivity of the material (there is no longer any reference to types of insulation as before).

Procedure 2   Specified U-values

This is similar to the earlier procedures, being based on U-values and an example is given on how to calculate these. There is no longer any equivalent of Schedule 11 which gave examples of various composite constructions for walls floors and roofs showing the thickness of various types of insulation required with each. This, however, is hardly necessary in view of the method now available in Procedure 1.

Window areas are dealt with in both these systems by simple factors for double and triple glazing.

Section B   Two procedures to limit heat loss without setting maximum areas for glazing or minimum standards for solid areas

Procedure 3   Calculated trade-off
This enables trade-offs to be made within the glazed area limits (windows for rooflights, single or double glazing) and within the solid parts (walls, roofs etc). In dwellings only, improved standards for the solid parts can be used to augment window area.

Procedure 4   Calculated energy use
In all buildings except dwellings, heat gains (eg solar, lighting, industrial processes) may be set off against losses. This is a matter for the experts and is only briefly described.

0.4   The requirements of L 2/3 only apply to exposed elements which are defined in L 1 above.

Section A   Procedures 1 and 2

1.1   The following apply to both procedures:
(*a*)   The area of perimeter wall on which window areas are based should include all openings. Note: this should really read 'perimeter or exposed wall' (see 1.3.)
(*b*)   An external door with 2 m² or more of glazing counts as window area.
(*c*)   Part of a roof pitched at over 70° counts as a wall.
(*d*)   An opening in a wall other than a window opening, and a meter cupboard recess may be counted as part of the wall area.
(*e*)   Lintels, jambs and cills may be counted as part of the window or rooflight area (see L 1)
(*f*)   Areas should be measured between finished internal surfaces, and in roofs on the plane of the insulation.
There is a great deal left to chance here:
1   The phrasing of item (*d*) above could be misleading, but previous usage clearly indicates that a meter cupboard recess should be counted as wall, not window.
2   Item (*d*) is also surprising since it leaves a great gap in the control exercised. It is presumably meant to refer to small openings required for ventilation and the like, but in fact leaves the possibility of any sized gap being left, so long as it is not a window.
However it is unlikely that anyone would try to maintain heating in such a space.
3   Item (*b*) is probably intended to cover the case of so-called French windows, but means that large doors such as might be found in industrial buildings can be totally ignored if they contain no glass, but if they contain 2 m² of glazing the *whole* area of the door must be treated as window. In this event, if double glazing is used would the whole area be treated as double-glazed window? Of course, the use of glazing in these circumstances is within the designer's control should it raise problems.
4   No information is given as to how window sizes should be measured, but in previous legislation a window opening was defined as 'any *structural* opening for a window' which suggested that the frame was included, and it must be presumed that this remains the case.
5   Item (*f*), measurement between internal surfaces could be interpreted in one of two ways. The stricter interpretation is the second, which would give a slightly smaller window allowance, and it might well be applied by some local authorities: diagram [12.8].
The examples in the Approved Document are no help since they include both interpretations.

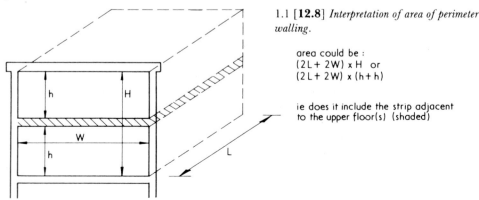

1.1 [**12.8**] *Interpretation of area of perimeter walling.*

area could be :
(2L + 2W) x H or
(2L + 2W) x (h + h)

ie does it include the strip adjacent to the upper floor(s) (shaded)

Thermal conductivity

* (Chartered Institution of Building Services Engineers Guide Section A 3 Thermal properties of building structures 1981 obtainable from Delta House, 222 Balham High Road, London SW12 9BS).

1.2   This is a measure of the rate at which heat passes through a material. It is expressed in terms of watts per square metre for one metre thickness and a temperature difference of one kelvin. In symbols this should be written $k = Wm/(m^2K)$, but in normal practice the square metre is left out and it becomes W/mK since the one square metre is constant and the value varies only with the thickness. The lower this figure is the better is the insulation value. The thicknesses of insulation given later are based on various values for this quality. These can be obtained either from the supplier of the material or Table A.3.22 of the CIBSE *Guide**, extracts from which are reproduced (p. 271). Table A.3.1 of this *Guide* also gives values for concrete blocks, and if the claimed thermal conductivity of a product is based on a value lower than these, the claim should be supported by test certificates, as required in Appendix 4 of the *Guide*.

Procedure 1   Specified insulation thickness

1.3   Using this method the thickness of insulation required can be direct from the Table. To satisfy the requirement it is necessary to:
(*a*)   Meet the conditions in (a) to (f) above.
(*b*)   Restrict window areas to the percentages in the Table.
(*c*)   Use insulation of at least the thickness shown in the three tables for walls, roofs and floors respectively.

Windows
Table 1 of the Approved Document, which shows maximum window areas, is reproduced below as it stands, but it clearly requires further explanation.

Table 1   Maximum single glazed area

Building type	*Windows*	*Rooflights*
dwellings*	windows and rooflights together 12 per cent of perimeter wall area	
other residential (including hotels and institutional*)	25 per cent exposed wall area	20 per cent of roof area
places of assembly offices* shops*[1]	35 per cent of exposed wall area	20 per cent of roof area
industrial* and storage	15 per cent of exposed wall area	20 per cent of roof area

NOTES
* These building types are defined in Regulation 4.*
[1] Not display windows in shops.
1 The meaning of perimeter wall area and exposed are given in Appendix.
2 Areas which are double glazed may have up to twice the single glazed area; areas which are double glazed with a low emissivity coating, or triple glazed, may have up to three times the permitted single glazed area.

* (Author's note) This note is incorrect and should refer to Regulation 2. This itself gives some definitions but refers to L 1 for residential and industrial buildings.

The brief note 'not display windows in shops' is a bit inadequate since L 3(3) states that where there are display windows, the whole storey in which they are situated should be disregarded.
Note 1 states that the meaning of 'perimeter wall area' and 'exposed' are given in the Appendix. This does explain 'exposed' but makes no mention of 'perimeter wall' (nor does L 1), although briefly mentioned in the diagram to 0.1(a) [12.7]. This is an essential part of the rules for dwellings, as for other buildings the window area is a percentage of the 'exposed wall area', which might amount to the same thing in detached houses, but in flats, for example, is quite different.
Previously, Part F of 1981 defined 'perimeter walling' as the walls enclosing all parts of the dwelling, but specifically excluding ventilated and partially ventilated spaces, garages, con-

servatories etc. Certain parts of these walls were given specific maximum U-values (less onerous than for the exposed parts). This now no longer applies and a wall is either exposed (requiring insulation) or not exposed (not requiring insulation and not considered as contributing to the total heat loss).

There seems little doubt however that the intention regarding perimeter walls was to retain basically the same definitions; otherwise the low figure of 12 per cent of exposed walls would be quite inadequate when applied to flats in a central situation. Diagram [12.9] shows examples of different situations affecting the relationship of exposed wall to perimeter wall and hence the proportion of the exposed wall which can be glazed.

[**12.9**] *Examples of perimeter wall/exposed ratios.*

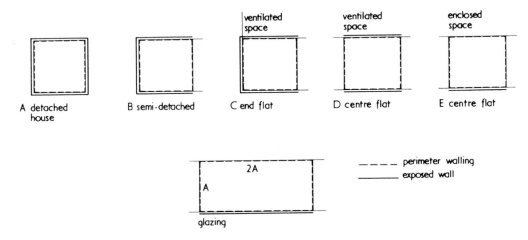

If all units are square, percentage of exposed wall which may be window (or rooflight) is:	Type of glazing		Assuming a flat with a 2:1 length to depth proportion and one long side exposed.
	Single	Double	Perimeter wall area = 6A
	A 12	24	Exposed wall area = 2A = $\frac{1}{3}$ of perimeter
	B 16	32	Therefore window allowance = 12×3
	C 16	32	= 36% single
	D 24	48	72% double
	E 48	96	

To facilitate comparison the units are all shown as square in shape but similar comparisons can be made with other proportions, and to illustrate this one example is shown of a flat with a 2 to 1 exposed wall to depth ratio. From this it can be seen that it would be possible using double glazing to have all the wall glazed from say 700 mm above floor to head height (72 per cent).

Solid parts

There are three tables which relate to exposed walls, roofs and exposed floors. The latter will be comparatively rare.

Part 1 of each Table gives a base level thickness of insulation for each building type in relation to the thermal conductivity of the material. This may be used as it stands, in which case a better than minimum standard will be achieved as the construction itself will contribute to the total insulation value.

If wishing to economise the designer may take account of the construction by using Part 2 of the Table which gives a set of figures showing the deduction from the base level thickness which can be made for various elements of structure.

The Tables are quite easy to use and may be the most convenient way. However there is little point in simply reproducing them here, and so to follow one of the principles of this Guide, Part 1 of each table is expressed below in graphical form and Part 2 in percentages of the base thickness level. (The graphical form also assists in using linear interpolation, which is permitted: diagram [12.10]).

1.3 [**12.10**] *Graphical representation of Tables 2, 3, 4, Part 1, Base level thickness.*

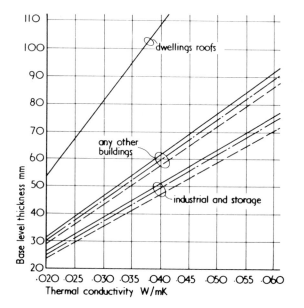

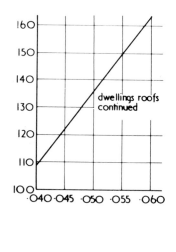

——————— roofs
——— · ——— exposed walls
— — — — — exposed floors

NOTE: The chart shows clearly how insulating material of the same thermal conductivity is more effective on floors than on walls, and on walls than on roofs, due no doubt to the tendency of heat to flow upwards.

Tables 2, 3, 4, Part 2 of Approved Document L Permitted reductions in base thickness for elements of structure expressed as a percentage.

Type of building		*Industrial and storage (1)*	*Any other building (2)*	*Dwelling roofs (3)*
		mm	mm	mm
Air space – minimum of 25 mm.		14†	12†	6
Brick leaf – min. 100 mm.		10	8	
100 mm solid concrete	500	48	40	
block-work leaf with dry density	800	35	30	
of – (kg/m^2)*	1100	24	20	
	1400	15	13	
	1700	10	9	
	2000	7	6	
	2300	5	4	
Lightweight plaster or plasterboard		6	5	3
Plasterboard on dabs or framing		17	15	8
Insulating, plasterboard on framing		26	22	12
Screed min. 40 mm.		7	6	3
100 mm. Concrete beams dry density 500 kg/m^3*		48‡	40‡	22
100 mm dense concrete beams or slab		7	6	
Screed min 75 mm.		14	12	
Wood block floor		6	5	
* as declared by manufacturer				
† Air space in floors		17	14	
‡ 100 mm. Light concrete beams (500 kg/m^3) in floors		52	43	

Extract from CIBSE Guide, Table A3.22

The reference in the Approved Document to this table can be confusing as there is more than one table A3.22. The correct reference is to Appendix 2 – Properties of materials – Table A3.22. Thermal conductivities and resistivities of miscellaneous materials.

It is very extensive (12 pp A4) and includes a wide variety of materials, not only those used specifically for insulation, but also many other materials used in buildings (eg floor and wall finishes). It does not include structural materials such as brick and concrete. In many cases a series of values is given for one material, varying with density or water content. In the extract below only one of these is quoted as a guide. Usually the variation with density is not great, nor is it always the lower density that has the better value. In selecting materials the actual value should always be checked. The examples included have generally been selected as falling within the range of values between 0.020 and 0.060 which are used in the tables for procedure 1 in the Approved Document. However a few which are a little outside this range but which may be useful are included.

Material	Density kg/m³	Thermal Conductivity W/mK
Air	1.17	0.026
Asbestos slabs, lightweight	70	0.050
Blanket, wool, closely woven	65	0.043
Carpet, Wilton type	–	0.058
Cellulose wadding	30	0.038
Cork, loose granules	115	0.046
Corkboard	130	0.040
Cork with resin binder	250	0.050
Eel grass blanket	80	0.039
Ebonite, cellular board	64	0.026
Felt, hair	80	0.039
Fibre building board	240	0.053
Flax, resin bonded board	300	0.070
Glass fibre, lightweight quilt	12	0.040
Hardboard, medium	600	0.080
Jute bonded fibre mat	50	0.036
Kapok quilt	20	0.035
Mineral wool, felted	16	0.040
Mineral wool, semi-rigid mat	130	0.036
Mineral wool, rigid slab	155	0.050
Papyrus grass insulating board	255	0.055
Perlite, loose expanded granules	65	0.042
Perlite, plaster	400	0.080
Vermiculite plaster	480	0.140
Phenolic foam board	30	0.038
Polystyrene, expanded board	15	0.037
Polyurethane foam (aged)	30	0.026
PVC rigid foam	25	0.035
Urea formaldehyde foam (UF)	8–12	0.031
Rubber, cellular slabs	80	0.040
Sawdust slabs, lightly bonded	160	0.050
Sponge clippings	30	0.043
Strawslab compressed	260	0.085
Vermiculite, loose granules	100	0.065
Wood chipboard, resin-bonded	350	0.070
Wood wool, slabs	400	0.080
Wood wool, fluffy	40	0.040

Examples

The Approved Document gives eight examples of how to use the tables to determine insulation thicknesses for five types of wall construction, two roofs and one floor. Three of these have been repeated here to demonstrate how to use the chart and percentage method above instead of the tables in the Document. One new example showing a wall to an industrial building is also included.

Example 1 [**12.11**] *To determine the thickness of thermal insulation required for an exposed wall to a dwelling constructed as shown in the diagram below:*

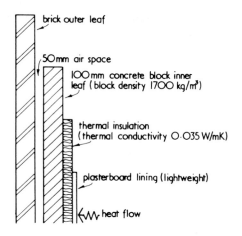

From graph base level thickness for   *mm*
thermal conductivity of 0.035.   52
To take account of construction deduct
percentages in Col (2).

air space	12
brick leaf	8
concrete block leaf	9
plasterboard	5
	34%

∴ *Insulation to be 66 per cent of 52 =*   34

Example 5 [**12.12**] *To determine whether an exposed wall to a dwelling constructed as shown in the diagram below, meets the requirements:*

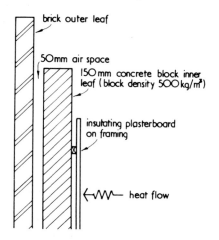

To take account of construction deduct
percentages in Col (2).

air space	12
brick leaf	8
150 mm concrete block 40 × 150/100	60
Insulating plaster board on framing	22
	102%

Therefore wall meet requirements without further insulation.

Example 6 [**12.13**] *To determine the thickness of thermal insulation required for a pitched roof to a dwelling as shown in the diagram below:*

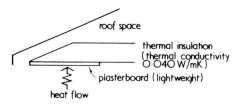

From graph base level thickness for   *mm*
thermal conductivity of 0.040   109
To take account of construction deduct
percentages in Col. (3)

roof space	6
plasterboard	3
	9

∴ *Insulation to be 91 per cent of*
109 =   99

New example. [**12.14**] *To determine the thickness of insulation required for an exposed wall of an industrial building as shown below.*

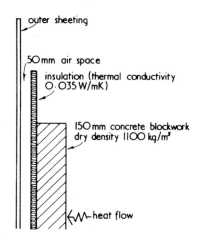

From graph base level thickness for   *mm*
thermal conductivity of 0.035.   44
To take account of construction deduct
percentages in Col. (1)

air space	14
150 mm cone block 150/100 × 24	36
	50

∴ *Insulation to be 50 per cent of 44 =*   22

1.4   The Approved Document says that this method allows full account to be taken of the insulating properties of the construction. The purpose of Part 2 of the Tables in Procedure 1 is also to enable the construction elements to be taken into account, by giving these a value equivalent to a certain thickness of insulation. This however ignores certain things, such as the thermal resistance of surfaces (see later).

U-values

1.5   The insulation value of construction (how quickly heat can pass through) depends on the thermal conductivity and thickness of the materials, the existence of air spaces and surface resistances. All surfaces have a degree of resistance to the transfer of heat from them to the adjacent air (or vice versa). This includes surfaces facing a cavity which taken together represent the thermal resistance of the cavity. The thermal resistance of a component is obtained by dividing its thickness (m) by the thermal conductivity (W/mK) of the material. The resistances of the several components can be added together to give a total resistance for the whole construction.

The reciprocal of this is called the thermal transmittance or U-value.

The definition of thermal conductivity has already been given in 1.2. The other two definitions required are:

Thermal resistance   = area required to pass one watt of energy when the temperature difference between faces is one kelvin $(m^2 K/W)$.

Thermal transmittance = rate of heat flow in watts through one square metre when the temperature difference between faces is one kelvin $(W/m^2 K)$.

1.5 [**12.15**] *Calculation of U-values.*

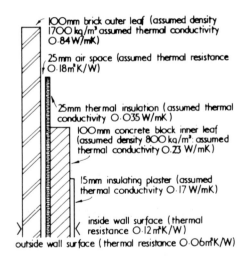

To determine if the requirements will be met by an exposed wall to a dwelling constructed as shown in the diagram.

The thermal resistance is obtained by dividing thickness of material (m) by thermal conductivity $(W/m^2 K)$.

The U-value (thermal transmittance) is obtained by adding the thermal resistances and taking the reciprocal of the result, as shown below:

Item	Thickness [m]	Thermal conductivity [W/mK]	Thermal resistance [m²K/W]
outside wall surface	–	–	0.06
brick outer leaf	0.1	0.84	0.12
air space	–	–	0.18
thermal insulation	0.025	0.035	0.71
block inner leaf	0.1	0.23	0.43
plaster	0.015	0.17	0.09
inside wall surface	–	–	0.12
total thermal resistance			1.71

U-value = total thermal resistance = $\dfrac{1}{1.71}$ = **0.58** W/m²K

The example above of how to calculate a U-value is taken from the Approved Document. This method of course requires information on the thermal resistance of surfaces and thermal conductivity of building materials, as well as of insulation. These and further information on calculation may be found in the CIBSE *Guide*, which also contains extensive tables giving U-values for composite elements of construction including exterior walls and roofs, also internal walls and floors (Tables A 3.16–A 3.21 of Appendix 1).

1.6   To satisfy the requirements it is necessary to:

(*a*)   Meet the conditions (*a*) to (*f*) in paragraph 1.1.

(*b*)   Restrict window areas as specified in 1.3.

(*c*)   Not exceed the U-values specified below.

There are now only three U-values, as follows:

Industrial and storage buildings	0.7
All other buildings	0.6

which apply to exposed walls, roofs (except dwellings) and exposed floors, plus:

Roofs of dwellings	0.35

Section B   Procedures 3 and 4

2.1   This section describes alternative procedures for designing the exposed building fabric without limiting the areas of windows and rooflights to the maximum percentages given in 1.3 and without limiting the thermal transmittance of the solid parts to the maximum values given in 1.6, whilst ensuring that the heat loss will be no greater.

2.2   The following conditions apply to both procedures 3 and 4:

(*a*)   The building used for calculating the heat loss should be of similar size, shape, orientation and use as the proposed building. This is rather a curious way of putting it since generally speaking it must be the same building, which is simply being subjected to studies of two or more ways of meeting the requirements.

(*b*)   In calculating the heat loss the following fixed U-values must be used for windows and rooflights

Single glazed	5.7
Double glazed	2.8
Triple glazed	2.0

(*c*)   As these procedures might allow U-values higher than the maxima specified in 1.6 some parts of the fabric might be subject to surface condensation, and it may in some circumstances be desirable to limit the U-value of any part to 1.2 W/m^{2}K.

Procedure 3   Calculated trade-off

2.3   The procedure allows trade-offs:

(*a*)   Between windows and rooflights.

(*b*)   Between walls, roofs and floors, independent of (*a*).

(*c*)   In dwellings only where the insulation of walls, roofs and floors is better than the standards given in 1.6, to allow larger window areas than 1.3.

It takes no account of heat gains.

This is virtually the *status quo* as represented in the recent Parts F (1981) and FF (1978) which were contained in the First and Second Amendments to the 1976 Regulations, but Part F (dwellings) only allowed a trade-off between walls and windows, whereas roofs and exposed floors are now brought into the equation. However, as exposed floors are rare, and the U-value required for the roofs of dwellings is already set at a figure which is difficult to improve on (0.35), this is unlikely to make much difference.

2.4   To meet the requirement:

(*a*)   Conditions (*a*) to (*c*) in 2.2 above must be met.

(*b*)   The calculated rate of heat loss must be no more than it would be if the window areas in 1.3 and the U-values in 1.6 were used.

The Approved Document gives four examples of this procedure including one industrial building, one office building and two houses. There is not much point in simply repeating these here and so a new example (diagram [12.16]) is provided to illustrate some points not picked up in the other four.

[**12.16**] *Procedure 3: example.*

It is desired to glaze the 4 storey office building illustrated continuously along both the long sides. There are some rooflights. What height of window (cill to head) can be used on each floor?

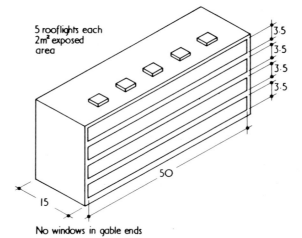

5 rooflights each
2m² exposed
area

3.5
3.5
3.5
3.5

50

15

No windows in gable ends

Total exposed height 3.5 × 4 =		14 *m*
Exposed wall area (15 + 50) × 2		
× 14 =		1820 *m²*
Roof area 50 × 15 =		750 *m²*
Allowable Single glazed window		
1820 × 35%		637
Allowable rooflights 750 × 20%		150
		787
Deduct rooflights 5 × 2		10
Available for windows		777 *m²*
Length of glazing 4 × 2 × 50		400 *m*
∴ depth of single glazing		
permitted = 777/400		1.94 *m*

Using double glazing area permitted becomes 777 × $^{5.7}/_{2.8}$ 1581 *m²*
Which is more than the area of the two long walls (50 × 14 × 2 = 1400).
Therefore whole area could be glazed.

Procedure 4   Calculated energy use

This may not be used for dwellings.

2.5   The procedure allows a full trade-off between glazed and solid areas (presumably both ways, including a lowering of standards for solid areas if glazing is reduced or eliminated) and account to be taken of useful heat gains. These may include solar gains and those from artificial lighting, industrial processes etc. Body heat is not mentioned although it can be a factor, especially in assembly buildings.

2.6   To meet the requirement:

(*a*)   The conditions in (*a*) to (*c*) of 2.2 above must be met, and

(*b*)   Either:

(i)   The annual energy consumption, after taking any useful gains into account, can be shown by calculation to be no greater than it would be if the previous figures for window areas and U-values had been used or

(ii)   The building meets an acceptable energy demand target in accordance with Part 2 of the CIBSE *Energy Code*, and

(*c*)   It can be shown that sufficient heating controls will be provided to ensure that the claims in respect of the contribution made by heat gains can be met (heat gains are clearly no use if they only result in overheating instead of a reduction in the heat input required).

No examples are given and this procedure is clearly a matter of involving experts at the very initial design stages. The prohibition on its use for dwellings is perhaps a little surprising, since they form the largest single part of the national energy consumption, and it is in this field that most of the experimental work has been done.

L 4   HEATING SYSTEM CONTROLS

This replaces the recently introduced Part Q of the 1976 Regulations but is somewhat less specific, leaving room for doubts which will probably be resolved in practice (like many others elsewhere) by referring back to the earlier legislation, on the assumption that the intention remains the same.

The requirement is as follows:

	Requirement	Limits on application
	Heating system controls	
Space heating and hot water systems.	L 4. Space heating or hot water systems in buildings shall be provided with automatic controls capable of controlling the operation and output of space heating systems and the temperature of stored water.	This requirement does not apply to – *(a)* systems in dwellings: *(b)* systems which heat or store water for the purpose of an industrial process; *(c)* systems provided to serve a building with a floor area which does not exceed 125 m²; or *(d)* individual appliances with an output rating of 10 kilowatts or less.

0.1/0.2   The acceptable performance level is that controls should be capable of regulating the output of space heating systems and temperature of stored water to meet conditions normal for the intended use of the building.

As may be seen above, these requirements do not apply to dwellings or to systems in other buildings serving not more than 125 m² of floor area, or to individual appliances not exceeding 10kW. Strictly speaking this does not exclude heating *systems* of less than 10kW, but an advisory note to Local Authorities which accompanied Part Q suggested that this was intended.

Also excluded are systems which heat or store water for industrial purposes. In Part Q the phrase 'whether exclusively or otherwise' was added, which sugested that if heat which is a by-product of industrial processes is used for space heating (as is frequently the case in large factory areas) these rules do not apply.

No mention is made of extensions or replacements of existing systems but here again Part Q made it clear that the rules did apply to replacements and to extensions over 125 m² floor area. Also in defining 'building work' Regulation 3(1)(c) includes 'the provision, extension or material alteration of a controlled service or fitting' and paragraph (3) refers specifically to a service or fitting to which (*inter alia*) L 4 and L 5 apply.

Room temperature control

1.1   The following should be provided:

(a)   Thermostats, thermostatic radiator valves or other equal form of sensing device for each separately controlled part of the system, and

(b)   If the system uses hot water, a temperature sensing device outside the building (weather compensating control) to regulate the temperature of the water in the system.

NOTE   Q 3 referred specifically to systems using radiators or non-mechanical convectors, but now all systems using hot water are included. Weather compensating controls are designed to adjust output in accordance with changes in outside temperature, wind speed and possibly solar radiation. They are not essential with quick response systems such as ducted air.

Intermittent heat control

1.2   This is necessary to avoid waste of energy during periods when the building is not normally occupied. The following are required:

(a)   For systems with an output not exceeding 100kW, a clock control which can be manually set to start and stop times.

(b)   For systems with an output exceeding 100kW a control arrangement (optimum start control) giving start times based on the rate at which the building reacts when the heating is restarted after being shut off (optimising control).

Controls may also be provided to maintain sufficient heating to prevent damage by frost, humidity or condensation.

NOTE   Q 4 did not actually include the requirement in (*b*) above but a DoE advisory circular which accompanied the Second Amendment suggested the same procedure. Optimum start controls actually work by being linked to an outside temperature sensor.

Boiler controls

1.3   Where two or more gas or oil fired boilers have a total output of over 100kW controls are required to start up or shut down one or more as the demand fluctuates. Boilers run most efficiently at close to maximum output, so that it is more economical to run one boiler at full capacity, than two at half capacity each. The control should be able to detect variations in the need for heat in the building and cut out or modulate boilers accordingly.

Care is needed in the hydraulic design to ensure stable control. Presumably this means to avoid boilers being continually switched off and on due to small variations in the load.

Hot water storage control

1.4 It is necessary to limit the temperature of stored hot water by:

(*a*)   A thermostat to keep the water at the required temperature, and

(*b*)   If the vessel exceeds 150 litres and is not heated by off-peak electricity, a time switch to shut off heat when there is no demand. Four diagrams are included, but as they add absolutely nothing to the amount of information or its clarity they are not reproduced here.

L 5   INSULATION OF HEATING SERVICES

This is virtually a repeat of the recently introduced Part R (1981) but omitting some of the fine detail.

The requirement is as follows:

	Requirement	Limits on application
	Insulation of heating services	
Hot water pipes and warm air ducts.	L 5. – (1) Hot water pipes and warm air ducts shall have adequate thermal insulation unless – (a) they are intended to contribute to the heating of a part of the building which is insulated, or (b) they give rise to no significant heat loss.	This requirement does not apply to systems which heat or store any water for the purpose of an industrial process.
Hot water storage vessels.	(2) Hot water storage vessels shall have adequate thermal insulation.	

0.1   The following measures will meet the requirements:

0.2   Insulation is not required where heat loss from a pipe, duct or storage vessel:

(*a*)   Contributes to the heating of an insulated space, or

(*b*)   Is not significant, ie a hot water pipe is within the limits shown below

Outside diameter in mm	Max. length in m
not exceeding 12	20
exceeding 12, not exceeding 22	12
exceeding 22, not exceeding 28	8
exceeding 28	3
These are what are usually known as 'dead legs' in water by-laws	

Note that the limits on application to L 5 itself (see above) also exclude systems which store water for industrial purposes.

It is also interesting to note that the requirement is restricted to systems using hot water pipes and warm air ducts, whereas the earlier Part R referred to heated gases or fluids. That definition would include steam, whereas L 5 would not. This seems rather a strange omission although there are probably very few heating systems today employing steam unless this is a by-product of an industrial process.

Heating and hot water pipes

1.1   The insulation material should:

(*a*)   Have a thermal conductivity not greater than 0.07 W/mK and a thickness equal to the OD of the pipe up to a maximum of 50 mm.

(*b*)   Limit the heat loss to that shown in the table (represented here as a graph), or

(*c*)   Meet the recommendations in BS 5422: 1977.

The first of these is a simple rule of thumb method which will no doubt be used in the majority of cases and is illustrated in diagram [12.17].

1.1 and 1.2 [12.17]
Thermal insulation (pipes and ducts)

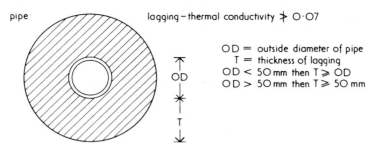

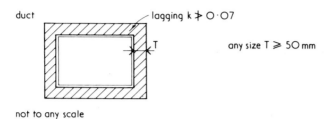

not to any scale

The heat loss values given in Table 2 of the Approved Document are here represented in the form of a graph which facilitates interpolation (not mentioned here but previously permitted in Part R). From these the thickness of insulation required can be calculated by methods shown in BS 5422 but this is a somewhat arduous business (see note on BS 5422 later). Since W/m^2 is a difficult standard to visualise in relation to small pipes it has also been shown in W per metre run and as may be seen these figures do not vary much regardless of pipe diameter.

1.1 (b) [12.18] Minimum requirements for thermal insulation of pipes.

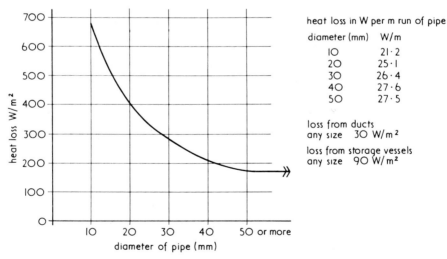

max heat loss in W/m^2 of actual surface area of pipe

Alternatively BS 5422 may be used. This gives tables for pipe and duct insulation thicknesses and also methods of calculating heat losses. The overall recommendations of Section Five of the BS is that in heating installations generally the basis of the design for insulation should be the 'economic thickness' (see note on BS 5422).

Warm air ducts

1.2   The insulation material should:
(a)   Have a thermal conductivity of not more than 0.07 W/mK and a thickness of not less than 50 mm (see diagram [12.17]), or
(b)   Limit the heat loss to 30W/m² of surface area, or
(c)   Meet the recommendations of BS 5422 (see below).

Hot water storage vessels

1.3   The insulation should:

(*a*)   Limit the heat loss to 90W/m^2 of surface area or

(*b*)   Meet the recommendations of BS 5422 or

(*c*)   Meet the recommendations of BS 5615: 1985 Specifications for insulating jackets for hot water storage cylinders or

(*d*)   Meet the recommendations of one of the following:

BS 699: 1984 *Copper direct cylinders for domestic purposes*

BS 1566: 1984 *Copper indirect cylinders for domestic purposes (Part 1 double feed, Part 2 single feed).*

BS 3198: 1981 *Copper hot water storage combination units for domestic purposes*

Although nothing is stated, the diagram attached to this clause (diagram [12.19]) suggests that insulation need not be applied to the base of the vessel.

[12.19]

The use of method (*a*) will require calculation as before. Table 6 to 9 of BS 5422 relate mainly to pipes but the last line of these may be used for flat surfaces which should be used therefore for ducts or vessels whether rectangular or cylindrical.

NOTE   It is interesting to compare the various heat loss figures. For example, the very much greater amounts for pipes (175 to 675W/m^2) than for ducts (30W/m^2) with yet another figure for storage vessels (90W/m^2). Looking at the figures for pipes converted into W/m run it can be seen that these are really quite small for pipes up to 50 mm diameter due to the small surface area involved. The table however leaves one with the same figure (175W/m^2) for all pipe diameters over 50 mm, and it would surely be advisable to improve on this for large diameter pipes, at least to the standard prescribed for vessels (90W/m^2), which is actually what happens in BS 5422. The lower figure for ducts, as compared with storage vessels, is no doubt because the temperature of the air contained will be very much less than that of the water in the vessels, and there is in effect, less heat to be lost, so that a small loss would have a comparatively greater effect on the residual temperature.

Notes on relevant British Standards

The following may be referred to:

BS 5422: 1977 The use of thermal insulating materials

This covers a much wider range than L 5. It includes information on the types and application of insulating materials, refrigeration, chilled water and process pipework as well as central heating and hot water supply. The last is contained in section Five.

This contains a lot of very useful information including tables showing recommended thicknesses of insulation at three thermal conductivity values (0.040, 0.055 and 0.070) for heating pipework at three different hot face temperatures, hot water supply pipework and ductwork. The last line of the pipework tables gives thicknesses for very large pipes which can also be used for flat surfaces.

There are separate tables for solid fuel systems and those using gas or oil, the latter showing marginally greater thicknesses. The reason for this is not explained but is probably because the tables are based on the concept of 'economic thicknesses' above which the cost of extra insulation would outweigh the savings on fuel cost. This however depends on relative fuel costs, which have fluctuated wildly since the date of this BS.

The use of these tables would generally result in thicknesses less than those obtained by using the method in 1.1 (*a*) except for small diameters below 25 mm OD, where thicknesses greater than the OD of the pipe are recommended. For ducts the recommendation is the same as in 1.2 (50 mm at k = 0.070) when the temperature of the air in the duct is 10°C above the ambient. This goes up to 75 mm when the difference is 25°C.

There is also a table of thicknesses to protect against freezing and advice on fire hazard and protection against condensation when pipe surfaces are cold.

Appendix B gives a method of calculating heat losses. However the formulae are complicated, especially for cylindrical surfaces and require information additional to the thermal conductivity. They are only likely to be used by experts in large installations. The same applies to Appendix E which is a method of calculating 'economic' thickness'.

BS 699: 1984 and BS 1566: Parts 1 and 2: 1984. Copper hot water cylinders for domestic purposes	These three standards are very similar each dealing with a type of hot water storage cylinder (direct and double and single feed indirect respectively). They each make a recommendation that where factory-insulated units are supplied, they should have a standing loss not exceeding 1W/L (one watt per litre) of capacity.
BS 3198: 1981 Combination Units for domestic purposes	This deals with a range of copper hot water storage units (both rectangular and cylindrical) which combine a hot water storage vessel with a cold water feed cistern. It contains the same recommendation that in factory-insulated units the standing heat loss shold be limited to 1W/L of capacity and in addition that the insulation between the hot water vessel and the cold feed cistern should be enough to prevent the cold water from rising to more than 38°C.
BS 5615: 1985. Insulating jackets for hot water cylinders	This lays down a performance standard which is based on a type 7 grade 3 cylinder (see BS 699) which has a capacity of 120 litres. This is that the standing loss must not exceed 2.5 kW/h per 24 hours. If a jacket passes this test it is also suitable for the usual range of sizes.

NOTE   It is interesting to compare the three differing standards for standing loss from hot water vessels by bringing them all to the same basis, namely W/L using the 120 litre cylinder as the vessel being compared, thus:

L 5 specifies 90 W/m^2 = 1.43 m^2* × 90/120 = 1.07 W/L

BS 5615 specifies 2.5kW/h per 24 hours

$$= \frac{2500}{24 \times 120} = 0.868 \text{ W/L}$$

BS 699, 1566 and 3198 all specify   1.0 W/L

The term 'standing loss' means energy consumption under steady state conditions.

* Surface area of type 7 cylinder (450 mm dia × 900 mm high)

References

The AD refers to the following documents on the page number given at the end of each entry.

Chartered Institution of Building Services Engineers. CIBSE Guide Section A3. *Thermal properties of building structures.* CIBSE. 1980. £12, p. 5.

Chartered Institution of Building Services Engineers. CIBSE Building Energy Code Part 3. £15·50, p. 12.

BS 699: 1984 *Specification for copper direct cylinders for domestic purposes.* £12·20, p. 18.

BS 1566 *Copper indirect cylinders for domestic purposes.* Part 1: 1984 *Double feed indirect cylinders.* £12·20. Part 2: 1984 *Specification for single feed indirect cylinders.* £12·20, p. 18.

BS 3198: 1981 *Specification for copper hot water storage combination units for domestic purposes* Amendment slip no 1: AMD 4372. £12·20, p. 18.

BS 5422: 1977 *Specification for the use of thermal insulating materials.* £22·80, p. 18.

BS 5615: 1978 *Specification for insulation jackets for domestic hot water storage cylinders.* £7, p. 19.

Approved Document M (M2/3/4) Access for Disabled People

This document dated 1987 now contains the substantive guidance regarding the regulations covering access for disabled people to buildings which were previously contained in Schedule 2 of the 1985 regulations, which it replaces. This change was forecast at the time of publication of the 1985 regulations, the intention being to bring these rules into line with the rest of the substantive regulations, by incorporating them into Schedule 1 supported by an Approved Document, permitting future detail changes without reference back to Parliament.

The contents are very similar in effect to Schedule 2 but there are some changes and where these occur some comment is included.

The document covers three requirements of Part M of Schedule 1, namely:

M 2   Means of Access.

M 3   Sanitary Conveniences.

M 4   Audience or Spectator seating.

NOTE   M 1 requires no Approved Document as it contains only definitions (see 0.1 to 0.7). The actual requirements are as follows:

Requirements	Limits on application
Interpretation	1. The requirements of this Part apply only to a building which is erected and which is, or contains, relevant premises.
M 1. In this Part – 'disabled people' means people with a physical impairment which limits their ability to walk and people who need to use a wheelchair for mobility; and	2. When an existing building is extended or altered, then in applying paragraphs (4), (5) and (6) of regulation 2 to determine whether the work shall be regarded as adversely affecting the existing building, there shall be disregarded any intended use as relevant premises of:
'relevant premises' means –	
(*a*) an office.	
(*b*) a shop.	
(*c*) so much (if any) of –	
(i) a factory (within the meaning of section 175 of the Factories Act 1961)	(*a*) the extension or any part of it,
(ii) a school or other educational establishment.	(*b*) any part of the existing building which was not used as relevant premises before the alteration,
(iii) any premises to which the public are admitted whether on payment or otherwise.	(*c*) any part of any existing relevant premises to which access was not, or would not have been, required by requirement M 2 before alteration.
as is (or are) on the storey of the building concerned which contains the principal entrance to that building.	
Means of access	
M 2. Reasonable provision shall be made to enable disabled people to gain access to the relevant premises, and to those parts of the relevant premises to which it is reasonable to provide access.	
Sanitary conveniences	
M 3. Where sanitary conveniences are provided in connection with relevant premises, reasonable provision shall be made for disabled people.	
Audience or spectator seating	
M 4. Where relevant premises contain audience or spectator seating, reasonable provision shall be made to accommodate disabled people.	

Foreword

The importance of recognising the problems of disabled people and of helping to solve these is stressed.

The Chronically Sick and Disabled Persons' Act 1970 (amended 1976) imposes a duty on building providers to make provision for access to and sanitary conveniences within buildings for the disabled, but it does not contain enforcement provisions. These are now taken over by Building Regulations.

The underlying philosophy is, that so far as is reasonable, the built environment should be as accessible to disabled persons as to able-bodied people. Buildings which are so accessible are usually also more convenient for the general public.

The object of the Approved Document is to ensure that, in the main, all relevant buildings are accessible to disabled people, but it is accepted that there will be circumstances when full provision may not be reasonable. Some of these are defined. *Nevertheless, designers etc. are encouraged wherever possible to go beyond the level of provision demanded by Part M.*

More information may be obtained from:

The Access Committee for England and the Centre on Environment for the Handicapped (both at 35 Great Smith Street, London SW1)

The Wales Council for the Disabled, Caerbragdy Industrial Estate, Bedwas Road, Caerphilly, Mid-Glamorgan

The Access Committee's *Design Guidance Notes for Developers* is especially recommended.

Scope and Interpretation

01   The document explains:
Where the requirements apply
What access and facilities should be provided
How these should be designed.
In the document:
02   'Access' means approach or entry convenient for disabled people
03   'Accessible' with respect to relevant premises and facilities means they are suitably designed for disabled people to reach and use them
04   'Suitable' as to access or facilities means designed to enable disabled people to use them
05   'Relevant premises' are:
(*a*)   Any storey or any part of a storey intended for use as:
    1 Office premises within the meaning of regulation 2(1) (see page 10)
    2 Shop-premises within the meaning of regulation 2(1) (see page 11)
(*b*)   The principal entrance storey (or any part thereof) intended for use as:
    1 A factory within the meaning of Section 175 of The Factories Act 1961 or
    2 A school or other educational establishment not exempted by Section 4(1)(a) of the Building Act 1984 or
    3 Any premises to which the public are admitted whether on payment or otherwise

NOTE   State run schools are exempted from 2 above, which therefore applies only to the private sector.
06   'Principal entrance storey' means the storey containing the principal entrance or entrances to the building. If an alternative entrance is provided as required in 3.2 or 3.3 the storey containing that entrance is the principal entrance storey.

NOTE   There has been a significant change here because Schedule 2 specified 'single storey buildings' only. The new description means that multi-storey buildings in these classes are now included, but only in so far as the entrance storey is concerned.
07   'Disabled people' means people with a physical impairment which limits their ability to walk and people who use a wheelchair for mobility.

Application of the requirements

1.1   New buildings: in newly erected buildings the requirements apply to any relevant premises.
1.2   Extensions: when a building is extended, the access to and facilities in the existing building, including the means of access from outside, must be maintained. Thus, if a building is extended at the point of access, the new entrance must be no less suitable and must give access to the existing building.
1.3   Material alteration: Part M is now included as one of the requirements defined in regulation 3(2) which must not be adversely affected. This means that when a building is

materially altered access and facilities must be maintained. They may be moved provided the general level is not reduced.

Introduction to the provisions

2.1   In a building containing relevant premises reasonable provision may need to be made for:
(a)   access to the principal entrance storey
(b)   access to and within relevant premises in this storey
(c)   access to and within relevant premises in any storey of shop or office premises
(d)   sanitary accommodation in relevant premises including access thereto
(e)   accommodation in audience or spectator seating.

2.2   These provisions may be intended for the benefit of occasional visitors, those that work in the premises, or both.

2.3   If relevant premises in a storey are on more than one level suitable means of access should be provided between levels.

2.4   It is not considered reasonable to require access to parts of the building used only for inspection, maintenance or repair.

2.5   Part M does not apply to outside features except those required to provide access to an entrance.

2.6   In schools etc. the requirements of M 2 and M 3 will be satisfied if the provisions comply with paragraphs 2.1/2/4/6, 3.1, 4.1/2/4/6 and 5.1 in Design Note 18, 1984, 'Access for Disabled Persons to Educational Buildings' published by the Sec. of State for Education and Science. NOTE   In Schedule 2 the 'deemed to satisfy' requirements for buildings except schools were laid down by reference to clauses 6.2 to 8.4.4 of BS 5810: 1979. Whilst the new document is clearly still based on these rules they are now rewritten in more detail in the Approved Document itself so that reference to the BS is no longer necessary. However, for school buildings, reference to Design Note 18 has been maintained.

M2   Access

3.1   Access should be through the principal entrance. If there are separate entrances for visitors and staff both should be accessible.

3.2   Exceptionally, if space outside the main entrance is restricted, congested, or on sloping ground, access may be through an alternative entrance if intended for general use.

3.3   Where car spaces are provided, but there is not suitable access from them to the principal entrance, an additional entrance should be provided which is also for general use.

3.4   Additional guidance is given in Appendix A.

Access inside the principal entrance storey

3.5   Access should be provided from principal entrances to:
(a)   all relevant premises in the storey
(b)   any lift, ramp or stairway provided to comply with Part M
(c)   any sanitary or other accommodation in the storey provided to comply with Part M

3.6   In restaurants and bars there should be access to the full range of services offered, including access to all bars and self-service counters, and at least half of each area where seating is provided.

3.7   In hotels and motels containing guest bedrooms on the entrance storey the following provisions should be made in respect of those bedrooms:
(a)   the entrance door to each guest bedroom should be accessible
(b)   one guest bedroom out of any 20 (or part thereof) should be suitable as to dimensions and layout for use by a person in a wheelchair.

3.8   Guidance on internal doors, guest bedrooms, corridors, internal lobbies and WCs is given in Appendices B and C.

Access to other storeys

3.9   The most suitable means of vertical access is by passenger lift but this may not always be regarded as a reasonable requirement.
NOTE   In the recent past some Local Authorities treated the previous regulations as requiring the provision of a lift in all cases where more than one storey was to be made accessible. This

uncertainty has now been resolved (see below).

3.10 Access by suitable lift or ramp should be provided to any storey above or below the principal storey which contains:

(a)   in a two storey building more than 280 m² of relevant premises

(b)   in a building over two storeys more than 200 m² of relevant premises and suitable means of access should be provided from that lift or ramp to any relevant premises within that storey.

3.11 The area of relevant premises in a storey should be measured as follows:

The areas of all relevant premises which use the same entrance from the street should be added together, whether they are in more than one part of the storey, or used for different relevant purposes. The area of any vertical circulation, sanitary accommodation and maintenance areas used by the relevant premises should be included.

The 1988 amendments (which have been incorporated in 3.11 as reproduced above) do clarify things and it now becomes clear that 3.10(b) above is referring to buildings with relevant premises exceeding 200 m² in any one storey.

3.12 In cases where there is no lift access a suitable stairway should be provided.

3.13 Guidance on the design of suitable lifts, ramps and stairways may be found in Appendix B.

Access within other storeys

3.14 This should be provided from any lift, ramp or stairway serving the storey to:

(a)   all relevant premises in the storey

(b)   any sanitary accommodation provided to comply with Part M.

3.15 Guidance on corridor widths may be found in Apendix B.

M3   Sanitary conveniences

Staff

4.1 Office or shop premises which contain sanitary conveniences for staff should have either 'unisex' or separate male/female conveniences designed as shown in [13.9]. If there is no access by lift or ramp to storeys containing sanitary conveniences these special units should be sited in the principal entrance storey (unless this contains only the entrance and vertical circulation). Each office or shop premises should have at least one unisex convenience and in larger premises additional facilities should normally be provided.

4.2 In factory premises containing sanitary conveniences for staff suitable accommodation [13.9] should be provided in the principal entrance storey.

4.3 The same requirement applies to public premises.

Visitors and customers

4.4 Wherever separate sanitary conveniences are provided for the use of visitors/customers, unisex conveniences [13.9] should be provided as per the guidance in 4.1/4.3 above.

4.5 In hotels and motels which contain guest bedrooms in the principal entrance storey, the sanitary accommodation in such bedrooms which are suitable for wheelchair users should be *en suite*, if that is the case in the rest of the bedrooms. Any sanitary accommodation which is not *en suite* should be unisex. These facilities are in addition to any provided elsewhere in the building by virtue of 4.4 above.

NOTE   The philosophy behind the so-called 'unisex' compartment is twofold. First, where situations do not merit provision on sufficient scale for both sexes the use of one facility by either sex is essential. Second, disabled people may need assistance within the compartment and the arrangement allows, for example, for a husband to help a handicapped wife, or vice-versa.

M4   Audience or spectator seating

5.1 In all relevant premises containing fixed audience or spectator seating, at least 6 or 1/100th of the total seats available to the public should be wheelchair spaces.

5.2 'Wheelchair space' means a clear space at least 900 mm wide × 1400 mm deep accessible to wheelchair users with a clear view of the event. It may be kept permanently clear or have seating which can be easily removed. Such spaces should not be all together but be dispersed within the general seating.

5.3 Further guidance may be found in Appendix D.

Appendix A Access into the building

In this Appendix the relationship between these rules and those for stairs and ramps generally in Part K are not altogether satisfactorily resolved, particularly as regards 'guarding'. In the notes below some effort is made to clarify this relationship.

Approach to the entrance

A 1 The general approach should not be steeper than 1/20 and have a clear width of at least 1200 mm.

Where site constraints necessitate a steeper approach a ramp should be provided designed as in A 2 or A 3 and any additional stepped approach as in A 4.

Ramped approach with associated stepped approach

A 2 These should be designed as shown in [13.1].

Guarding and handrails should be provided in accordance with the rules described in Approved Documents to requirements K 1 and K 2.

NOTE See the notes on Part K which follow A 4 and which also apply to ramps in respect of handrails and guarding.

A 2 [**13.1**] *Ramped approach with associated stepped approach.*

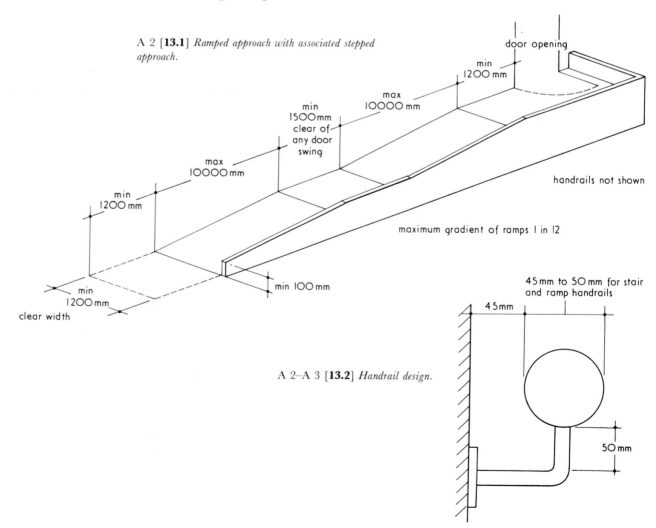

A 2–A 3 [**13.2**] *Handrail design.*

Ramped approach without associated stepped approach

A 3   The same rules apply as in A 2 except that:

The unobstructed width should be not less than 1010 mm and not more than 1800 mm and notwithstanding the handrail requirements by virtue of K 1 there should be a suitable handrail (see [13.2]):

(a)   on at least one side

(b)   on each side if the ramp is steeper than 1 in 15 and longer than 3 m.

NOTE   K 1 requires all ramps of 1 m or more in width to have handrails on both sides. (a) and (b) above appear to over-ride this. It is however difficult to see why these rules should vary from those in A 2. This was not previously the case (see also A 4 below).

Stepped Approach

A 4   To be suitable a stepped approach should comply with diagram [13.3]. In all other respects the approach should satisfy the requirements of Part K 1.

A 4 [**13.3**] *Stepped approach.*

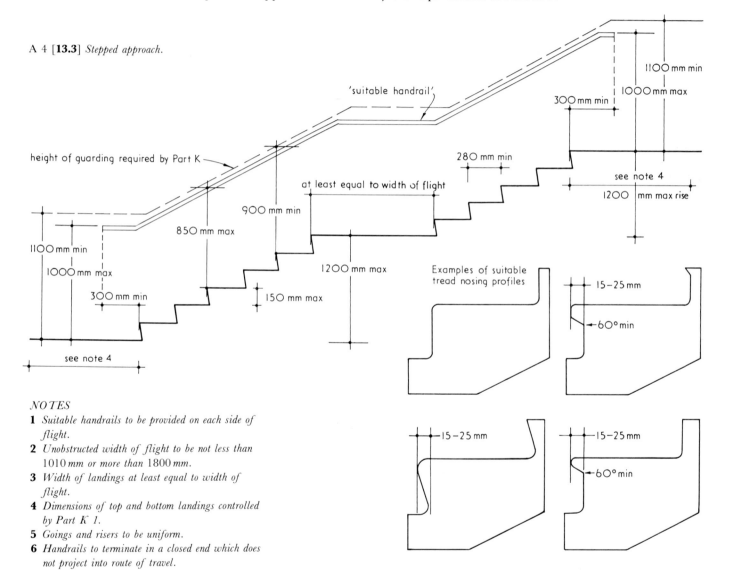

NOTES

1 *Suitable handrails to be provided on each side of flight.*

2 *Unobstructed width of flight to be not less than 1010 mm or more than 1800 mm.*

3 *Width of landings at least equal to width of flight.*

4 *Dimensions of top and bottom landings controlled by Part K 1.*

5 *Goings and risers to be uniform.*

6 *Handrails to terminate in a closed end which does not project into route of travel.*

NOTE   The rules of K 1 which are not confirmed or over-ridden by Part M, A 4 (above) will include:

1.6   Sloping ground

1.7/8   Formula $2 \times \text{rise} + \text{going} \geqslant 550\,\text{mm} \leqslant 700\,\text{mm}$ (controls in Part M limit the lower figure to 580 mm).

1.9   Headroom.

1.10   All steps to be level.

1.15   Stairways over 36 risers to have a change of direction. Stairs of this length are clearly unlikely to be used.

1.16/17   Tapered treads: although not specifically mentioned the use of tapered treads in conjunction with Part M seems unlikely.

1.19/20   K 1 differentiates between handrails and 'guarding' (the one for support, the other to prevent falling over a drop at the side). A 4 covers only handrails. The height of guarding required by K 1 exceeds the handrail heights given in A 4 (see dotted line on [13.3]).

1.21   Landings at top and bottom to be equal in width and depth to the width of the stair.

1.22/23   Landings to be clear of obstruction except certain door swings.

1.24   Exceptions re certain external doors.

1.25   Landings forming part of the ground (slope permitted).

1.26   Guarding:- required where there is a drop exceeding 600 mm.

1.28   Guarding: see 1.19/20 Resistance to horizontal force, use of glass.

Entrance door

A 5   The minimum clear opening should be that provided by a 1000 single leaf external door set (850 mm) or one leaf of an 1800 double leaf external door set (810 mm) to Table 2 of BS 4787 and never less than 800 mm. There should be an unobstructed space next to the leading edge as shown in [13.4].

Revolving doors

A 6   Any entrance with revolving doors should also have an entrance complying with A 5.

Entrance lobby

A 7   These should have at least the dimensions shown in [13.5].

A 5 [**13.4**] *Doors: minimum clear openings etc.*

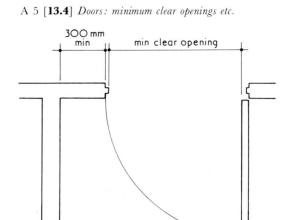
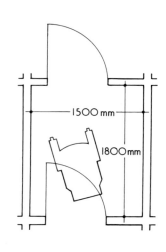
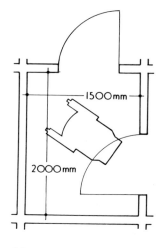

A 7 [**13.5**] *Entrance lobbies.*

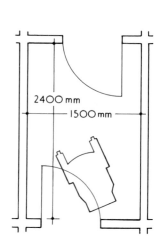
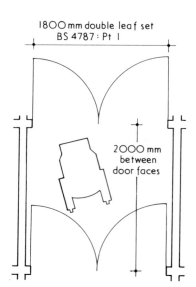
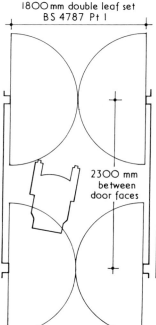

Appendix B Inside the building

Internal doors

B 1   The minimum clear opening should be that provided by a 900 single leaf internal door set (770 mm) or one leaf of an 1800 double leaf internal door set (820 mm) to Table 1 of BS 4787 and never less than 750 mm.
There should be an unobstructed space as in [13.4].
The exception is that WC compartments should be provided with a 1000 single leaf door set to Table 1 of BS 4787.
NOTE   Single leaf door sets required to provide a degree of fire resistance must be limited to 900 mm overall.

Corridors and passageways

B 2   These should have a clear width of at least 1200 mm.

Internal lobbies

B 3   To be suitable should have at least the dimensions shown in [13.6].

Hotel and motel bedrooms

B 4   To be suitable the entrance door to each guest bedroom in the principal storey should comply with B 1. [13.7] shows one example of a suitable arrangement for wheelchair users.

B 3 [**13.6**] *Internal lobbies.*

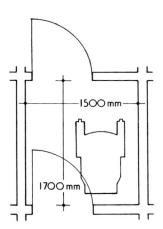
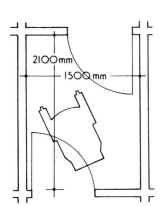
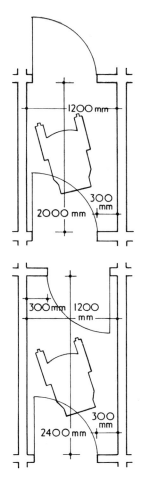

B 4 [**13.7**] *Example of accessible hotel bed and bathroom suite.*

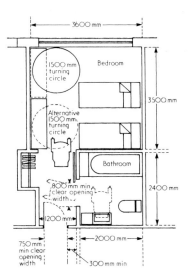

Lifts

B5 These should have a clear landing accessible from the relevant premises which it serves and have the minimum dimensions shown in [13.8].

B 5 [**13.8**] *Lift dimensions.*

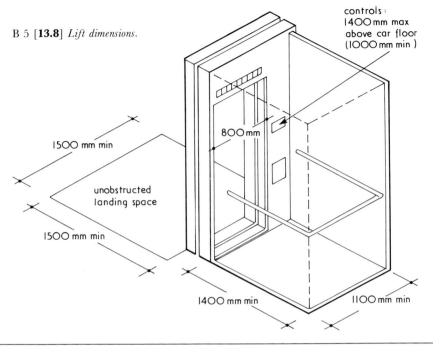

controls:
1400 mm max
above car floor
(1000 mm min)

800 mm

1500 mm min

unobstructed
landing space

1500 mm min

1400 mm min

1100 mm min

Stairways

B 6 Internal stairways should be as described in A 4 except for the following limiting dimensions:
Going 250 mm minimum
Rise 170 mm maximum
Rise of flight between landings 1800 mm maximum (except where particular storey heights or need for access below intermediate landings dictate).

Internal Ramps

B 7 To be suitable these should be as described in A 2/A 3.

Appendix C Sanitary accommodation

C 1 WC compartments should have at least the dimensions and equipment shown in [13.9].
NOTE This is the type known as a 'unisex' compartment and is the only type recommended. Previously BS 5810 included an alternative smaller type for ambulant disabled people.
C 2 Because the users and their companions may not be of the same sex a unisex compartment should be approached separately from all other sanitary accommodation.
NOTE Nevertheless the same provisions are recommended for compartments for disabled persons within normal single sex provision.
C 3 If a building contains more than one such compartment the opportunity of handing the layouts should be taken.

Appendix D Audience or spectator seating

D 1 Any wheelchair space should be:
(*a*)   in a theatre located as shown in [13.10].
(*b*)   in a stadium designed as shown in [13.11].

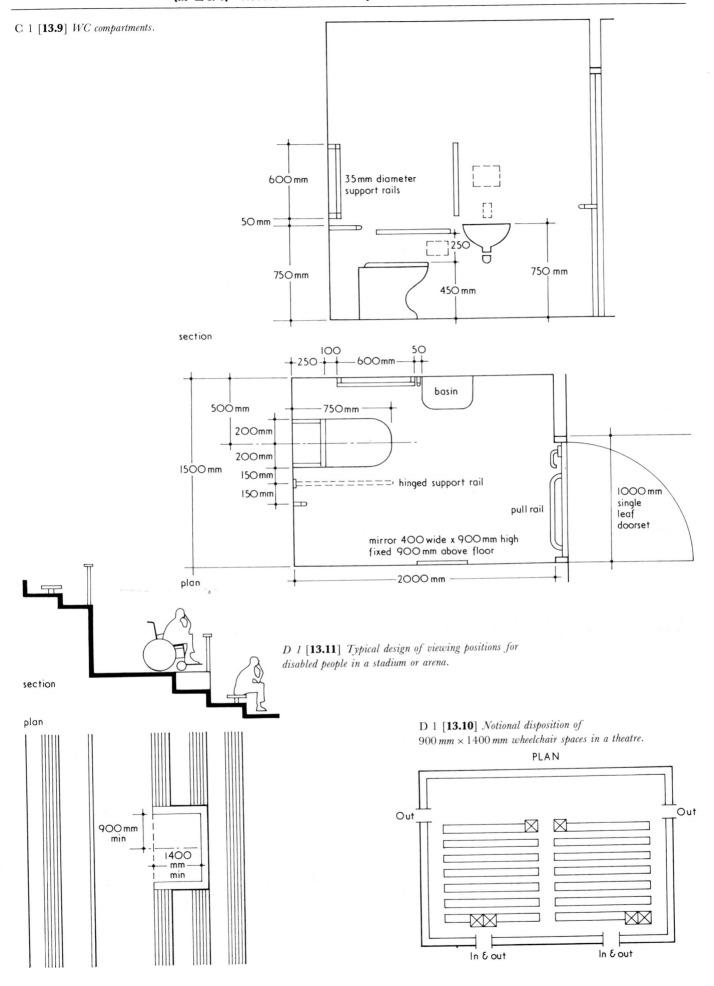

C 1 [**13.9**] *WC compartments.*

D 1 [**13.11**] *Typical design of viewing positions for disabled people in a stadium or arena.*

D 1 [**13.10**] *Notional disposition of 900 mm × 1400 mm wheelchair spaces in a theatre.*

**Note on DES Design
Note 18 Access for the
physically disabled to
educational buildings**

This document covers all educational buildings but is particularly directed to schools.

It includes recommendations for arrival and parking facilities in addition to those for buildings.

It also contains notes on the problem of means of escape from fire for the disabled.

Broadly speaking its recommendations are the same or very similar to those in BS 5810: 1975. It is however rather more detailed. The principal differences are listed below:

1   The recomendations for ramps are rather more extensive and include length limitations: see diagram [8].

2   Stairs   splayed risers are preferred to nosings.

3   Doors   these should have vision panels, attention should be paid to door closers and there are recommendations on door furniture.

4   There is an illustration of a dual access corridor divided into a ramp and a stair. This seems a doubtful advantage as there would seem to be no reason why all traffic should not use a ramp.

5   Lifts   short rise lifts with entries on opposite sides can facilitate access to and from mezzanines.

6   There is advice on surfaces: floors and lift enclosures.

7   Sanitary accommodation. There are illustrations showing the conversion of two normal WCs into one unit for disabled use (diagram [9]) and where more than one unit is provided the handing of two adjacent units to suit right or left transfer from wheelchairs.

The recommendations for escape from fire are very tentative and broadly in line with those for shops and offices in BS 5588 (see B 1 of Schedule 1).

References

BS 4787: *Internal and external door sets, door leaves and frames.* Part 1: 1980 *Specification for dimensional requirements.* Amendment slip no 1: AMD 4737.

Index